THE HISTORY OF
WOODWORKING
TOOLS

Statens Historiska Museum, Stockholm

Handled Bronze Age Tools

THE HISTORY OF WOODWORKING TOOLS

W. L. GOODMAN

G. BELL AND SONS LTD

LONDON

York House, Portugal Street
London, W.C.2

First published 1964
Reprinted 1964, 1966, 1967, 1969

DEDICATION

To Edward and Eva Pinto

SBN 7135 0489 7

Printed in Great Britain by
William Clowes and Sons, Limited, London and Beccles

Preface

THIS BOOK first appeared as a series of articles in 'Practical Education', the Journal of the Institute of Handicraft Teachers, and I am grateful to the Editor, E. W. Luker, F.Coll.H., for his valuable help and encouragement, and to the Council of the Institute for permission to make use of many of the blocks. The articles have been extensively revised in the light of subsequent research, and some of the matter is new. During the autumn and winter of 1961–62, with the help of a grant from the Leverhulme Trustees, I made a tour of Italy, Sicily, Greece, and Egypt, and this enabled me to fill in some of the gaps in my knowledge, and broaden the basis of the study.

I have been greatly helped by conversation and correspondence with Mr. R. A. Salaman, Mr. and Mrs. E. H. Pinto, Miss Joan Liversidge, Mr. G. C. Boon, and Herr J. M. Greber. I am also grateful for much valuable information from Mr. Thijs Mol, Mr. Christian Waagepetersen, Dr. Gösta Berg, Mr. G. A. Norman, Mme. Levasheva, and Mr. B. A. Kolchin, and very many others. I must also acknowledge my indebtedness to the Directors and Trustees of many museums and private collections for permission to use photographs of tools and other illustrations to this book, the sources of which are indicated in detail in the text.

W. L. G.

Contents

Introduction

THERE ARE several ways of arranging a history of woodworking tools. One method would be to take each cultural period in turn and describe the complete kit of tools of the craftsman of that time. Another method would be to take each common tool, roughly in the order of its first appearance, and trace its evolution separately. This makes for a certain amount of repetition and cross-reference, but lends itself to a tidier and more logical arrangement, and is the method adopted in this study.

There seems to be a general impression that down the ages there has, in fact, been very little change in the form of the commoner tools. To the average museum-goer the Roman hammer, axe, or saw look very similar to those in use today. There are, of course, superficial resemblances, but in almost every detail of their design and construction there have been considerable changes and improvements in the course of time. It is a curious thing that the axe, the first, the simplest, and for a long time the commonest cutting tool of all, with a continuous history extending over 10,000 years, shows as much variation in detail as any, so that it is possible to date any example within fairly close limits, yet on the face of it very little variation is possible. In essentials, all that is needed is a piece of fairly heavy material capable of bearing and retaining a sharp edge, with provision for attaching a handle of some kind; yet the variations that human ingenuity has played on these simple themes are almost incredible. It is true that development has often been unaccountably slow, sometimes appearing to stop altogether for hundreds of years, while in other cases, such as the bronze palstave, it found itself at a complete dead end. But occasionally, after centuries of stagnation, there appear to have been sudden spurts of invention. As far as Europe is concerned, one of these occurred during the Roman period; the second seems to have taken place between 1400 and 1500; the third and last during the 18th century, the Golden Age of woodwork, before the invention of machinery drove hand tools into the background. Progress may take several forms: improvement in detail of a tool in general use; the invention of an entirely new tool such as the saw or plane or brace; or the specialisation of tools for particular jobs. As a rule a new tool first appears in its most general form, and while this form is retained for ordinary purposes, increasing specialisation occurs later. The overall effect is an increase in the number of tools in the woodworker's kit at any given time. This tendency is shown in Table I. In this connection there have been one or two cases of what might be called reversed specialisation, where a tool, originally developed for a particular purpose, is found to be more generally useful. Examples that come to mind are the spokeshave and the coping saw.

TABLE I

WOODWORKERS' TOOL KITS AT VARIOUS PERIODS

Tool	*Stone Age*	*Bronze Age*	*Early Iron Age*	*Greek and Roman*	*Dark Ages*	*Middle Ages*	*1600 to 1800*	*1800 to 1962*
Axe	×	×	×	×	×	×	×	×
Adze	×	×	×	×	×	×	×	×
Knife	×	×	×	×	×	×	×	×
Chisel	×	×	×	×	×	×	×	×
Auger	×	×	×	×	×	×	×	×
Hand-saw		×	×	×	×	×	×	×
Cross-cut saw		×	×	×	×	×	×	×
Bow drill		×	×	×	×	×	×	×
Drawknife			×	×	×	×	×	×
Rule				×	×	×	×	×
Plane, smooth				×	×	×	×	×
„ jack				×	×	×	×	×
„ plough				×	×	×	×	×
„ moulding				×	×	×	×	×
T-axe					×	×	×	×
Breast auger					×	×	×	×
Brace						×	×	×
Plane, try						×	×	×
„ mitre						×	×	×
„ shoulder						×	×	×
Saw, fret						×	×	×
„ tenon							×	×
Spokeshave							×	×
Marking gauge							×	×
Breast drill								×
Screwdriver								×
Twist bits								×
All-metal planes								×
Metal brace								×

Generally speaking the number of different tools available at any time depends upon the prevailing level of culture, which determines the kind of work the craftsman is called upon to do. For example it is probable that the tool kit of the average Roman joiner in Rome or Trier or London was more extensive and specialised than that of his medieval counterpart in a small French or English village 1,000 years later.

Taking the tools individually, they seem to follow a fairly well-defined course of development. Once the general principle of the instrument is established, the growing points, to adopt a biological term, appear to confine themselves to one or two particular features, leaving the rest of the tool more or less unchanged. Since most woodworking tools consist essentially of a blade with a cutting edge or edges, and a block or handle to hold and manipulate it with, the point where these two components meet is as often as not the most variable and ingenious feature.

One of the limiting factors of a study of this character is the amount and kind of evidence which has survived. This is not confined to tools alone. For the Stone Age, there are a few sledge-runners and skis found in the northern peat bogs as well as a large number of prehistoric dug-out boats and canoes with their paddles. The Landesmuseum at Zürich displays some large jointed balks which formed the framework of the piled dwellings of the Swiss Neolithic lake villages, some of which show clear traces of the polished flint axes and chisels used in their fashioning. But as a rule, for this period the tools themselves have survived in greater numbers than the woodwork.

Similarly with the Northern Bronze Age; there are thousands of bronze axes, chisels, knives, and other tools in our museums, but only very exceptional circumstances preserved the remarkable wooden folding stool, found with an oak-coffin burial at Guldhoj in Jutland, together with other wooden objects of the same period. The Bronze Age in Egypt, however, lasted a very long time, and besides a fair number of surviving tools, we also have a large quantity of beautifully made wooden furniture and other objects, kept more or less intact in the hot, dry climate, as well as the sculptured reliefs and models of carpenters at work, to fill out our knowledge of the Egyptian craftsman's methods.

For the Early Iron Age, and particularly the Roman period, the absolute number of surviving tools appears to fall sharply, owing to the fact that iron is more vulnerable than the preceding stone or bronze. Very little contemporary woodwork has come down to us either, but there is enough at Herculaneum, Pompeii, and other places, to give us some idea of the scope of their work. In addition, there are a number of references to woodworking in classical literature, but it is not always easy to assess their value in practical terms.

For the Middle Ages, however, although we can be sure from the woodwork we have from that period that they used a very wide range of tools, very few actual examples have come down to us, and for the most part all we have to go on is the literary evidence, the pictures in the illuminated manuscripts and early printed books, the woodcarvings in the churches, stained-glass windows, and other clues of this type.

When we come to the 17th century the establishment of first private and then public collections of relics of earlier times, which form the nucleus of our modern museums, resulted in the accumulation of a fair number of craftsmen's tools, some of which are minor works of art in themselves. In this connection it is likely that the large number of carved and dated planes in our museums owe their survival more to their carving than to their value as tools; it is doubtful whether the planes of the 18th-century joiner were all as elaborate as this.

Finally, the spread of education in the 17th and 18th centuries among the artisan classes made it profitable to write books about some of the more important trades, and from this period we have the earliest technical handbooks, of which Moxon's 'Mechanick Exercises' is a typical example in this country, and Roubo's 'L'Art du Menuisier' in

France. These, and the relevant chapters of Diderot's and other encyclopedias, give valuable accounts of the tools used during the Golden Age. Later still, when tools began to be made and sold commercially, the trade catalogues are a useful source of information. In spite of all this, there are still many gaps in our knowledge, and several unsolved problems, which will be discussed later in their proper place. The following study has been put together as an attempt to display the evidence as far as it is known at present.

SECTION I

THE AXE AND THE ADZE

1: The Stone Ages

ANY COMPREHENSIVE study of the history of woodworking tools must of necessity begin with the axe; it was not only the first, but for many years almost the only woodworking tool of any kind, and it was still important right up to the end of the Middle Ages. At the present time it is still used a good deal for its original purpose, the felling and preparation of timber, and it occupies a modest but useful place in the modern carpenter's kit.

The invention of the axe and its development as a woodworking tool, as far as Europe is concerned, may be attributed to certain groups of Mesolithic peoples living on the fringe of the northern forest about 8000 B.C. Their earliest tools, made of reindeer antler, with the stump of the brow tine sharpened to a cutting edge, are known as 'Lyngby axes', from the site at Norre-Lyngby, in Denmark, where they were first found. Later the stump end was hollowed out to take a piece of hard stone, usually flint.

The next stage was to mount the flint head in a short length of antler, perforated to take a wooden handle. The earliest culture to adopt this device is known as the Maglemosian, from the type-site, also in Denmark, dating from about 6000 B.C., but the pattern was in use throughout Europe for several thousand years, indeed one of the finest intact examples is that from Penhoet, Loire-Inférieure, now in the museum at Saint-Germain, of the later Neolithic period, about 2000 B.C.

It was not long before it was realised that a good deal of the efficiency of an axe lay in the sheer weight of the head, but it was found difficult to mount a large head in an antler sleeve. One solution was to shape the butt end to a point and let it directly into a hole in the handle (Fig. 1). The drawback to this method may be seen from the the illustration; the shaft has fractured at its weakest point. In the case of a similar example from Spain, the shaft is intact, but only because it is almost as thick and heavy as the head itself, with a consequent loss of efficiency. Half the effort expended in using this tool would be wasted on the handle.

Other methods of hafting a fairly heavy celt, as these plain axe-heads are often called, are shown in Fig. 2. In one case the head is let into a piece of wood or antler, which is in turn driven tightly into the thickened end of the wooden handle. In other cases lengths of antler or suitable branches of trees with short ends at the desired angle were selected, and the heads inserted into slots or lashed directly to the prepared ends. These examples are all of adzes, but similar methods were used for the axe, with the slot arranged to bring the cutting edge in the same plane as the handle, instead of at right angles to it.

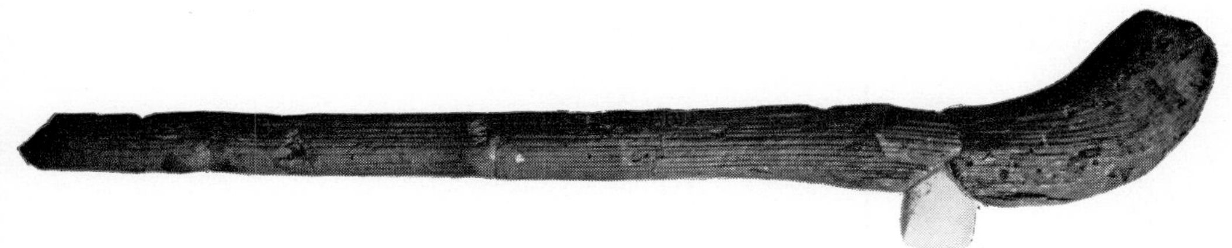

1. Neolithic Axe in Wooden Handle, Schotz, Kanton Luzern *Schweiz. Landesmuseum, Zürich*

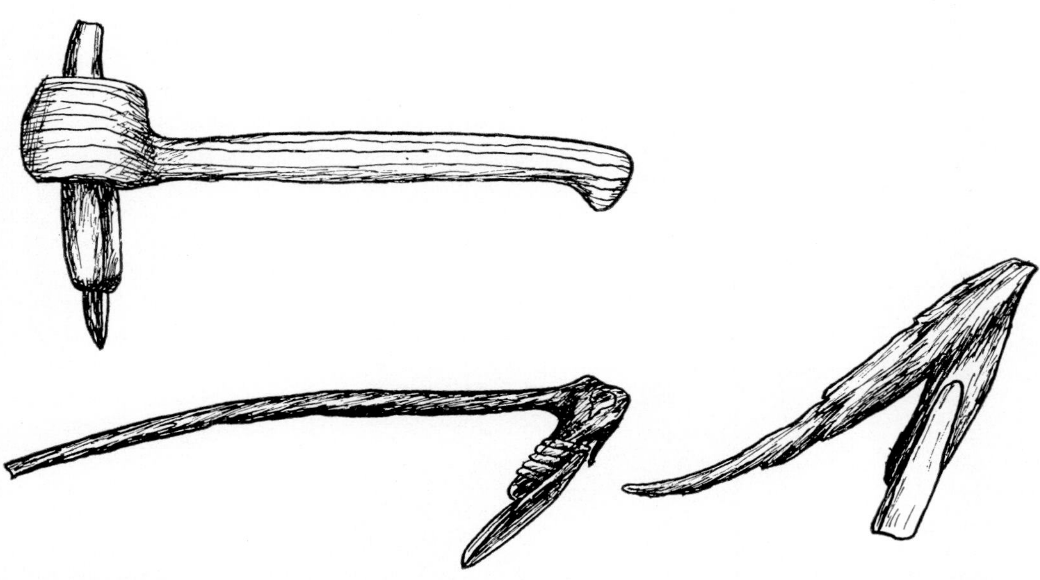

2. Neolithic Handled Adzes, Swiss Lake Villages *Landesmuseum, Zürich*

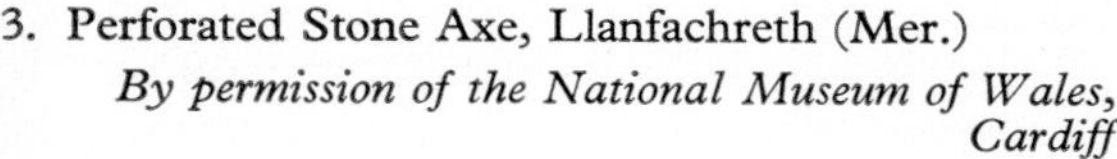

3. Perforated Stone Axe, Llanfachreth (Mer.)
By permission of the National Museum of Wales, Cardiff

It is clear why these rather elaborate methods of hafting were used, and not the obvious way of boring through the head itself. Drilling a hole big enough to take a suitable shaft was only possible in thick pieces of comparatively soft stone, and although many examples of these perforated stone 'axes' have come down to us (Fig. 3), they must have been very crude tools, very likely not used for woodwork at all, but as weapons or for dispatching game. The fact that many of them are chance finds, probably lost on hunting or marauding expeditions, and occur in all contexts, from the Early Neolithic to the Bronze Age, as in our example, seems to confirm this theory.

2: The Bronze Age in the West

Although the use of copper and later bronze for tools and weapons was known in the Middle East before 2000 B.C., it took over five hundred years for this knowledge to seep through to Western Europe. Stranger still, in spite of the fact that the earliest Mesopotamian cultures soon evolved the shaft-hole axe and adze, the Bronze Age peoples of the West retained their traditional method of hafting the head to a knee-shaped, cleft handle. In the course of time the shape of the head was drastically modified, yet even when casting was adopted they still kept to the old way of lashing the head to the shaft. Indeed the inertia was such that this method was still used for some of the forged iron axes of the Early La Tène period in Switzerland and other places! This was perhaps one of the most curious blind alleys in the whole chequered history of human progress.

Some of the more important stages in the development of the bronze axe-head are shown in Fig. 4, and various methods of hafting in Fig. 5 and on the frontispiece. The plain flat axe (Fig. 4*a*), which was simply a copper or bronze version of its flint predecessors, with the cutting edge flared out more or less by hammering, is shown hafted on the right in the Haslemere group. To give better lateral fixing the edges were hammered over, and later cast, to form a flange on either side (*b*), and lashed to a cleft shaft in a similar manner (Fig. 5, second from the right). To prevent what must have been a common misfortune, the splitting of the wooden handle, a ridge was formed about half-way along the head (known as the Tinsdahl type), which later developed into the pronounced stop in the palstave (*c*), shown hafted in the centre on Fig. 5, and at the extreme right on the Swedish group. In some cases a loop was provided to make the lashing more secure (*d*). Some Spanish palstaves were cast with two loops, one on each side. In a parallel line of development, centred mainly in North Italy and Switzerland, the flanges of (*b*) were hammered right over to form a sort of socket on either side of the head (4*e*), shown with a loop unhandled in Fig. 5. The weak spot up to now had always been the necessity to use a cleft shaft, but when the technique of casting became sufficiently advanced, the heads were made with a hollow socket (*f*), with or without a loop, to take the stub end of a crooked shaft. It was suggested at one time that the cast socketed axe was a direct development from the wide-flanged type (*e*), but this supposed inter-

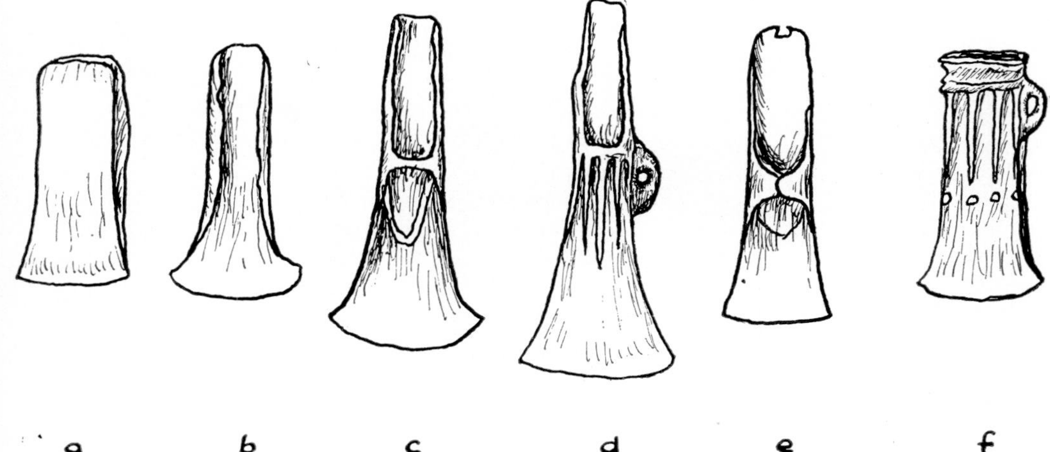

4. Development of Bronze Axes

5. Hafted Bronze Axes

Haslemere Educational Museum

mediate pattern does not occur at all in Russian bronze hoards, in fact the palstave itself only appears in a very rudimentary form, while the socketed head seems to have made a spontaneous appearance. It is possible that an enterprising bronze-smith, having been casting weapons like spear-heads with sockets for some time, suddenly decided to make his axe-heads in the same manner.

Some of the later Spanish socketed axe-heads were cast with two loops like their palstaves, and this feature occurs quite frequently on socketed axes from the other end of the Eurasian land-mass, between Siberia and the Urals. There is also a small number of double-looped socketed axes in the Etruscan collections in Florence and the Villa Giulia at Rome, but nobody else seems to have adopted this very sensible idea. In general, the shape of these heads varies from square, as in the Haslemere example (Fig. 5, second from the left), to oval or round (Fig. 4*f*), with various decorative patterns cast on the head, according to the locality of origin. Fig. 6 is a curious freak, having the body of a palstave with traces of a loop, and a square-socketed butt. Other variations are

6. Socketed Palstave, St. George (Denb.) *By permission of the National Museum of Wales, Cardiff*

possible, and they were all tried from time to time, but the really surprising thing is that although all these different types of head were finally produced by casting, the Bronze-Age smiths were so hidebound by the tradition of the bent shaft that it never seemed to occur to them to cast a shaft-hole at right angles to the axis of the head, as in the modern tool. They even made their hammers in exactly the same way, with a round or square socket.

Heads of this shape could of course also be used for adzes, merely by cutting the cleft in the shaft in the required direction, or in the case of the plain socket, by turning the head itself through 90 degrees. There are, however, three bronze tools in the Landesmuseum at Zürich, from Eastern Switzerland, with the wide flanges of Fig. 4 type (*e*), bent over the edge of the blade, instead of the flat sides, so that when fitted to a haft cleft for an axe, they could be used as adzes.

One feature of these bronze tools has always been a source of wonder, their extremely small size for the work they were presumably called upon to do. There are a few fairly large ones in the York, Zürich, Bologna, and Villa Giulia collections, but the majority seem little bigger than toys, and can only weigh a few ounces at most. Apart from the cost of the material, which was so expensive that flint tools were still being made right up to the end of the Bronze Age, and the difficulty of making large castings, the limiting factor was always the strength of the handle at the crook. This makes it all the more surprising that the simple solution to the problem, that of making the hole right through the head, already well known in the Middle East, was never stumbled on.

3: The Egyptians

The story of the axe and the adze during the long Egyptian period was another example of a technological cul-de-sac, and owing to the time-span involved, some 3,000 years, the stagnation seems to have been even more pronounced than in the case of the bronze palstave.

The stone and flint axes of the Pre-Dynastic period, some time before 3200 B.C., were little different from those of other Neolithic cultures, except perhaps in their size and the skill shown in their manufacture. The earliest axes of copper and later bronze took the form of a flat semi-circular plate with a straight back and two projecting lugs, and sometimes a row of holes bored through the plate to take the leather or hempen thongs which bound it to the handle. Axes of this type with long handles are shown in use for felling trees on the celebrated reliefs in the mastaba of Tiye at Saqqara, dating from the Vth Dynasty (about 2500 B.C.). This axe also appears in the frieze of tools intended to serve the deceased in the next world, which were painted inside the wooden coffins of the XIth and XIIth Dynasties. A typical example is that of the court official Sopi (about 2100 B.C., Fig. 7) in the Louvre. There is a similar group inside the outer coffin

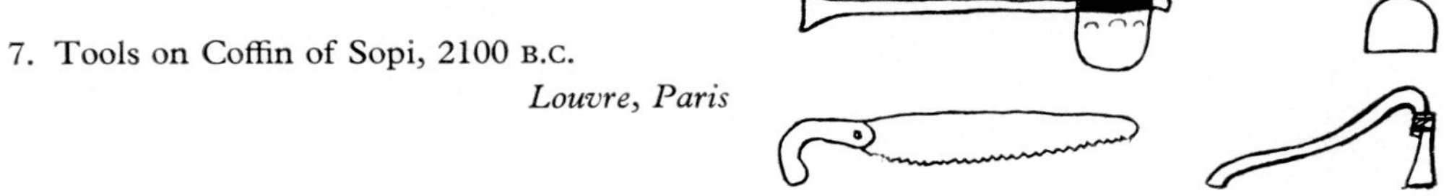

7. Tools on Coffin of Sopi, 2100 B.C.
Louvre, Paris

of Gua, one of the chief court physicians of the same period, in the British Museum, and there are other examples at Cairo. In these schematic drawings the method of fixing the head is not clear, but the dark colour used by the artist probably indicates a thonged binding (visible in the earlier mastaba relief) covered with bitumen.

In the axes of later periods the shape of the head gradually approximated to that of a modern axe, with curved sides and a slightly flared cutting edge, but the flat butt and the two lugs were retained right up to the Iron Age, about 770 B.C., as shown by the iron axe, No. 20762, in the British Museum.

Judging from the number of surviving tools, and from the pictures on the tomb reliefs and so on, the Egyptian craftsmen made much more use of the adze than the axe for dressing their timber, as in fact they still do to this day. Its importance to the ancient Egyptians is shown by its use as the hieroglyph s – t – p, meaning 'to choose',

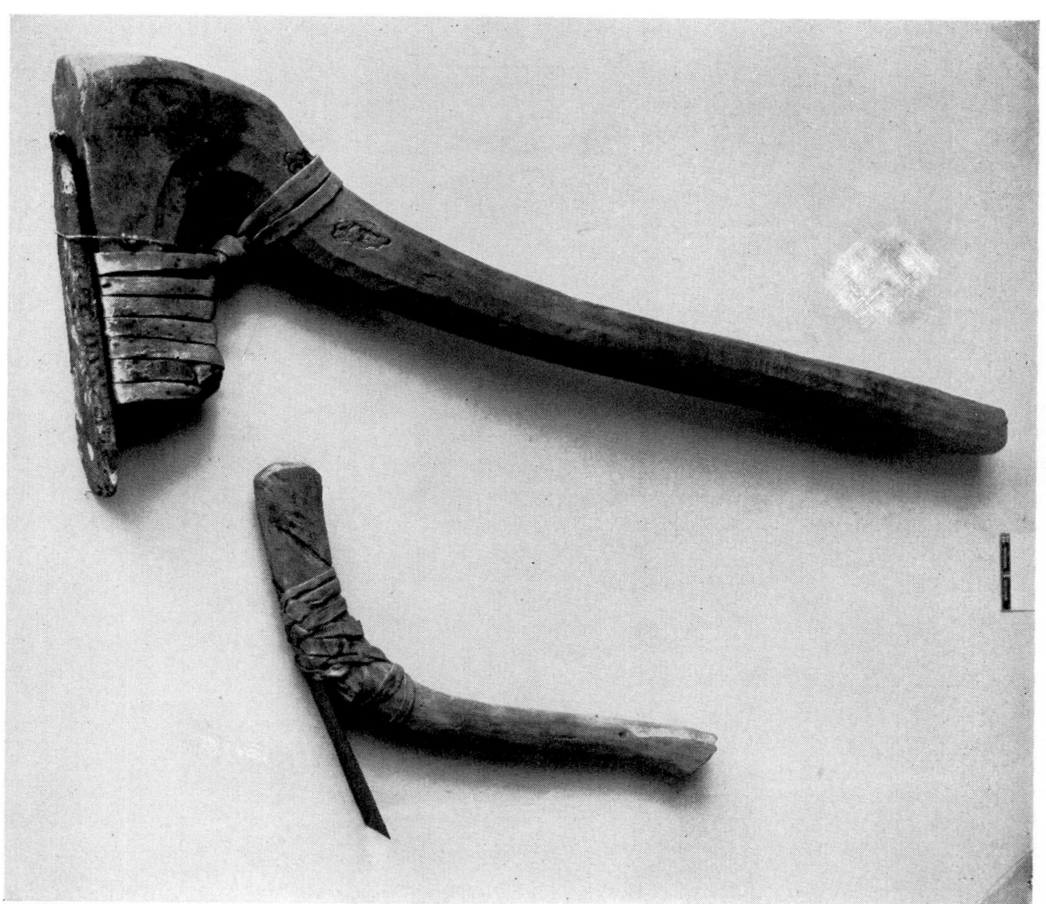

8. Egyptian Copper Adzes, 17th and 18th Dynasties *Trustees of the British Museum*

often accompanied by a saw, w – s, to give the sense of 'builder' (or perhaps 'craftsman'). This hieroglyphic pair occurs several times on the stele of a priest of the IIIrd dynasty (about 2750 B.C.) from Saqqara, in the Cairo museum, and also in the mastaba of Tiye mentioned above. In both cases the beautifully executed detail of the reliefs brings out very clearly the method of fixing the blade to a knee-shaped handle by means of thongs.

Over a thousand years later these adzes were still being made in exactly the same way, as illustrated by the copper tool from the tomb of Ani (Fig. 8), dating from the XVIIth Dynasty (1650 B.C.). The shaft is roughly chamfered, and is about 2 ft. 2 in. long, so it must have been quite a useful tool. The purpose of the knob at the top end of the blade, also present in other adzes, is not clear from the present method of mounting, but it is likely that the binding was lashed once or twice over the shoulders to give lateral rigidity.

The smaller adze in the same figure, inscribed with the name of Queen Hatshepsut (XVIIIth Dynasty, 1501–1479 B.C.), is much simpler; a thin copper blade lashed to the thick end of a curved piece of wood. This tool resembles very closely the adzes being used by the chairmakers in the tomb fresco of this period in the Science Museum at South Kensington.

Small models in copper or bronze of these axes and adzes, together with model saws and other tools, were often buried in the foundations of Egyptian buildings, and show that no important changes took place in their design for something like 2,000 years. The smiths of the Bronze Age in the West did make some attempt to improve the fixing of their tools by modifying the shape of the head in course of time, but the Egyptians kept the same flat blade for both axes and adzes throughout. One possible reason for this lack of enterprise was the fact that the Egyptian craftsman was usually a serf or slave, merely taking his orders from his lord and master, who had more important things to think about than how they were carried out. In contrast to this, the farmers and herdsmen of the West were comparatively free men. The climate may also have had something to do with it. But the same inertia is characteristic of almost all aspects of Egyptian life; even their wonderful art, after its initial break-through, became monotonous and repetitious towards the end.

4: The Bronze Age in the Mediterranean Area

As Gordon Childe pointed out in 'The Dawn of European Civilisation', speaking of one of the earliest Bronze Age cultures in the Mediterranean area, the Minoan civilisation of Crete: 'For axes the flat celt of the copper age did not lead, as in Cis-Alpine Europe, to flanged and socketed types, but was superseded by the shaft-hole axe, which had been current from prehistoric times in Mesopotamia.' In another passage he suggests that the first copper shaft-hole axes were copies in metal of the stone axe-hammers of the Late Neolithic (Fig. 3), which they resemble closely both in shape and size.

There are a number of cast bronze axes and adzes in the British Museum (Fig. 9*a*), dating from the Early Dynastic period at Ur (2900–2700 B.C.). These tools, with the characteristic ribs on the butt, show that the bronze-smiths of Ur had already advanced considerably from the crude stone prototypes. They had also evolved an entirely new feature, which, with one or two exceptions, was retained throughout the subsequent history of the axe, the asymmetrical shape of the blade. This form spread northwards through Asia Minor to the Greek islands (Fig. 9*g*), and also through Armenia and Georgia and the steppe region of the Northern Caucasus (Fig. 9*i*), to the Urals, where about 1,000 years later large bronze axes were being made, of which the example from Gorbunovo (Fig. 9*h*) is typical. Similar tools have been found further east in Kazakhstan.

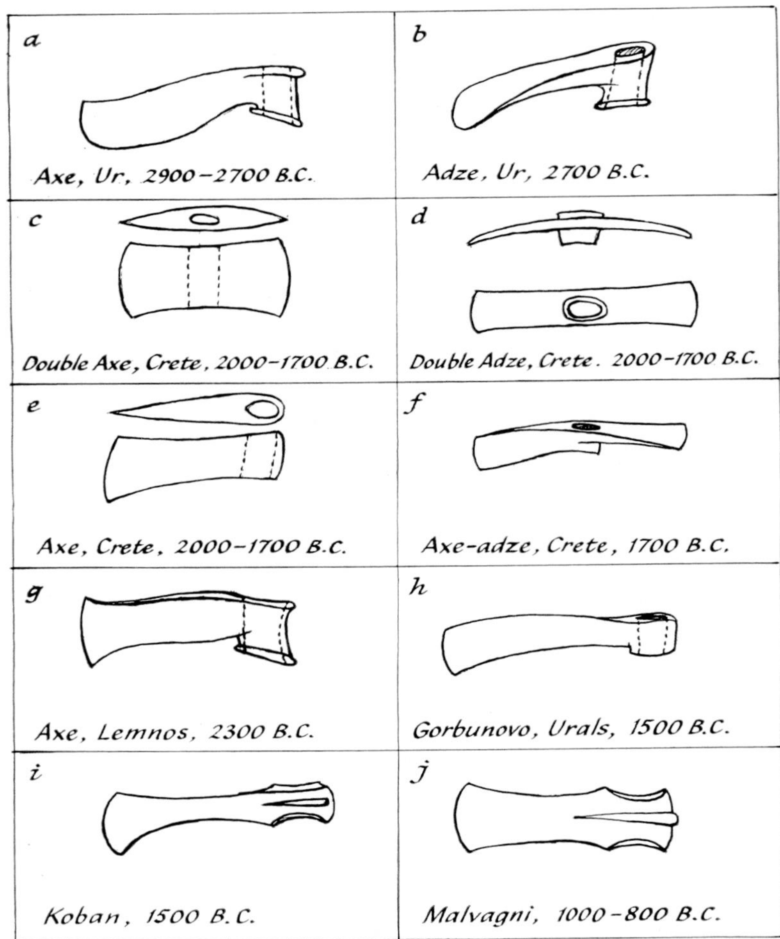

9. Bronze Shaft-hole Axes and Adzes: (*a* and *b*) *British Museum;* (*c, d, e,* and *f*) *Heraklion Museum, Crete;* (*g*) *National Museum, Athens;* (*h* and *i*) *Material and Researches in 'Archeology', No. 35, Moscow, 1953;* (*j*) *Museo Nazionale, Syracuse, Sicily*

The distinctive contribution of the Minoan civilisation of Crete to the development of woodworking tools, also, in its way, a bit of a dead end, was the double-bladed axe. It first appears in the Prepalatial period (2600–2000 B.C.) as a religious symbol, laid in the tomb to protect the dead. The earliest example in the Heraklion museum came from the vaulted tombs of the Messara, a votive axe made of two thin bronze plates riveted together, but later proper tools were cast in bronze to the same shape (Fig. 9*c*). Two stone moulds for casting these implements were found at Mallia. The Minoans also carried this idea over to the design of adzes (Fig. 9*d*). It is not clear what practical advantage there is in having two identical blades in an axe or adze, except that when one blade becomes blunt, the tool can be simply turned round and the other brought into use. After their conquest of Crete about 1300 B.C. the Myceneans adopted this 'gimmick', perhaps as much for its religious and political significance as for its value as a tool, and many examples were found in the shaft graves at Mycenae itself, and other parts of Greece, while later in the Iron Age the Etruscans and Romans also used this pattern for similar reasons. Single-bladed axes were also used in Crete (Fig. 9*e*), but surviving examples are rare. Another double-purpose tool of the Minoans, the axe-adze (Fig. 9*f*), first encountered in the Neopalatial period (1700–1400 B.C.) was also taken over by the Greeks, and an example in bronze has been found at Taormina, one of their colonies in Sicily. In the succeeding Iron Age this tool became very popular with the Romans.

The characteristic shaft-hole axe of the Late Bronze Age peoples of Sicily, of which the best example is that from Malvagni in the collection at Siracusa (Fig. 9*j*), still retains the symmetrical shape of the blade. This was no doubt due to the influence of the traditional flanged axes and palstaves, which were still being made and used in large quantities, in fact the writer noticed that in one hoard from Toscana in the Pigorini Museum at Rome the proportion was roughly one shaft-hole axe for about twenty palstaves.

It is sometimes difficult to realise that the heroes of the Homeric epics were still living in the Bronze Age. There are several passages in the 'Odyssey' mentioning the axes and adzes of the period, usually reckoned to be about 800 B.C., when the poem took its present form. The following extracts are from E. V. Rieu's translation in the Penguin Classics:

> 'First she (Calypso) gave him a great axe of bronze. Its double blade was sharpened well, and the shapely handle of olive wood fixed firmly in its head was fitted to his grip. Next she handed to him an adze of polished metal, and then led the way for him to the farthest part of the island, where the trees grew tall . . . Twenty trees in all he felled, and lopped their branches with his axe; then trimmed them in a workmanlike manner and trued them to the line . . .'

> 'I was reminded of the loud hiss that comes from a great axe or adze when the smith plunges it into cold water—to temper it and give strength to the iron . . .'

> 'The Queen reached the store-room and mounted the oaken threshold—the work of some carpenter of bygone days, whose adze had smoothed it well and true to the line . . .'

> 'Inside the court there was a long-leaved olive tree, which had grown to full height with a stem as thick as a pillar. Round this I built my room of close-set stonework, and when that was finished, I roofed it over thoroughly and put in a solid, neatly-fitted, double door. Next I lopped all the twigs off the olive, trimmed the stem from the root up, rounded it smoothly and carefully with my adze and trued it to the line, to make my bedpost . . .'

It is interesting to note that in all three cases where the adze is mentioned, it is insisted that the work was made 'true to the line', a very practical Homeric formula which shows that both narrator and audience must have known how difficult a process this was. The Greek carpenter in Fig. 10, shown using an adze of very stylised form, was probably intended to illustrate the last quotation from the 'Odyssey' above. The handle seems much too long and thin for this kind of work, and although the head seems to be of the shaft-hole type, possibly an axe-adze, the artist has gone to considerable trouble to indicate the way it was lashed by thongs to the handle. Indeed the remark about the axe in the first extract, that the olive handle was fixed firmly in the head, is very suggestive. Generations of exasperated carpenters had been puzzling their wits for several thousand years to find some way of doing just that.

10. Greek Carpenter using Adze *Trustees of the British Museum*

5: The Early Iron Age and the Romans

Iron copies of bronze socketed axes have already been mentioned as being a continuation of the Northern European tradition in the new material. In the earlier Hallstatt period they were forged with round sockets, and several examples, notably the one from the Berwin Hills in the British Museum, have a loop in addition. In the later La Tène period the socket was often made square (Fig. 11*a*), and a similar construction is shown in a number of adzes in the Etruscan collections in Florence and the Villa Giulia at Rome. Some of these tools are displayed in the Zürich Landesmuseum with the usual knee-shaped wooden handles.

It was about this time, between 500 and 200 B.C., that this traditional method was finally abandoned, and the axe assumed the form familiar to us today, a heavy wedge-shaped forging, with the shaft-hole, usually elliptical in cross-section, made by folding a rectangular billet of iron in the middle, leaving the eye parallel to the cutting edge. One of the earliest of these axes is shown at Fig. 11*b*. The head is about $6\frac{1}{2}$ in. long and 3 in. wide at the cutting edge, with the hole approximately $2\frac{1}{4}$ in. by 2 in. The standard general-purpose Roman tool is that shown in Fig. 12, with a very businesslike

a *b*

11. (*a*) Iron Socketed Axes; (*b*) Iron Shaft-hole Axe. Port, Kanton Bern
Landesmuseum, Zürich

12. Roman Axe *Photo, Reading Museum. From H.G. the Duke of Wellington's Collection*

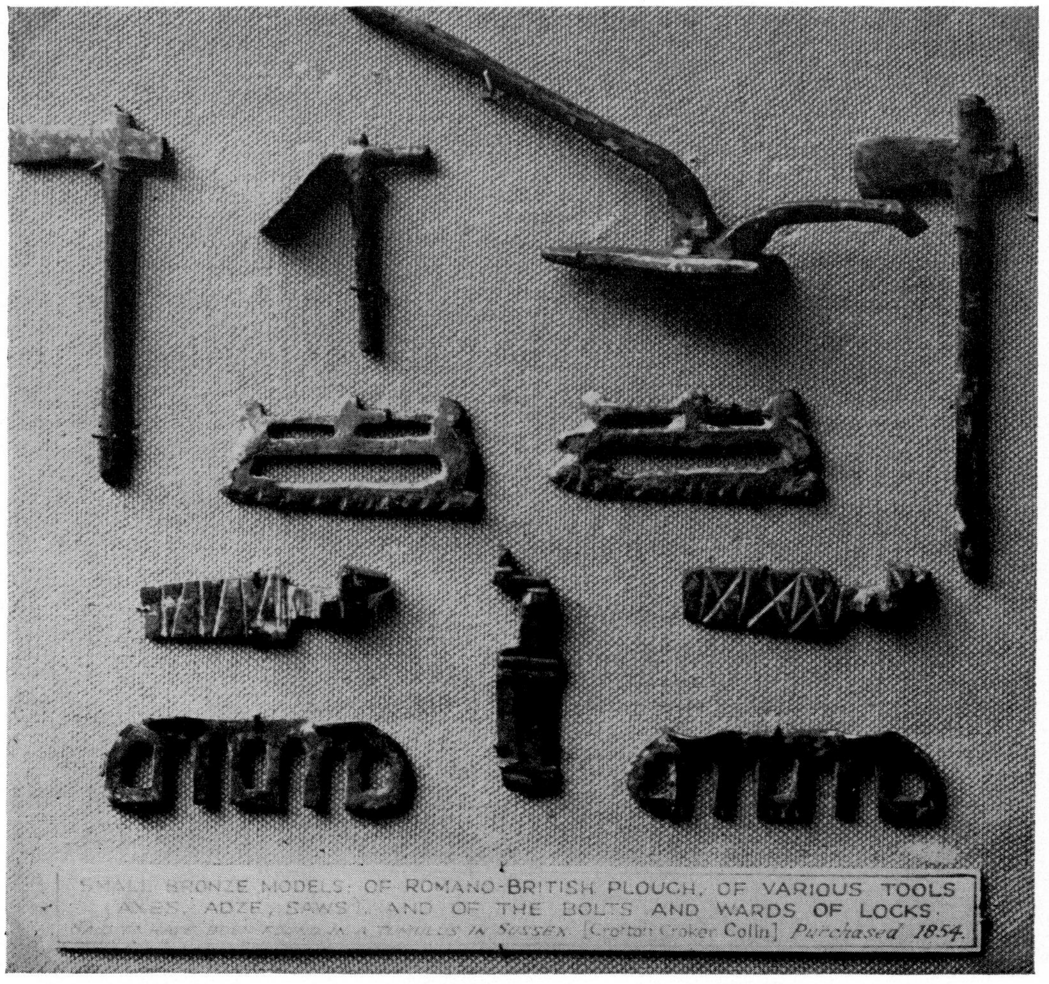

13. Romano-British Bronze Model Tools *Trustees of the British Museum*

flat butt and plain, gracefully curved blade. It was usually fitted with a straight wooden handle like those in the bronze models in Fig. 13. The Romans also made flat-butted axes with the same blade shape, provided with lugs above and below the eye to improve the fixing of the handle, suggested in the model on the right of Fig. 13. The axe-hammer from Augst, near Basel, a very important Roman station in Northern Switzerland (Fig. 14*b*), is another fairly common Roman type. It is about 7½ in. long overall, and the cutting edge is prolonged downwards to form a pronounced 'beard'. On similar axes in the Roman museum at Fiesole near Florence the cutting edge is about 7 in. wide, and Jacobi, in 'Das Romerskastell Saalburg', 1891, figures a number of Roman axes of this advanced type. The axe-adze from Vindonissia (Fig. 14*a*) was also a standard Roman woodworking tool, derived from the Minoan prototype, but this particular example is further notable for the hinged bronze guard for the cutting edge.

For adzes, the Silchester Collection at Reading includes a spoon-shaped adze with a plain butt (Fig. 15*a*), and a hammer-adze with the deep socket characteristic of these Roman tools. The blade of this adze is also curved slightly upwards, a feature which also occurs in three very similar tools in the Cirencester Museum. The bronze model adze second from the left in Fig. 13 brings out another typical point about the Roman adze, the acute angle between blade and handle, in many cases something like 45 degrees. In a normal modern adze the angle varies between 60 and 75 degrees.

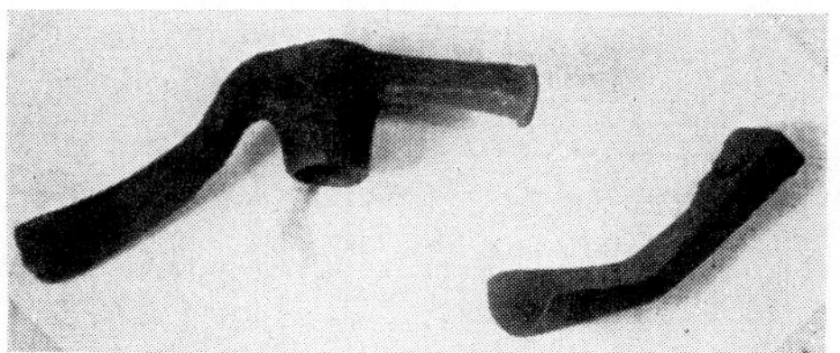

15. Roman Adze Heads

Photo, Reading Museum. From H.G. the Duke of Wellington's Collection

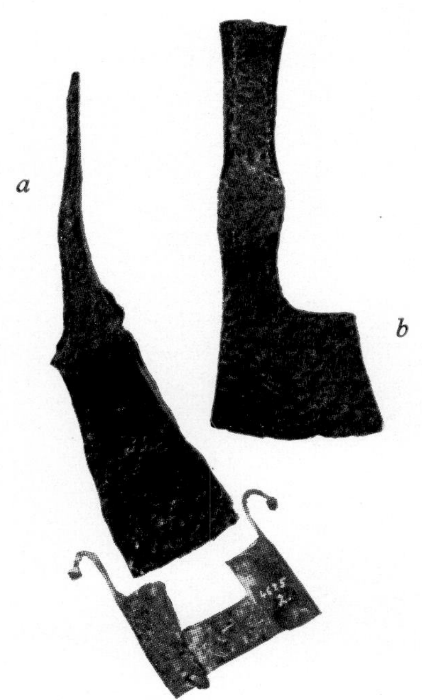

14. (*a*) Axe-Adze with Bronze Guard, Vindonissia; (*b*) Axe-Hammer, Augst

Landesmuseum, Zürich

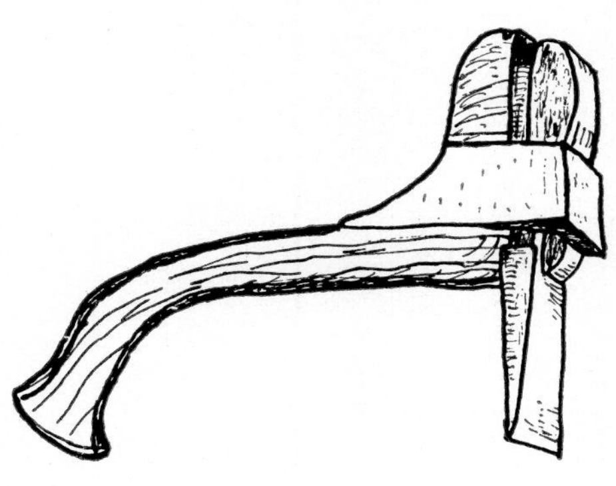

16. Iron-collared Adze

Louvre, Paris

The iron adze shown in Fig. 16 is quite different from any previously discussed, and has several original and interesting features. Its construction clearly derives from the Egyptian bronze adzes such as that shown on Fig. 8, but a completely new departure is the fixing of the blade to the bent handle by means of an iron collar and a wedge. This is the earliest instance in the history of woodworking tools where a wedge is used to secure the blade in this manner. Altogether, three complete examples of this adze are known: two in the Egyptian Museum at Cairo from Abydos (Fig. 38), and Dar el Bahari respectively, figured in Flinders Petrie, 'Tools and Weapons', Pl. XVIII, No. 132; and one in the Louvre, Paris, dating from the Basse Epoque, Egypt, but whose provenance is not known. In addition to these, a model of the same type occurs in the group of tools from Qustul in Nubia, also in the museum at Cairo, dating from between A.D. 150 and 400. This same Nubian group also includes the iron parts (collar and blade) of two further examples. All these have the characteristic iron collar shaped like the upper of a shoe, following the contour of the curved wooden handle. Besides these six examples, the writer is of the opinion that the iron blade and collar from Thebes in Egypt, No. 2452 in the collections at Manchester Museum, described in Flinders Petrie, op. cit., Pl. XXVIII, C. 107, as a 'wide chisel', is another tool of this type. It is said to be Assyrian in origin, and to date from about 660 B.C. Through the courtesy of Mr. Burton-Brown the writer has been able to make a close inspection of this blade and collar, and make a model of it in balsa (Fig. 17), showing how they may be assembled to form an adze of the type under discussion.

17. Iron Adze with Collar and Wedge

In the same case as the Abydos adze in Cairo there is a similar, but longer, iron blade with an almost identical collar. There are also two plain shouldered iron blades, described as 'wide chisels', one of which has a narrow rectangular collar of iron, in the British Museum (Nos. 23064 and 30089). These are said to be of the Roman period in Egypt, and are dated to after 30 B.C. All ten of these curiously devised tools were found in or near Egypt, and with the exception of that from Thebes, are all of the Roman period. The point is of interest, as J. M. Greber, in his scholarly 'Geschichte des Hobels' ('History of the Plane'), Zürich, 1956, suggests that this tool was one of the early stages in the development of the plane. This theory will be dealt with in its proper place; what is remarkable and perhaps little known is that wedged adzes of this pattern are frequently shown in use by shipbuilders in Italian medieval frescoes and mosaics of Noah's Ark, while the writer saw a Sicilian wheelwright using a similar tool in Ragusa in January, 1962.

6: The Middle Ages

During the Middle Ages the axe was the carpenter's tool *par excellence.* Whenever they are depicted in illuminated manuscripts or stained glass, one or more of them will almost certainly be brandishing an axe, often of a pattern which looks more like a battle-axe than a practical tool. A good example of this kind of thing is the group of workmen building the city of Novgorod in the Radzivil MS. of the 'Povest Vremennikh Let' ('The Russian Primary Chronicle'), written in the 15th century but almost certainly copied from an earlier manuscript. The events it describes occurred from the 10th century onwards. It will be noted (Fig. 18) that the battle-axe type is shown in use both for felling and preparing the timber. A similar scene is shown on the page for July in an 11th-century calendar among the Cotton MSS. in the British Museum, and there are innumerable other instances.

18. The Building of Novgorod *'Russian Primary Chronicle', Radzivil MS. f. 3*

Although the medieval artist was very fond of this kind of axe, largely because it was easy to draw and was most men's idea of what an axe ought to look like, as far as surviving examples go it was not very common. There were, in fact, four main types of medieval axe (Fig. 19), considered as a tool rather than as a weapon: type 1, the heavy, comparatively long and narrow felling axe; type 2, the T-shaped axe, used as a rule as a side-axe; type 3, the 'bearded' axe, with a broad blade, used two-handed with a long handle or with a short handle with one hand as a side-axe; and type 4, a light axe or hatchet, more or less symmetrical in shape, used by the joiner or cooper or by non-craftsmen generally for various purposes (including aggression and defence). B. A. Kolchin, in his 'Blacksmith's Work in Old Russia', Moscow, 1953, based on material excavated from 10th- and 11th-century burial mounds, excludes type 2 from the tools, classing his T-shaped axes as *toporika* or battle-axes, but there is plenty of evidence for their use by the woodworkers of the period in Western Europe.

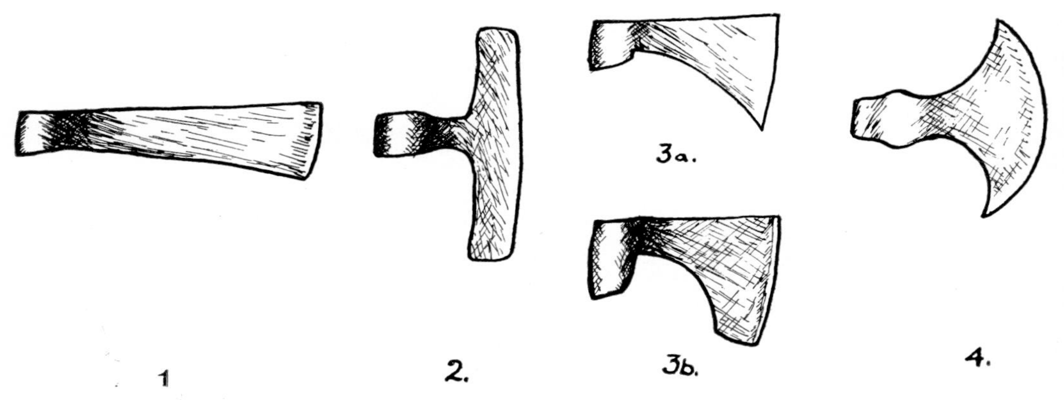

19. Types of Medieval Axe

The standard woodcutter's axe (type 1) had a comparatively long, narrow head, with a parallel or slightly flared blade, very much like its Roman predecessor but usually narrower and heavier and lacking the hammer-like projection at the butt. This threw the effective weight nearer the cutting edge, and enabled the tool to be used for cleaving the timber by striking the flat butt with a hammer or maul. Similar implements are illustrated in the frontispiece and at Fig. 8 in 'London and the Vikings' (London Museum Catalogues, No. 1).

The T-shaped axe (type 2) is first known as a weapon of the Goths and Franks (A.D. 200–800) from an example in the Pitt-Rivers Museum at Farnham from Mainz, and another at Saint-Germain, illustrated in the Guide at Fig. 83, No. 3, together with other *armes mérovingiennes* (A.D. 700–800). Both these implements have thick flat butts, with the blade tapering gradually to the cutting edge. The true T-axe, with a rounded socket and a narrow, thin neck connecting it to the blade, occurs in two examples from the Saxon site at Hurbuck, Co. Durham (Fig. 11, 'The Anglo-Saxons', Wilson). The author dates them to A.D. 700–1000. An axe very similar to these, one of several in the

Reading Museum from chance finds in the Thames Valley, which makes them difficult to date precisely, is shown at Fig. 20.

A T-axe of this pattern, except that the neck is usually shown much shorter, is quite common in the manuscripts from the 10th to the 14th century, where it is almost always used as a side-axe for trimming the edges of the timber. It occurs four times in the Bayeux Tapestry (*c.* A.D. 1080); one in the hands of Duke William's foreman shipwright; another for squaring a balk after felling; the third in one of the lewd pictures in the lower border, showing a man trimming the edge of a plank; and the fourth as a side-axe for

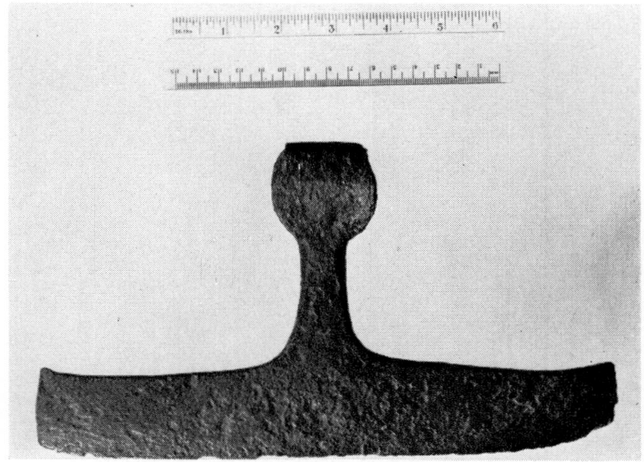

20. Saxon T-Axe, Thatcham, Berks *Reading Museum*

cleaning up the hull of a boat. The man using this latter is shown working left-handed, and must have been using a special tool with the bevel ground the other way. One wonders whether he was paid more per day than the other ship's carpenters, as his modern counterparts the left-handed boiler-makers of the Clyde used to be. The picture of Noah building the Ark in the Holkham Bible (*c.* 1326) shows two T-axes, one with a long handle being used two-handed for working the edge of a board, and the other with a short handle, hanging on the Ark. T-axes of a rather more flamboyant shape are also shown in the 12th- and 13th-century mosaics of the same subject in St. Mark's, Venice, and the Duomo at Monreale, near Palermo in Sicily. According to the evidence of the manuscripts, the T-axe was gradually superseded from the middle of the 14th century onwards by the short-handled version of type 3 (Fig. 19), with a broad asymmetrical blade, often set at an angle to the socket to protect the workman's knuckles from injury.

The majority of surviving medieval axes are of types 3*a* or 3*b*, with various permutations of long or short socket, rounded or flat butt, the blades with a single or double curve to a point at the heel (3*a*) or single curve with 'beard' (3*b*). A Swedish example, of type 3*a* is shown in Fig. 21, with a short socket and the cutting edge prolonged downwards to a point. This kind of axe is shown in the well-known picture of St. Joseph by the Maître de Flemalle which used to be in Brussels but is now in New York. A type 3*b* variation, with a broader and heavier blade, and a correspondingly longer socket, comes from Orreby (Fig. 22). A similar tool is shown resting against the trestle in the Jost Ammann woodcut of the Zimmermann (Fig. 23). It is interesting to compare this picture of a 16th-century carpenter at work with that in Rodler's 'Perspectiva', Frank-

21. Medieval Axe
Nordiska Museet, Stockholm

22. Medieval Axe, Orreby
Nordiska Museet, Stockholm

23. 16th-century Carpenters at Work
Jost Ammann. Bibliothèque Nationale, Bern

furt, 1546, illustrated in Salzman's 'Building in England', Oxford, 1952, p. 196. Both men are squaring a round log into a balk or deal; in the Rodler picture, the workman is cutting notches in the log to act as a guide for trimming with a side-axe which lies in the foreground; in the Ammann woodcut the notches have been cut and the sides are being trimmed. It is curious, however, that the workman here seems to be using a felling axe for this purpose, while the side-axe remains unused; moreover, he seems to be working away from himself. The correct method is shown in an illustration to a 15th-century French MS. of the 'Livre de Rustican' (B.M. Add. MS. 19720), where an axe of type 3*b* is being used. Mercer, in 'Ancient Carpenter's Tools', refers to this process as 'scoring-in' and says it was still common in the States about sixty years ago.

A very elaborate and highly stylised example of the 17th-century German *Breitbeil* or broad axe comes from the Trier Municipal Museum (Fig. 24). Like many German tools of this period, it doesn't appear to have been used a great deal.

24. 17th-century Broad Axe
Städtisches Museum, Trier

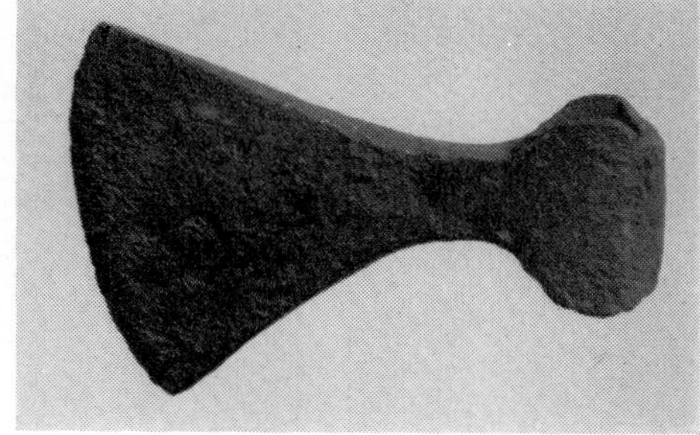

25. Medieval Axe
Nationalmuseet, Copenhagen

In spite of the medieval artist's fondness for the symmetrical (type 4) axe, comparatively few tools of this pattern have come down to us. A very good example is the one from Copenhagen (Fig. 25), and there are others at York, Reading, and in the London Museum.

With regard to adzes, the Saxon group from Hurbuck, Co. Durham, referred to earlier, includes a shaft-hole adze similar to the Roman tool shown on left in Fig. 15. This is essentially an axe with the blade forged at right angles to the eye, and several tools of this common pattern were found in the pre-Mongolian settlements of European Russia (Fig. 26). A small T-shaped adze was also found at Hurbuck, and a much larger implement of this form appears in a group of shipbuilder's tools of the late Viking period (A.D. 950–1000) from Mastermyr in Gotland (Fig. 128). A much simpler type of adze, forged from a flat plate with the flanges bent round to form a socket (Fig. 27) recalls similar tools from the Late Bronze Age, and would have required a similar knee-shaped wooden haft. In addition to those described in Kolchin's book cited above, identical tools from the 13th century are illustrated in Viires' 'Esthonian Folkcrafts in Wood', Tallinn, 1960. Actually in Russian the term for thin prepared boards, the equivalent of the English 'wainscot', is known as *tyoss*, from the name of the tool, the *teslo* (adze), with which it was prepared, while the workman who used the tool was known as a *tessalshchik* from the same root.

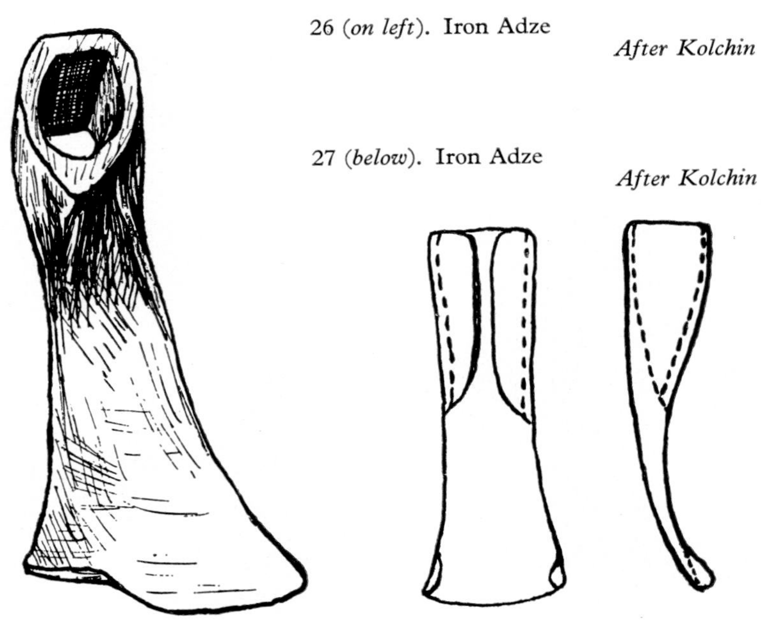

26 (*on left*). Iron Adze *After Kolchin*

27 (*below*). Iron Adze *After Kolchin*

Illustrations of adzes are rare in the medieval manuscripts, indeed Mercer remarks that he has never seen one in drawings of the period. Yet the documentary evidence is quite definite that the adze was one of the most useful tools in the medieval woodworker's kit. Salzman (*op. cit.*) quotes an account for work on Restormel Castle in 1343 where 6d. was paid for 'an ades for smoothing old timber, because it was so full of nails that the carpenters would not set their own tools to it'. This entry is also interesting for showing that in spite of the comparative abundance of timber, a certain amount of old stuff was used again, and in throwing some light on a question which has always interested the writer: to what extent the workmen in the Middle Ages owned their own tools. Evidently they all possessed a kit of their own, but the employer had to provide special implements for emergencies like this. This cost of this 'ades' would have been the equivalent of a day and a half's wages for the artisan of that period.

Most of the adzes depicted in the mosaics and frescoes of the late Byzantine period in Italy and Sicily (St. Mark's, Venice, the Duomo at Monreale, and the Capella Palatina at Palermo) appear to be of a similar pattern to the Romano-Egyptian adze described earlier, with an iron collar and wedged blade, although the nature of the medium makes their construction rather doubtful. A clear example of this type, however, occurs in the sculptured soffit over the main door at St. Mark's, illustrating the building of the Ark, showing that this form of adze was still current in the countries surrounding the Mediterranean Sea, where indeed it still is to this day.

Referring back to the Ammann woodcut (Fig. 23), the workman in the left foreground is chopping out a mortice in a large timber scantling with a tool known in English as the 'twybill'. This is a medieval specialisation of the Minoan and later Roman axe-adze, with both cutting edges narrowed and lengthened, and provided with a long handle to be used as shown in the cut.

7: The 18th Century to the Present Day

Owing to the increasing efficiency of hand and later machine sawing and planing, the axe and the adze have suffered a progressive decline in importance from the 18th century to the present day, while some types have almost disappeared altogether from general use. The first of the medieval axes to drop out was the type 2, which was already being superseded by the different forms of side-axe in the 15th century. There are no T-axes in Diderot's 'Encyclopédie' (1751–69), while the only modern representatives are the various forms of cooper's axe. The section 'Charpente' in Diderot's work shows the *cognée*, or heavy, general-purpose axe (Fig. 28*a*), with a slightly flared blade and a long cylindrical socket (a feature which has been completely discarded in modern times), and the heavy *hache* (Fig. 28*b*), the successor of the type 1 felling axe. The lighter *hachette à marteau* (Fig. 28*c*) sustains the tradition of the symmetrical type 4.

For adzes, Diderot illustrates the *herminette à marteau* (Fig. 29*a*), the *herminette double* (Fig. 29*b*), with one cutting edge straight and the other with a deep curve, and the *herminette* proper (Fig. 29*c*), with the blade wedged against an iron collar as in the Romano-Egyptian and Italian tools described earlier. The 'Encylopédie' also shows a form of twybill called the *besaiguë*, similar to that in the Ammann woodcut of the carpenters, but without a handle. This might be considered at first glance to be an error on the part of the engraver, but fortunately Plate 1 of the 'Charpente' article shows a workman using the paring-chisel end of this tool to true up the shoulder of a halving joint on a large timber scantling, gripping the short socket with the right hand and controlling the tool with the left. The mortice chisel end, called in the French the *bec-d'âne*, must also have been used without a handle as well, as a similar tool to Diderot's is illustrated in the painting 'The Dream of St. Joseph', by Phillippe de Champaigne (1602–74) in the National Gallery. Part of the tool is concealed under St. Joseph's gown, but the short, handleless socket is in full view. Bringing the discussion of this implement up to modern times, a catalogue of the Goldenberg tool firm of Saverne, Alsace, dated 1875, gives a twybill almost identical with Diderot's, except that the chisel end is bevelled on the sides as well. This tool is 2 ft. 6 in. long, has no handle, and is described as the 'Parisian pattern'. Another catalogue in the collection of Mr. R. A. Salaman, of Schmidt of Elberfeld, undated, but probably about 1880, shows a 'cross-axe' exactly like the twybill, with a short, hollow, hexagonal socket. On the other hand Mercer, in 'Ancient Carpenters' Tools', illustrates three handled twybills on Fig. 159, dating from

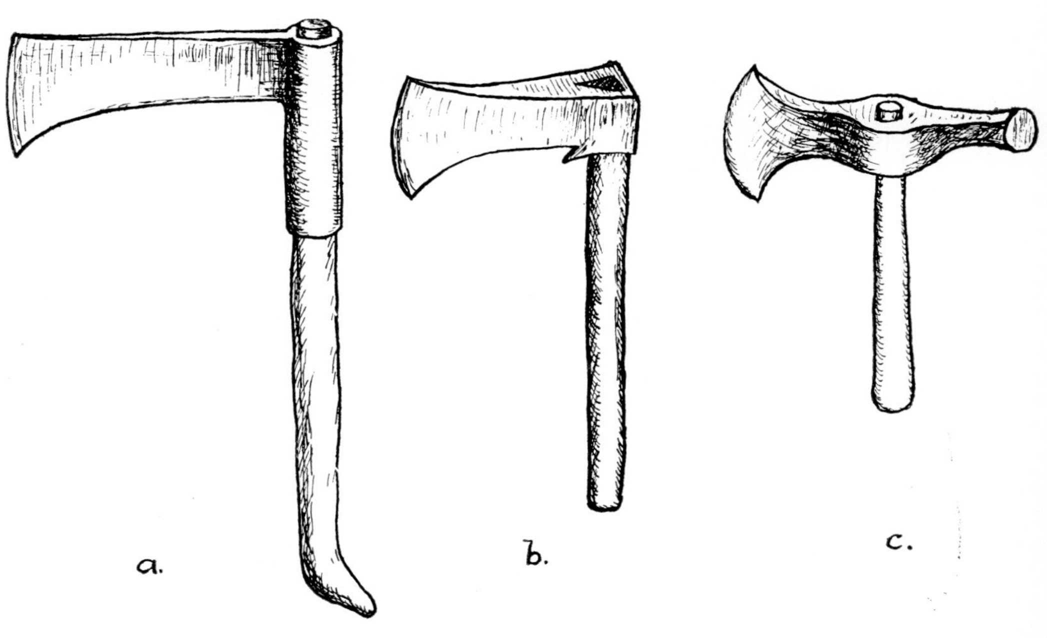

28. (*a*) Heavy Axe (*Cognée*) (*b*) Felling Axe (*Hache*) (*c*) Hatchet (*Hachette à marteau*)
Diderot, 'Encyclopédie', 1751–69

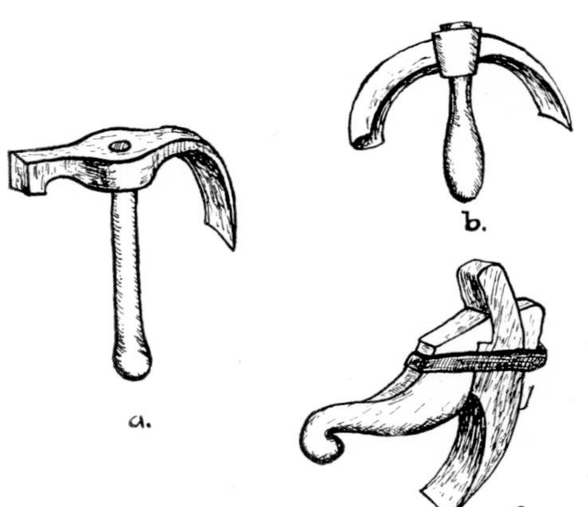

29. 18th-century French Adzes
Diderot

about 1830 through to about 1900, which were used in the States during the last century for cutting mortices. My friend Mr. Christian Waagepetersen, of the Kalundborg Museum, Denmark, who has done a good deal of research on the twybill there and is now engaged on a monograph on the subject, says that these tools are found both with and without handles. A handled example from his collection, very similar to those in Mercer, is illustrated in Fig. 30. A much commoner tool in Denmark, known as the *Stikøkse*, which only retains the paring-chisel end of the twybill, with an identical short, empty socket, is also used as in the Diderot engraving, like an ordinary chisel. The Goldenberg catalogue quoted above lists this tool as a 'mortising axe (pioche)', while the Schmidt catalogue calls it simply the 'mortice axe'.* It is unlikely that either of these implements has been used in this country since the Middle Ages, while the twybills shown in Mercer were only common among the 'Pennsylvania Dutch' (mostly German immigrants) in the United States.

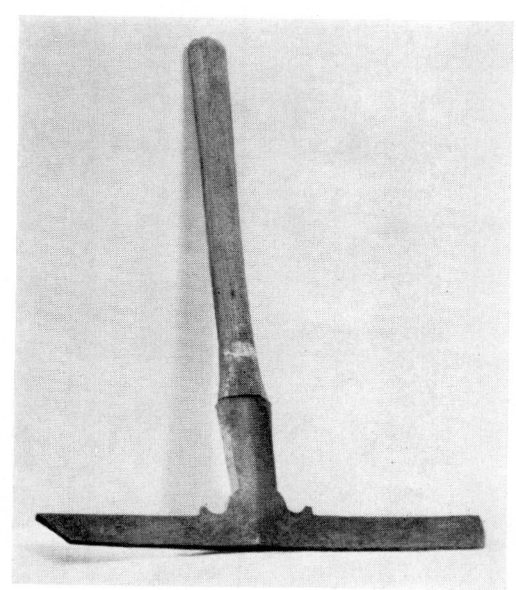

30. Danish Twybill
Kalundborg Museum

In England about a hundred years after Diderot the axe seems to have made one last flourish before its eventual eclipse. The 1868 catalogue of W. Gilpin Senr. of Wedges Mills, Cannock, lists no less than forty-seven different patterns. These vary according to trades: coachmaker's, wheelwright's, shipwright's, mast-maker's, and cooper's; purposes: mahogany squaring, felling, hedging, rafting, lopping, beating, mortice, and pitching; and localities: Kent, Norfolk, Yorkshire, Lincolnshire, American, Canadian, Kentucky, Australian, Spanish, Ohio, Scotch, Irish, Plymouth, Banbury, Manchester, Guildford, Newtown and London wheelwright's, Wantage, Marychurch, Chichester, Newcastle, and Dublin. In the Goldenberg catalogue Gilpin's 'Spanish' axe, with a

* Mr. Waagepetersen sent the writer one of these tools, brand new from the German makers, as a Christmas present last year.

rounded butt and flared blade like the medieval type 3*a*, is called the 'Biscayan', while Sorby's of Sheffield (*c.* 1900) list a similar tool as the 'Brazil' adze. Names from catalogues other than Gilpin's include: Dutch side, New Zealand, Suffolk, Westmorland, West Indian felling, and Columbia. A large number of these different patterns were clearly for export, but even for the home market it seems as if every separate trade and every locality had its own special type. Some of the commoner varieties are illustrated in Figs. 31 and 32, taken from the 1864 catalogue of William Marples and Son, Sheffield, kindly loaned to the writer by Mr. A. O. C. Fenton. With the exception of Fig. 32*a*,

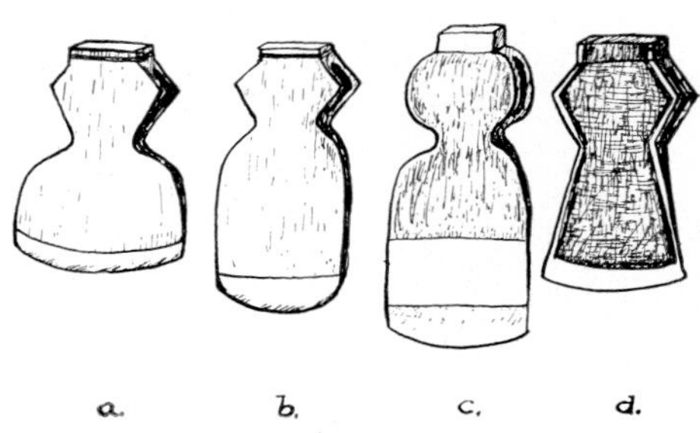

31. 19th-century Axes: (*a*) Kent Axe; (*b*) Suffolk Axe; (*c*) Scotch Axe; (*d*) Irish Axe
William Marples & Sons, Sheffield. 1864 Catalogue

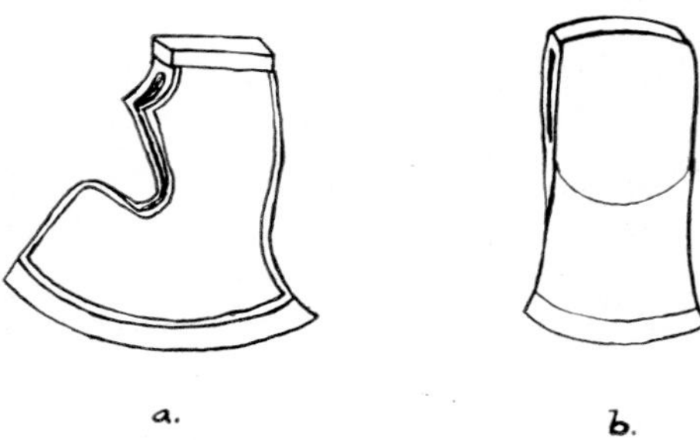

32. 19th-century Axes: (*a*) Coachmaker's Side Axe; (*b*) American Wedge Axe
William Marples & Sons, 1864

these are symmetrical axes with a flat poll or butt, with slight variations in shape and proportion. This reversion to the symmetrical shape of the Late Bronze Age is peculiar; in the Gilpin list the ratio of these to the asymmetrical patterns is about 1:1. The type 3 medieval axe survives in the coachmaker's (Fig. 32*a*), and in some of the other special trade tools, but the felling axe is represented by an entirely new type, with a blunt, heavy, wedge-shaped symmetrical blade and long handle, known as the American wedge axe (Fig. 32*b*).

In the present-day catalogues, such as those of Tyzack & Son and Buck & Hickman, the only survivor of the 'county' type axe is the Kent. In most modern lists the appellation 'American' has been dropped from the description of the wedge or felling axe, but several makers have a smaller version, sometimes rather fancifully designated the 'American Hand Axe or Tomahawk'. It is curious to reflect that this, the final product of 6,000 years of incessant trial and experiment, is perhaps the simplest and most

33. Danish Double Axes
Skagens Fortidsminder, Denmark

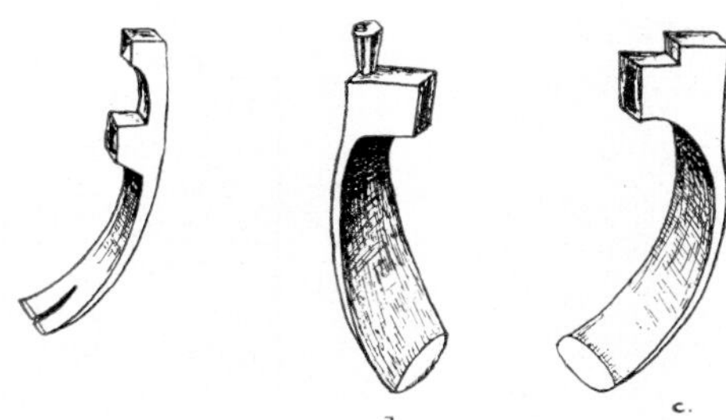

34. Adzes, 1864: (*a*) Cooper's; (*b*) Carpenter's; (*c*) Wheeler's
William Marples & Sons

functional of all. In spite of this, however, Tyzacks still list an 'English Felling Axe' in the direct line of the medieval type 1, while the type 3 still survives in the coach side-axe, practically identical with Fig. 32*a*, and the cricket-bat maker's side-axe.

Finally, to show that there is nothing new under the sun, a form of double-bladed axe similar to the Minoan and later Greek and Roman 'bipennis' was in use recently by carpenters breaking up wrecked ships at Skagen in Denmark (Fig. 33).

The adzes in the Marples 1864 catalogue, of which the usual varieties such as the cooper's, carpenter's, and wheeler's are shown (Fig. 34*a*, *b*, and *c*), have assumed their modern form, with a square or rectangular socket and hammer-headed butt. The collared adze with the wedge is shown in the 1875 Goldenberg catalogue and in Sorby's of Sheffield *c.* 1900 under the name of the Brazil or Spanish slot adze, and as was mentioned earlier, the writer saw one of these tools in use recently in South Sicily. There is also an example in the museum at Ludlow, but its age and provenance are unknown.

Regarding the material used for these tools, the two most important innovations in the history of the axe, the adoption of metal (in the first place copper) instead of stone, and the later substitution of iron for bronze, were both cases of *reculer pour mieux sauter*, as neither metal in its crude form is any harder than the material it replaced. In the first case the only immediate advantage lay in its weight (copper being over three times as heavy as flint) and perhaps its greater malleability, giving the tool a longer life. But only the further step of adding tin to form bronze (with a slight loss in specific gravity) gave the new tools the edge, in both senses, over the old. Similarly in the case of iron; the conservative Bronze Age woodworker was perfectly justified in looking askance at the new material, until the rustic smiths, persevering with the cheaper and more available metal, found ways of adding carbon to form steel. This must have occurred fairly early in the development of the iron axe, and Roman axes similar to those in Fig. 12 have recently been analysed and found to contain steel.

In his researches on the 11th- and 12th-century Russian carpenters' tools, B. A. Kolchin and his assistants made extensive metallurgical tests of the axes, chisels, knives and other implements found in the settlements and burial mounds. Of 22 axes tested, 7 had a steel tip welded over the iron base; in 7 others the steel was inserted between the folded iron of the head. Seven others were solid steel, and only one of iron throughout. In most cases there were signs of hardening and subsequent tempering, confined, of course, to the cutting edge. Some examples showed a hardness of 724 Vickers units.

Modern tools have benefited from the intensive research work carried out by metallurgists on steel alloys, indeed in 1864 Marples listed a 'Best Electro Boracic Steel Axe', probably produced in an electric furnace, at 1s. per lb., compared with the average price of about 9d.

Note: The double-bladed axe (Fig. 33) has in fact been in use since about 1840 in the United States for felling timber. Known as the 'Yankee double-bitted axe', it appears to be a re-invention (it is first recorded in Maine) of the Minoan and Roman tool, and although most felling is done nowadays by portable electric saws, it is still in the catalogues of the mail-order firms for sale to farmers and so on. The double edge has the advantage that the tool can be used all day on the lot without going back to the shack for re-sharpening.

SECTION II

THE PLANE

1: Origins

ALTHOUGH A large amount of advanced furniture and other woodwork has come down to us from Egyptian times, it is certain that the highly skilled craftsmen who made it knew nothing of the plane. Normally the wood was left as it came from the axe or adze, but if a smoother surface were required to take paintings or inscriptions, it was rubbed down with stone blocks, using sand as an abrasive (Fig. 35). It is possible that the semi-circular object in the Sopi coffin frieze (Fig. 7) is intended to represent one of these blocks.

35. Egyptian Woodworkers, 2540 B.C.
Mastaba of Tiye *Saqqara. Author's photograph*

This method, however, was of little value in preparing the wood to the finer limits required for framed and panelled work which became fashionable in early classical times. The need arose for a cutting tool which could be easily adjusted and which depended less on the skill of the craftsman, so frequently emphasised in the passages in Homer describing the adze. We therefore find the Romans, at about the beginning of the Christian era, already in possession of the plane, which must have had a long history behind it. There is a tradition that it was invented by the Greeks, and the name of Daedalus, as the archetypal craftsman, is invoked in this connection. As usual, the Greeks had a word for it (*rhykane*), but so far no actual Greek planes have come to light.

The earliest known planes are those from Pompeii, dating from before A.D. 79, when the town was overwhelmed by a volcanic eruption. Pliny the Elder, who was himself an indirect victim of this catastrophe, wrote of the plane in terms which show that it must have been a common tool in his day. Discussing the fir, he notes: 'The shavings of this wood, when briskly planed, curl up in circles like the tendrils of the vine.' Here he puts his finger unerringly on the essential feature of the new tool, the fact that it takes off a continuous shaving, instead of the chips removed by tools like the axe or adze, chisel or knife.

It has already been suggested that the wedged adze of the Roman period in Egypt may have been an early stage in the development of the plane. Basing himself on the example in the Louvre, J. M. Greber (*op. cit.*) makes a simple modification of the stock (reproduced by his kind permission in Fig. 36), converting the adze to a shaving tool

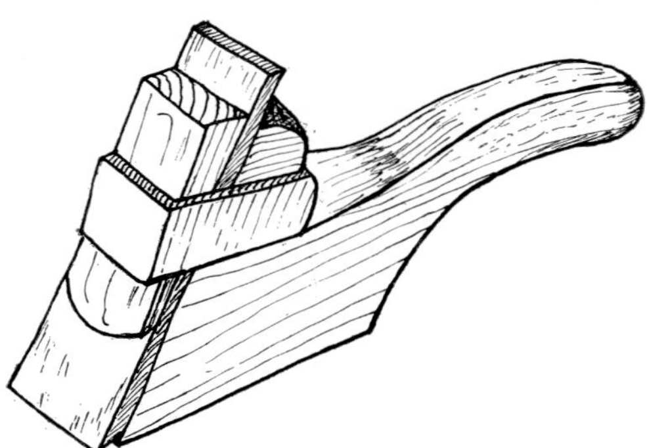

36. Suggested Modification of Wedged Adze

Courtesy J. M. Greber

similar to a bullnose rabbet plane. The next stage would be to enclose the iron in the stock so that part of the latter projects in front of the cutting edge, thus holding down the fibres of the wood. The iron strap or collar would then be modified to a bar across the mouth, and the blade firmly wedged against it. In this way all the essentials of an efficient plane would be present. But all this is pure conjecture, as no intermediate stages have as yet been identified. Furthermore, the Qustul adzes are still unchanged as late as A.D. 150–400, when some sort of plane had already been in use for a century or more, in fact similar tools were in use right through the Middle Ages and up to modern times. This seems to indicate that whatever tool was modified to develop the early planes, it could hardly have been the wedged adze.

Another, and more likely line of development could have been through the scratch stock to the moulding plane and plough, and then, by widening the iron, to the smoother and jack plane. One point in favour of this theory is that a large number of Roman plough- and moulding-plane irons are still extant (Greber lists twenty from the German sites alone), while all the known Roman smoothing- and jack-plane irons are comparatively narrow, from $1\frac{1}{4}$ in. to $1\frac{3}{4}$ in. at most, as compared with the 3 in. to 4 in. of the wedged adzes. In this connection the Lapp moulding plane in Fig. 37 is of some interest. The block is similar to Herr Greber's modified adze, except that the iron blade is held against a face sloping the opposite way, the tool being pulled instead of pushed. G. A. Norman, of the Sandvigske Samlinger, Maihaugen, Norway, to whom the writer is indebted for Fig. 37 and much valuable information, suggests in his 'Hovelens Historie' ('History of the Plane'), Lillehammer, 1954, that the Lapp planes were developed from the *båtastrek* or 'boat-moulder', used by the Vikings to work the mouldings on the edges of the planks forming the hull of their long-boats, e.g., the Oseberg ship. Modern examples of the *båtastrek* have a stock similar to that of Fig. 37 with a longer handle, and detachable pins at the sides acting as a fence, so that the moulding can be struck from either hand (the dovetailed grooves on either side of Fig. 37 serve to take a similar fence).

37. Lapp Moulding Plane
Sandvigske Samlinger, Lillehammer

It is possible that the famous Vimose plane, which has hitherto seemed to escape classification altogether, belongs to this line of development. This tool, with the fragments of two others, was found in the Vimose bog on the Danish island of Fynen, near Odense; part of a mass of tools, weapons, and other gear, the booty of war, broken up and thrown into the bog in accordance with an old pagan custom. From the style of the weapons, and from associated coins, the find is dated to A.D. 300–400. The plane is just over 10 in. long and about $1\frac{1}{2}$ in. wide in the middle. The mouth is exactly in the centre; the iron was probably about $\frac{9}{16}$ in. wide, and held in place by a wedge against a peg across the mouth. The sole is hollowed out underneath to a depth of about $\frac{1}{8}$ in. It appears to be some kind of rounding plane, possibly for the shafts of spears or wheel-spokes.

The Romans may have reached the same destination by a slightly different route. In the Egyptian Museum at Cairo there is the wooden stock of a small rounding plane (Fig. 38), 6 in. long by 3 in. wide, and about $1\frac{1}{2}$ in. thick. The iron was wedged into a slot on the face of the stock, with the lower end opened out to allow the shavings to escape. This method of fixing the iron of a plough or narrow rebate plane was retained up to the middle of the 18th century, and is illustrated in Diderot. A reconstructed plough plane (using an original Roman iron) in the exhibition of joiners' tools in the Landesmuseum at Zürich shows the iron in the centre of the stock, as in the modern tool, but

38. Roman Moulding Plane, Kom Washim *Egyptian Museum, Cairo*

Prof. Dr. E. Vogt, the Director, admits that the museum joiner, who made the reconstruction, had no actual Roman original to work on.

This account of the origins and development of the plane is of necessity vague and inadequate in the absence of trustworthy evidence. A recent tour made by the writer through Italy, Greece, and Egypt failed to discover any tools at all resembling planes except the Cairo example mentioned above. The fact that no planes were found in Greece does not necessarily mean that the Daedalus legends are false; very few tools of any kind are found there anyway, particularly from the Early Iron Age. But even in Egypt the plane is not known at all until Roman times, although the Greeks had been there before them as traders or conquerors for several hundred years. The only certain thing is that by the 1st century of our era Roman joiners and cabinet-makers already possessed a range of planes suitable for the advanced work they were called upon to do.

2: The Roman Period

A list of the known planes of the Roman period is set out in Table II. This is based on the list in J. M. Greber's book mentioned above, re-arranged according to the method of construction. Besides the planes, a large number of separate plane irons are known from various Roman sites in Germany, France, Switzerland, and Scotland. There are also a number of sculptures, frescoes, and so on, with representations of the plane and other tools, which help to confirm the conclusions arrived at concerning the design and use of this tool in Roman times.

TABLE II

KNOWN ROMAN PLANES

Source	*Date of Find*	*Method of Construction*	*Size, cm.* L.	W.	H.	*Width of Iron, mm.*	*Angle, deg.*
Pompeii	1850	Folded iron plate with wooden core	21	6	4·5	35	50
,,	,,		21	6	5	40	50
Kom Washim	1924	Wood (moulding)	16	5	9·5	20	50
Saalburg	1907	Wood (jack)	38	4·5	5·5	30	52
Seltz	1887	Iron sole with four rivets	34	4·5	5	30	—
Caerwent	1904		36·5	4·5	—	30	66
Verulamium	1958		44	7·5	7	40	—
Feldburg	—	Iron sole with rivets and side plates	36·8	4·8	5·5	32	58
Saalburg	1885		36·2	4·8	4·5	32	—
Zugmantell	1934		35·2	4·4	5·5	28	—
Silchester	1890		34	5	6	38	65
Cologne	1880		32·4	5	5	40	53
Caerwent	1904	Iron sole	32·5	5	—	30	66

Besides being the earliest known, the Pompeian planes (Fig. 39) are the only surviving examples of Roman smoothing planes. They are also unique in the way they are made. An iron plate about $\frac{1}{4}$ in. thick was bent into the shape of a letter U to form an open-sided box and filled in with wood, which appears to be either chestnut or oak. The mouth was cut in the sole about one-third the way back from the toe, and the iron, set at an angle of about 50 degrees, was held with a wedge against a round iron bar across

39. Roman Smoothing Planes *Museo Nazionale, Naples*

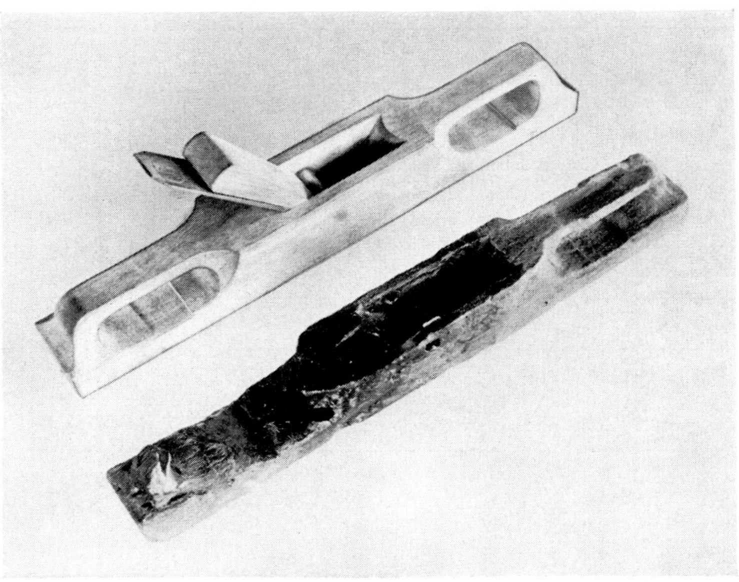

40. Roman Wooden Jack Plane, with Reconstruction *Saalburgmuseum, Homburg v.d. Hohe*

the opening. This method of wedging the iron is a characteristic feature of Roman planes, in fact it was used for all planes up to the end of the 15th century, and is retained to this day for small block planes, violin planes, and some Continental smoothers. The slotted wedge of the modern wooden plane was introduced at the close of the Middle Ages; it first appears in Dürer's engraving 'Melancholia', dated 1514.

The slotted grip for the right hand is another characteristic of Roman planes. It is interesting to note that except for the narrow iron, the dimensions of these Pompeian planes agree very closely with those of the Stanley No. 3 smoother.

The Kom Washim plane has already been described. The reason why small planes like this have not survived in greater numbers is probably because as soon as they are worn out they are thrown away and a fresh stock made.

The next ten planes on the list, apart from the recently discovered tool from Verulamium, show a striking uniformity of size and pattern, and no doubt represent the standard Roman jack plane. The method of construction varies from the tool made entirely of wood through intermediate forms with an iron sole to give greater accuracy and longer life, sometimes provided with side plates to strengthen the wooden stock, to the advanced Silchester and Cologne examples, where the wood merely acts as a core for a metal body.

The Saalburg wooden plane (Fig. 40) owes its preservation, like the Silchester tools, to having been thrown down a well when the settlement was attacked and destroyed by barbarians. It is of beechwood, and rather longer than the others, except the Verulamium example. The handle at the back is damaged badly, but the front grip is practically intact, and it is clear that the reconstruction shown in the upper part of the photograph, suggested by Dr. Jacobi of the Saalburgmuseum, is the correct one. The sandstone relief of a workman using one of these planes (Fig. 41), also from Saalburg, is further

41. Roman Workman with Jack Plane, Sandstone Relief, Saalburg

Landesmuseum, Trier

42. Monument to Roman Carpenter

Museo Nazionale, L'Aquila

confirmation. The planes shown on the pediment of a carpenter's memorial in the Museo Nazionale at L'Aquila (Fig. 42) and on the funerary *cippo* of Eutyches from Priolo in Sicily (Fig. 43) have similar grips. The holes for the cross-bar to take the wedge, semi-circular in section in the case of the Saalburg plane, can be clearly seen in the cheeks of the stock (they are also visible on the L'Aquila monument tool). An interesting feature is the curved shape of the front of the mouth opening, but the purpose of the wide, shallow grooves across the bottom of the handle slots is so far unexplained.

The surviving fragments of the next group consist of an iron sole turned up at both ends. The Seltz and Verulamium (Fig. 44) planes also have four rivets, two on either side of the mouth, while the Caerwent plane (Fig. 45) has the corresponding holes. The iron sole from Seltz, near Hagenau, in Alsace was found with other carpenters' tools and bronze utensils in a cache buried for safety during a raid by German tribesmen towards the end of the 2nd or the beginning of the 3rd century A.D. It was published by F. A. Schaeffer in 'Un dépôt d'outils et un trésor de bronzes de l'époque gallo-romaine

43. Eutyches 'cippo' from Priolo.
Museo Nazionale, Syracuse

44. Roman Plane *By permission of the Verulamium Excavation Committee*

découverts à Seltz (Bas-Rhin)', Hagenau, 1927. It consists of a thick iron bar with both ends turned up; a wide mouth cut about half-way along; the iron is missing, but four rivets, 2 in. high, and spaced about $3\frac{1}{2}$ in. apart, are still in position, two on either side of the mouth.

On the first Caerwent plane on the list (Fig. 45) the sole is about 1 in. longer, and although the iron is still present, the rivets are missing. As with all the iron plane soles of this type, the mouth opening is not exactly central, but about 5% of the total length nearer the toe than the heel. In its present position the iron of the Caerwent plane slopes towards the toe, but the sharpening bevel is on the top, which is the wrong way round for an iron with a slope of over 60 degrees. It could hardly have been used like this, and may have been forced over accidentally to the wrong position; if it were made to slope the other way, the bevel would be underneath in the usual manner. The holes for the rivets on either side are about 4 in. apart.

45. Roman Plane Sole and Iron, Caerwent *Newport, Mon. Museum*

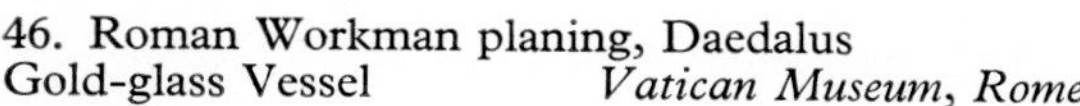

46. Roman Workman planing, Daedalus Gold-glass Vessel *Vatican Museum, Rome*

The sole of the Verulamium plane (Fig. 44) is the largest and heaviest to have been found so far, being $17\frac{1}{4}$ in. long, 3 in. wide, and $\frac{5}{8}$ in. thick, with a turn-up of about 1 in. at each end. The substantial rivets of $\frac{3}{8}$ in. iron are roughly $2\frac{3}{4}$ in. high, and the two middle ones are capped with circular plates which were probably originally about $1\frac{1}{2}$ in. diameter. The distance between centres of the front pair is $4\frac{3}{8}$ in. and of the back pair

5⅛ in. giving plenty of room for ample grips. Although the sole is so wide and heavy the iron could not have been more than 1½ in. across. This plane approximates to the apparent length of the tools in use on the Pompeii fresco and the Daedalus glass vessel (Fig. 46).

The planes of the next group, from the German frontier posts at Saalburg, Feldburg, and Zugmantell, when originally found, consisted of two separate parts: a sole with rivets like the preceding examples, and a box-like arrangement composed of two plates connected by three cross-rivets, one of which acted as the bar to secure the wedge and the iron. These plates are about ¼ in. narrower than the distance from the sole to the top of the rivets, and there is a narrow strip along the top edge turned over at right angles. A reconstruction of these planes (minus the iron and wedge) is given in Fig. 47, and shows that this type consisted of a wooden stock with an iron sole secured by four rivets as before, with the additional reinforcement of two plates to strengthen the cheeks of the stock at its thinnest point. The bottom of the iron rested on the bevelled portion of the mouth opening and it was supported by the sloping bed of the stock, and a wedge secured it against the central cross-rivet. There is in each case about 4 in. of clearance between the pairs of upright rivets in the sole, giving plenty of room for handles.

The Silchester plane (Fig. 48) resembles the previous six in many respects, but there are differences in detail. The sole with the turned-up ends and four rivets is practically the same, but the side plates are fixed to the sole and appear to have extended along the whole length of the wooden core. There is no angle strip at the top of these plates, in fact the top edge is about ¼ in. below the top of the rivets, and the plates must have been

47. Reconstruction of Roman Planes from Saalburg, Fledburg, and Zugmantell
After Jacobi

48. Roman Plane, Silchester
Photo. Reading Museum. From H.G. The Duke of Wellington's Collection

that much narrower than the stock. From information supplied by Mr. G. C. Boon, formerly of Reading Museum, it seems unlikely that this plane had the usual hollow grip in front of the iron, as the distance between these two rivets is only about $2\frac{3}{4}$ in., while the off-side plate extends into this space, as can be seen from the photograph. The space between the two rivets at the back, about $3\frac{3}{8}$ in., would allow of a grip for the four fingers of a small hand. A suggested reconstruction of the plane is given in Fig. 49.

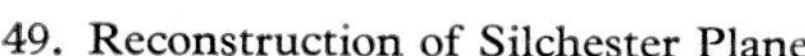

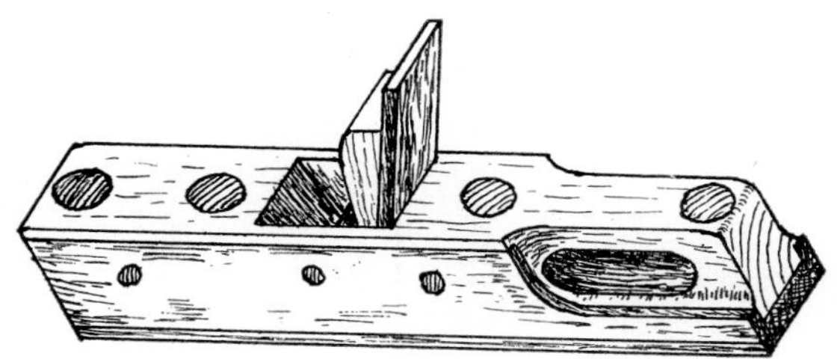

49. Reconstruction of Silchester Plane

50. Roman Plane from Cologne *Rhein. Landesmuseum, Bonn*

The rivet across the mouth secures the iron in the usual way; the other rivet behind the iron holds the side plates together, and a similar rivet is conjectured between the two vertical rivets in the front half. This back rivet is covered with lead, and there is a narrow space between it and the iron itself, and it has been suggested that originally there was another wedge at the back, but this is unnecessary if we assume that the iron was bedded in the usual way against the slope cut in the wooden stock. This tool may have been made somewhat as follows: the wooden block is first prepared to size, the mouth cut out, and drilled to take the vertical rivets. This is fixed to the iron sole, and finally the side plates are riveted in position, the handle slotted out, and the whole filed and smoothed to shape.

The Cologne plane (Fig. 50) is by far the best preserved of all the Roman tools which have survived. It was found in 1880 under the ruins of the former Colonia Agrippina, the present-day Cologne, and is now in the museum at Bonn, while there is a copy at Mainz. The tool consists of a stout iron sole $12\frac{3}{4}$ in. long and 2 in. wide, with a sort of box in the middle composed of two side walls $3\frac{1}{2}$ in. long by 2 in. high, with a straight cross-piece at the back against which the iron is bedded, and in the front a curved piece concave towards the front of the plane. The usual cross-rivet is provided to take the wedge. The resemblance between the curved front of the box and the shaped front end of the mouth in the wooden Saalburg plane is remarkable. The fretted harp-like front and back grips, or rather, grip reinforcements, are held by rivets near the box, and with a combed joint to the curved supports at each end. The whole assembly looks very much like the Saalburg wooden plane carried out in iron by an accomplished metalworker. The curved shape of the front and back supports, the curved front of the box itself, quite easy to do in wood, but very difficult in metal, and unnecessary for the efficiency of the tool, give point to this conclusion, while the vertical rivets are clearly vestigial. There can be little doubt that the spaces below the fretted pieces were originally filled in with wood, with slots cut in to form grips.

The iron rests against the bevelled edge of the mouth opening in the sole and the back of the box, giving a slope of about 53 degrees. It is 7 in. long and $1\frac{5}{8}$ in. wide, with fine V-shaped grooves in the lower quarter of the face, forming a series of teeth at the cutting edge. Other examples of toothed irons occur in the Saalburg collections. But although the Roman joiners were well acquainted with the technique of veneering, which is frequently mentioned by Pliny and other authorities, the fact that a toothed iron is used here need not imply that this was a veneering plane in the modern sense. Like present-day violin makers, who use toothed irons in their little compass planes, the Romans were more concerned with getting the wood true than with obtaining a smooth surface, which could be done with more traditional methods. With hard or cross-grained woods, especially bearing in mind the comparatively soft steel used for the irons, and in the absence of a cap iron, this could be more easily accomplished with a toothed iron.

The appearance of the tool was further enhanced by a pattern of concentric circles inscribed on the upper surface of the fretted grips and the side walls of the box. These markings are similar to those on a number of Etruscan bronze tools such as axes and adzes, but in spite of their wonderful skill as metalworkers, there is no evidence that the Etruscans used or even knew anything about the plane. But it is some indication of the prestige of the Roman joiner and the style of work he was called upon to do, that one of them should have gone to the trouble to get a blacksmith colleague to turn out such a practical and at the same time such a handsome tool.

The second plane from Caerwent (Fig. 51) is in such a dilapidated condition that it is difficult to assign it to any of the foregoing groups, although the closest resemblance is to the Cologne plane itself. In the first place the sole is almost the same size, and there are no rivet holes. When it was first found the iron was embedded in a mass of rusted metal at an angle of 66 degrees, perhaps the remains of the side plates of the box and the wedge.

Taking the series as a whole, the range of size (apart from the Pompeii and Verulamium planes) is comparatively narrow, from about 15 in. down to 13 in., corresponding more or less to the average jack plane of modern times. But as has already been pointed out, most of the representations of Roman joiners working at the bench show them using rather longer tools, something like the Verulamium tryplane.

In addition to the plane described above, six of which have irons, a large number of separate plane irons have been found at the various German sites, at Compiègne in France, Newstead in Scotland, and also in Switzerland. Greber (*op. cit.*, pp. 98 and 99) lists fifty-nine examples from the German frontier posts, about half of which are

51. Roman Plane Sole and Iron, Caerwent *Newport, Mon. Museum*

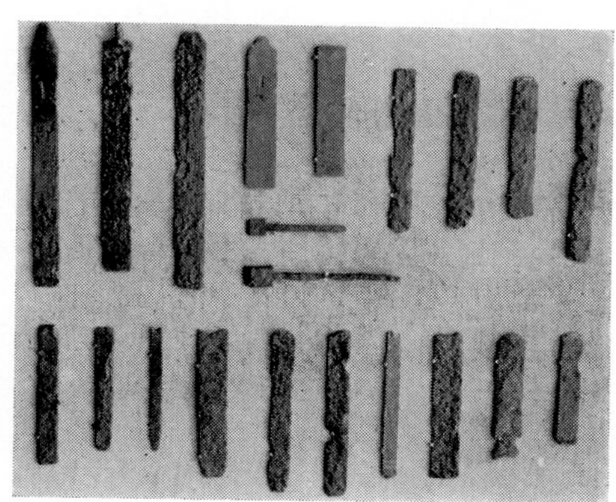

52. Roman Plane Irons
Saalburgmuseum, Homburg v.d. Hohe

smoothing- or jack-plane irons, ranging in width from $1\frac{7}{8}$ in. down to $\frac{7}{8}$ in. A selection of these is shown in Fig. 52, the first five in the top row being toothed irons, with an average width of about $1\frac{1}{4}$ in., which would have fitted most of the planes hitherto described. The remainder include moulding plane irons, beads, hollows and rounds, rebate- and shoulder-plane irons, and plough irons. Some of the latter, not shown on the photograph, have a projection at the side to allow for adjustment or removal, something like the modern plough iron, which indicates that they were fitted in a stock similar to the Kom Washim plane at Cairo.

The irons from Compiègne, now in the Saint-Germain Museum, are said to be toothed smoothing-plane irons, but the writer has not been able to get any detailed information about them. The moulding-plane iron from Newstead (Fig. 53) is about 1 in. wide at the cutting edge, and would give a profile not unlike that shown in the cupboard door described below. It is also not without interest that the finds at Saalburg included a number of iron dogs or bench stops (Fig. 54), used for holding the wood down to the surface of the bench while it was being planed.

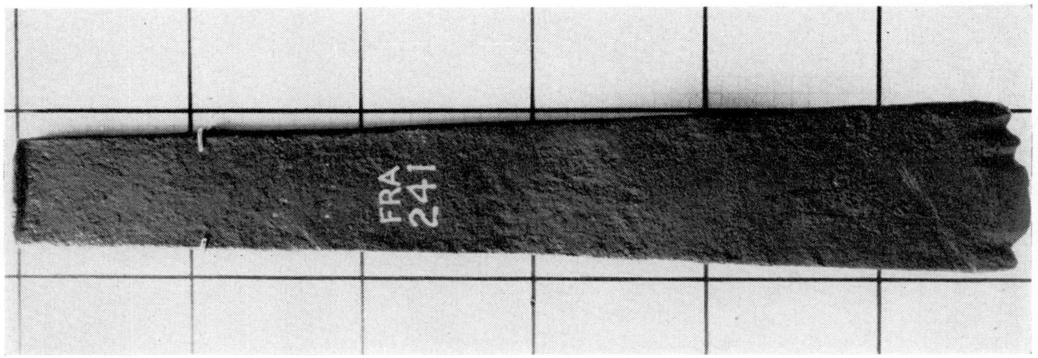

53. Roman Moulding-plane Iron, Newstead, Roxburgh
National Museum of the Antiquities of Scotland, Edinburgh

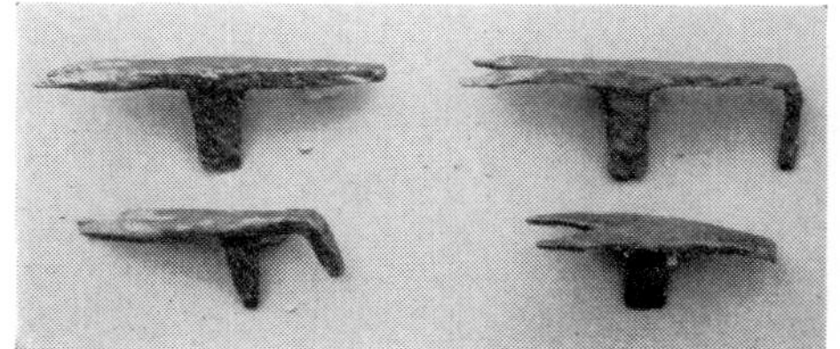

54. Roman Bench Stops or Dogs
Saalburgmuseum, Homburg v.d. Hohe

Owing to the climate, hardly any Roman woodwork has survived in this country, but there is a good deal at Herculaneum near Naples, which was buried by a sea of mud from the slopes of Vesuvius during the same eruption as that which nearly obliterated Pompeii. Among the furniture surviving in various states of preservation there are couches, beds, children's cots, a small wooden cupboard and shrine, and so on, and a large amount of joinery work in the shape of doors, panelled and trellised partitions, staircases, and other constructional work.

In the Bristol Museum there is a very fine example of Roman cabinet work from Rubaiyat in the Fayoum, Egypt, said to date from the 3rd or 4th century A.D.* It gives valuable evidence of the use the Roman joiners made of the tools we have been considering. The craftsman who made this door must have had in his kit, apart from the usual jack and smoothing planes, a wide variety of moulding, plough, rabbet, and shoulder planes.

This cupboard door, in a light-brown hardwood, appears to have been the right-hand leaf of a pair, as the pin hinge is slightly longer at the top. The position of the middle rails, about one-third of the way down from the top, appears unusual to us, but there is a parallel in the panelled doors of the little cupboard in the Simpelveld sarcophagus in Leiden Museum, illustrated at Fig. 49 in Olwen Brogan's 'Roman Gaul'. Two very similar doors are fitted in the shrine at Herculaneum referred to above.

The construction of the frame is very curious, the hanging style being continuous, probably to take the pin hinges, while the meeting rail is tenoned between the top and bottom rails. The joints themselves are stub tenons, haunched and pinned in a very modern manner. All the members are grooved for the panels, and moulded solid on the face with a kind of combined bead and ogee moulding. The corresponding beads on the raised panels, rather narrower in width, may have been done with a scratch stock. The returns of the raised panels are let in and fastened with three pins right through the panel, which is rebated slightly at the back to fit the grooves.

It is worthy of remark that one feature of this door, the fully mitred mouldings, does not appear in English woodwork until the beginning of the 17th century, and for at least a century before that it was usual to mitre the upper corners of a frame only, the lower corners being scribed. The method of building up the returns of the raised panels is also remarkable, and recalls the panelled panels of the 10th- and 12th-century mosque doors in the Islamic Museum at Cairo. There is a similar door dating from the 14th century from Samarkand in the Victoria and Albert Museum.

Greber illustrates a cupboard about 6 ft. high from Abusir in Egypt, from the 2nd century A.D., now in the Berlin Museum. This has a pair of doors, with the middle rail about two-fifths of the way down from the top, with moulded members also fully mitred. Pliny speaks of panelled doors on several occasions, indeed in one passage ('Nat. Hist.', XVI, 82) he remarks: 'The wood of the fir is strongest in a vertical direction (by this he probably means along the grain); it is remarkably well adapted for the panels of doors and all kinds of joiner's work, whether in the Greek, Campanian, or Sicilian styles.' One would give a good deal to know what the differences in these styles amounted to, but the mere mention of different styles gives us some indication of the scope and sophistication of the Roman joiner's work.

* Fig. 15 in the author's '*Woodwork*', Blackwell, Oxford, 1962.

3: The Dark Ages

It has been suggested that the plane was somehow forgotten during the Dark Ages, and then re-invented some time in the 12th or 13th centuries, but recent discoveries have shown that there is a thin but continuous link between the Roman period and the Middle Ages. A plane from the terp or village mound at Finkum in Frisia in Holland was at one time thought to belong to the Roman period, but no conclusive evidence has ever been brought forward to prove this, and for several reasons it is likely to be of a much later date. The body of the plane, which is 6½ in. long and about 1¼ in. wide, is of bone or horn, with a bronze sole turned up at the front, and projecting slightly at the back. The scroll-shaped handle abuts against a short, upright pillar, and the bed for the iron is cut to an angle of about 45 degrees. The hole for the peg across the mouth to take the wedge is clearly visible. Before discussing this tool any further it would be as well to consider the other Frisian planes in the Leeuwarden Collection.

The three in Fig. 55 are all of the Late Merovingian period (A.D. 700–750) and are made similarly of bone or horn. The plane at the top, from Hallum, is 6½ in. long; the one at bottom right, from Oosterbeintum, is 5¼ in. long; and the smaller one on the left, from Beetgum, 4½ in. long, and the slope of the iron in each case is about 40–45 degrees. The Beetgum plane is much cruder than the others, and has an accidental resemblance to

55. Bone planes from terpen Hallum, Beetgum, and Oosterbeintum *Fries Museum, Leeuwarden*

the Pompeii smoothing planes, but the other two are practically identical in shape with the Finkum plane.

Finally, a wooden plane from Aalsum, $8\frac{1}{2}$ in. long and $1\frac{1}{2}$ in. wide, obviously, from the interlacing carving on the front of the stock, something like that on our contemporary Saxon crosses, Late Merovingian or Early Carolingian (A.D. 750–800), has the same flat angle for the iron, and the same scroll handle with the short, round, upright pillar. As the Finkum plane has very similar features to this, it must be later than was earlier assumed, especially as that type of handle does not occur on any known Roman plane. Besides, the slope of the iron indicates a later date, as no Roman plane has an angle of less than 50 degrees, while the succeeding medieval planes are still flatter than the 8–9th-century Dutch ones. This may have been due to improvements in the steel for the cutting irons, allowing a flatter and thinner sharpening bevel.

The other unusual feature of the Finkum plane, the bronze sole with the turned-up end, has a close parallel in the Saxon plane from Sarre, Kent (Fig. 56). When first discovered it was described in 'Archeologica Cantiana', Vol. VI, p. 161 as: 'Found with bronze balance and scales and 19 weights in Sarre grave 26—iron lock, with bronze plate containing a hole for its bolt', and in George Payne's 'Catalogue of the Kent Archaeological Society's Collection', p. 19, No. 775, as 'lock-plate, bronze, attached to wood'. A closer examination has confirmed that this object is a small plane, with features relating it both to the Roman planes described above, and to the little tools from Leeuwarden. The stock is of horn, $5\frac{3}{8}$ in. long, $1\frac{1}{4}$ in. wide, and $1\frac{1}{4}$ in. high, with a bronze sole $\frac{1}{8}$ in. thick projecting at each end to make a total length of exactly 6 in., and turned up a short distance at both ends. The sole is attached to the stock by three iron rivets passing through the horn, and fastened to three small bronze plates let into the upper surface. A small grip is hollowed out behind the iron, which is $\frac{3}{4}$ in. wide, and has a slope of 43 degrees. The rivet across the mouth and the wedge and iron itself are the only conjectural features, but they are well vouched for in the Roman and Frisian examples.

56. Horn Plane with Bronze Sole, Sarre, Kent *Maidstone Museum*

With the help of a detailed drawing made by Mr. L. R. A. Grove, B.A., F.S.A., the curator of the Maidstone Museum, the writer has made a reconstruction in wood of the original plane. The tool is remarkably easy to use, and resembles the small violin planes described in Edward Heron Allen's 'Violin-making'. It may even be suggested that some such tool as this formed part of the kit of the craftsman who made the famous harp which was found among the treasure unearthed from the Sutton Hoo ship burial.

The fact that all the surviving tools of this period, both from Frisia and from Anglo-Saxon England, are smaller in size and cruder in form than the preceding Roman tools is a reflection of the lower standard of life and the unsettled political conditions which obtained for some centuries in North-western Europe after the Roman débâcle and which justify the description of this period as the Dark Ages.

4: The Middle Ages to 1600

However unfortunate it may be that so few planes from the Roman period and the Dark Ages have survived, it is still more curious and annoying that for the next eight hundred years or so, from about A.D. 800 to nearly 1600, no actual planes have come down to us at all, and very few other tools either, for that matter. So that the only information we have about the medieval plane comes from the documentary evidence, such as the pictures in the illuminated manuscripts, wood-carvings, stained-glass windows, and the like. This is not in the nature of things particularly reliable, for besides the limitations of the medium itself—the difficulties of showing detail in small-scale carvings, miniatures, or stained-glass—in many cases there is reason to suspect that the artist, rarely a craftsman himself, and interested in more important things than workmen's tools, has sometimes allowed his imagination to run away with him. But such as it is, it is the only evidence we have, and we must make the best use of it we can.

It is fortunate for the historian of woodworking tools that the inspiration of this medieval art was religious, and one of the most popular Old Testament episodes, and one very often depicted by the painters and miniaturists, was the building of the Ark. This usually shows the patriarch Noah supervising a gang of workmen, mostly carpenters, with a fairly representative selection of the tools of their trade around them. It is also fortunate for us that by a strong tradition Joseph, the father of Jesus, was a carpenter. Hence the innumerable Holy Families, Annunciations, and the like, with the Virgin Mary busy with her needlework, and Joseph himself, often with the assistance of the Holy Child, if old enough, working at the bench. Since the medieval and Renaissance artists were not as historically minded as we are today, they made no attempt to find out the sort of tools Noah's assistants or Joseph may actually have used, so that these pictures often given us some extremely valuable information about the tool kits of the various periods, especially since the paintings are usually fairly closely dated by the art historians.

Reviewing the evidence as a whole; it seems that south of a line Basel–Lake Constance–Vienna; that is, Italy plus the old Roman province of Raetia (roughly the modern Switzerland and the Tyrol), the Roman method of cutting a hollow grip through the stock of the plane, usually behind the iron, was retained right up to the 17th century and beyond. North of this line, in France, Germany, the Low Countries, Great Britain and Scandinavia, another line of development can be traced. The stock of the plane was left intact, while an upright handle was provided at the fore end to take the left hand. There does not seem to be any particular reason why this difference arose, but the evidence is clear enough. On the other hand, the Roman method of securing the wedge and iron against a rivet or bar across the mouth was retained by both traditions, at any rate until the early 16th century, and even later in the south. With one or two exceptions planes were made mostly of wood, the only metal tools being small block planes.

Taking the southern group first, a 13th-century mosaic in the porch of St. Mark's, Venice, of Noah building the Ark shows one of the workmen using a plane (Fig. 57*a*)

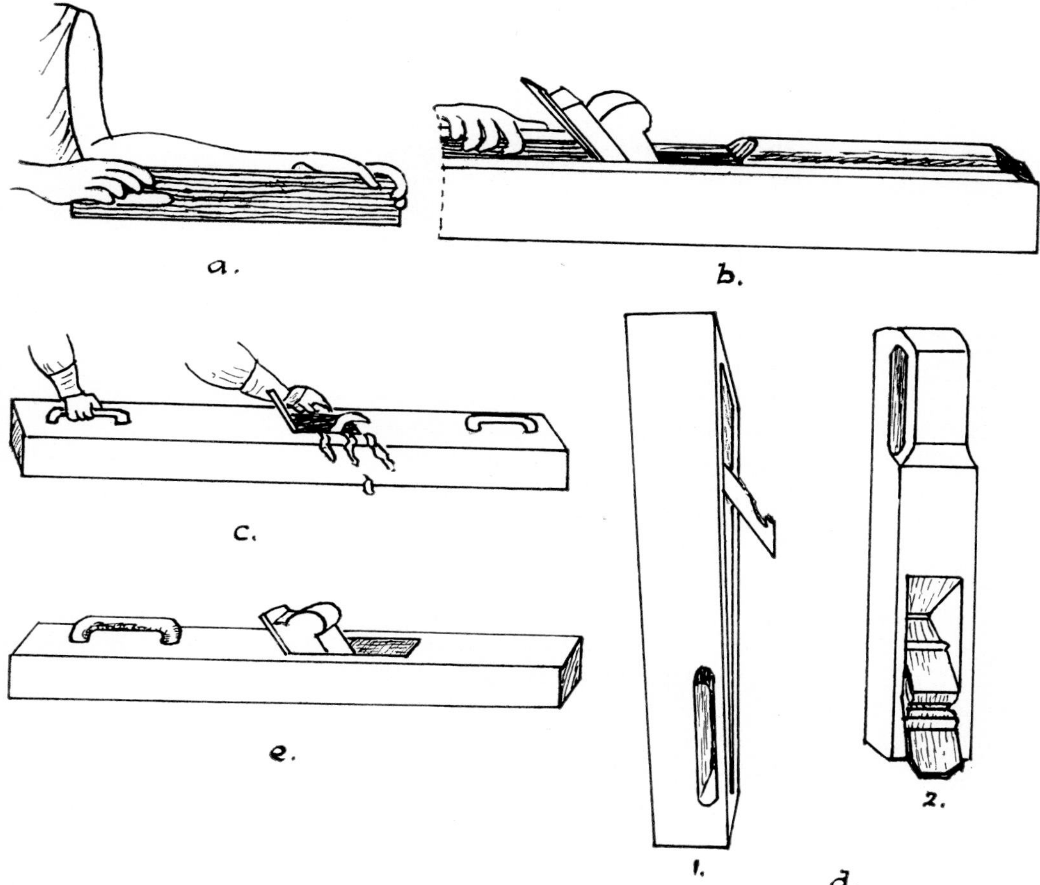

57. Italian Planes, 13th to 17th Centuries: (*a*) Mosaic, St. Mark's, Venice (13th century); (*b*) Fresco, Guildhall, Siena (*c*. 1340); (*c*) Fresco, Campo Santo, Pisa (1390); (*d*) Inlay, San Petronio, Bologna (1470); (*e*) 'Holy Family', Annibale Carracci (1560–1609)

about as long as his own forearm (say 14–15 in.), with the iron about one-third of the way back from the fore end, and a hollowed-out grip for the right hand. Apart from the position of the cutter, which in the earlier planes was usually about central, this tool is clearly in the direct Roman tradition.

One of the figures in the Hall of Peace in the Guildhall at Siena, painted by Ambrogio Lorenzetti in 1338–40, is holding a palm branch in one hand and in the other an unusual symbol of peace, a large tryplane inscribed 'Concordia' (Fig. 57*b*). During a recent visit to Siena the writer was able to verify that the ribs along the top of the stock are definitely hollowed out to form grips both before and behind the iron. One curious detail of this picture is that the iron is provided with two distinct wedges. There is a close resemblance between this plane and the large instrument shown in the Bedford Book of Hours version of the Noah's Ark theme, discussed in detail below.

Pietro Puccio's fresco on this same subject in the Campo Santo at Pisa, painted about 1390, shows one of the workmen using an enormous plane (Fig. 57*c*), which, judging from the size of the man pushing it, must be at least 3 ft. long. The mouth is rather less than half-way back from the fore end, and there are two handles, both shaped like the handle of an old-fashioned flat-iron. The plane is so long that the workman is holding it by one handle and with the left hand near the wedge; normally the front handle would be used by an assistant. The rest of his kit is shown in a basket in the foreground, but the fresco is now in such a dilapidated state that it is difficult to be sure of the details.

The tools shown in some inlaid panels in the choir stalls of the church of San Petronio at Bologna, executed by Agostino de Marchi in 1468–77, revert to the earlier Roman tradition (Fig. 57*d*). The artist has shown the tools as if lying in a tool chest; the try-plane (1) has a slotted grip at the back, with the iron fixed very close to the fore end, while the jack plane (2) has a similar grip at the front. In the latter the top view clearly shows the cross-bar to take the wedge and iron.

A typical Holy Family picture by another Bolognese painter about a hundred years later gives us a tryplane (Fig. 57*e*) apparently about 22 in. long, with a plain stock and a flat-iron handle similar to that in the Pisan fresco.

This discussion of the southern group may be rounded off with a beautifully carved 17th-century Spanish plane, where the handle is an elaborate version of the Roman hollowed-out grip. An almost identical plane, with the lion replaced by a carved dolphin at the fore end, also said to be of the 17th century, is in the Tiroler Volkskunstmuseum at Innsbruck (Fig. 58). These two planes are almost exactly the same size—35 in. long—and although coming from places so widely separated, they are clearly inheritors of the same tradition. The details of the plane being used by St. Joseph in Correggio's 'Vierge au panier' in the National Gallery, London, are not clear, but he seems to be using a tool similar to those just described.

With regard to smoothing planes, the earliest example of the northern tradition is taken from the 13th-century stained-glass windows in Chartres Cathedral. The one donated by the guild of joiners and dedicated to St. Julien shows two workmen, one of whom is using a smoothing plane (Fig. 59*a*), apparently left-handed. The details of the plane's construction are obscure, but from the position of the workman's hands it is clear that the block was flat, with an upright handle at the fore end for what would normally be the left hand. The artist may have arranged his figures in this curious manner either to show as much of the plane as possible, or to keep his design symmetrical, with the two men facing each other. Alternatively, the workman may actually have been left-handed, but that we shall never know.

A much clearer illustration of the northern medieval smoothing plane occurs in a miniature from the 'Mendel'schen Stiftsbuche' (cartulary) in the Nuremberg Municipal Library, painted about 1410 (Fig. 59*b*). This shows the front grip (shown off centre), the cross-peg to secure the wedge, and the comparatively flat angle of the iron, a characteristic of the medieval plane.

58. Try and Jointer Planes, 17th–18th Centuries *Tiroler Volkskunstmuseum, Innsbruck*

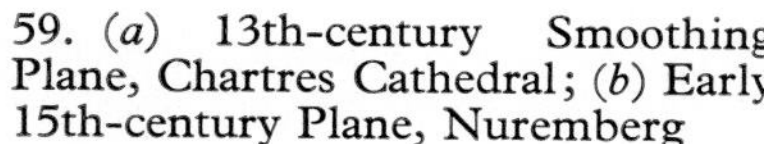

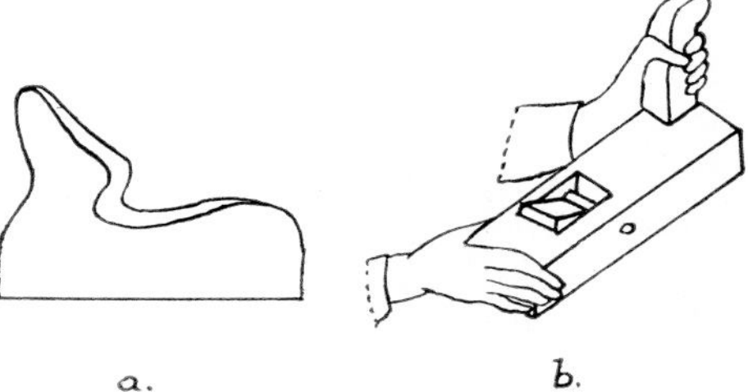

59. (*a*) 13th-century Smoothing Plane, Chartres Cathedral; (*b*) Early 15th-century Plane, Nuremberg

Referring to Littré's dictionary for the etymology of the word *rabot* (plane), the writer stumbled on an interesting and profitable line of research. One of the earliest quotations came from the 15th-century 'Accounts of the Dukes of Burgundy', No. 2391: 'Une autre couppe blanche, verrée (dorée au bord) à la devise des rabots (le rabot, devise de Jean sans Peur, Duc de Bourgogne'.

A query addressed to M. Henri Quarré, curator of the Dijon Museum, brought the information that the plane was the personal emblem or device of Duke John the Fearless (1404–19), adopted in opposition to his cousin and rival Louis, Duke of Orleans, whose emblem was a ragged staff. In the crude schoolboy fashion of the time, the plane was intended as a symbol of the way John of Burgundy would deal with the pretensions of Louis to the French throne. As his personal device it figures on the recumbent effigy on his tomb in the Chartreuse of Champol (after having Louis assassinated in 1407, he himself was ambushed and murdered in 1419), on various portraits, and in the Book of Hours which used to belong to him and is now in the Bibliothèque Nationale, Paris (MS. N.A.L. 3055, 172 v.). This miniature (Fig. 60), shows the crucifixion of St. Andrew, with a plane on the left, and another carpenter's tool, a level, on the right.

60 (*on left*). Miniature from Book of Hours of John the Fearless, Duke of Burgundy
Bibliothèque Nationale, Paris

61. Early 15th-century Planes, Book of Hours of John the Fearless

The larger tool to the left of the saint (Fig. 61*a*) seems to be made of metal, with a curved grip in front for the left hand, while the cross-bar to take the wedge and iron is quite distinct. The iron itself, however, is drawn at so low an angle that it appears to be almost flat. The background of the miniature is filled in with a diaper pattern of repeated planes and levels, and most of the tiny planes, shown in a very schematic manner with white lines (Fig. 61*b*), indicate the iron by a short, sloping line. Similar small planes are shown in gold on the crimson cloak of Duke John in another MS. in the Bibliothèque Nationale (Fr. 2810, f. 226), where he is receiving a copy of a book from the author.

An 18th-century copy in Brussels of a contemporary portrait of Duke John shows on the hood a pattern of planes of a different kind altogether. There are two alternative views of the same tool (Fig. 62*a* and *b*), one laid on its side to reveal the sole, and the other viewed from above. In the latter case the peg for the wedge can be clearly seen. This plane was obviously made of wood, with the usual grip at the fore end, and for good measure another, but smaller handle for the right hand. This cape is further embellished with pearls and rows of shavings!

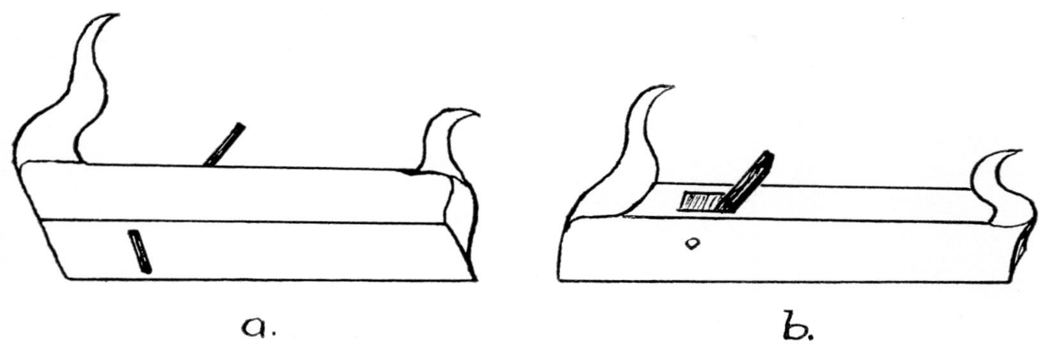

62. Planes on the Hood of Portrait of John the Fearless

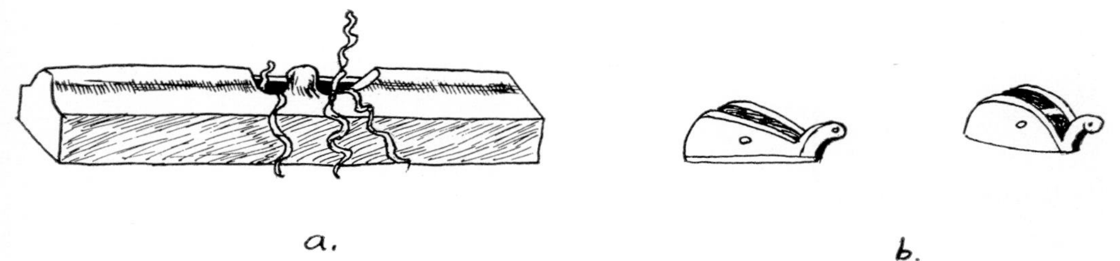

63. Early 15th-century Try and Block Planes *Bedford Book of Hours, British Museum*

The picture of Noah building the Ark in the Bedford Book of Hours, a French manuscript of the early 15th century, shows a very large plane in use (Fig. 63*a*) similar in many respects to the Siena fresco plane (Fig. 57*b*), especially in the shape of the top of the stock. The details of the wedge and iron are not clear, and it has been suggested that this plane had two irons, but it is difficult to see how this would have worked in practice. Among the other tools scattered about the foreground there are two curiously shaped objects (Fig. 63*b*) which somewhat resemble the small planes in the diaper background of Fig. 60. They may be boxes to hold a chalk line, a very common tool in the Middle Ages, but in the writer's view they are almost certainly small block planes of metal, with a curved handle in the front and the iron set so flat that it can hardly be seen.

A very similar tool to this is shown in a miniature (Fig. 64) in an early 15th-century manuscript of the poems of Christine de Pisan, a famous blue-stocking at the court of Charles VII (who earlier in his career was Joan of Arc's Dauphin). It has the same curved handle in the front and the rivet to take the wedge can be seen quite clearly.

There is, in fact, a small shoe-shaped metal *Vergatthobel* (block plane) of the early 16th century (Fig. 65) in the Arts and Crafts Museum in Vienna, showing all these features. The stock is made of iron, and is about 4 in. long and 2 in. wide, with the iron at an angle of 27 degrees. Another similar tool in the same collection has the wedge carved in the shape of a man's head with a long beard. It is fairly certain that the plane in Fig. 65 was the kind of thing the artists of the miniatures were aiming at.

64. Early 15th-century Plane, Harl. MS. 4421, f. 196v
Trustees of the British Museum

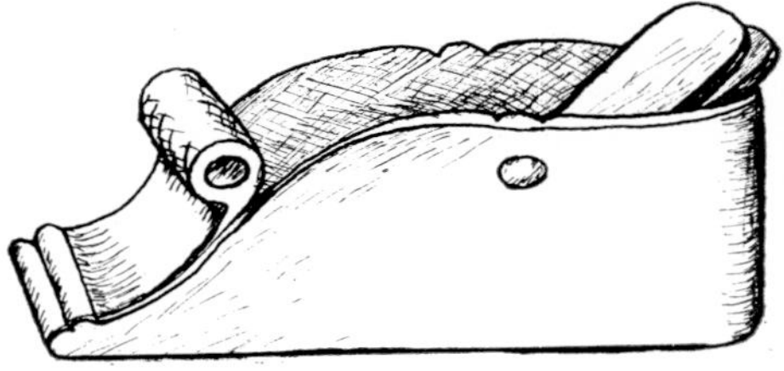

65. 16th-century Block Plane (Vergatthobel)
Kunstgewerbemuseum, Vienna

Returning to the larger and more commonly used planes, Bourdichon's picture of a Parisian joiner's shop of about 1510 gives a detailed representation of a late medieval tryplane and smoother. The complete miniature is reproduced on p. 91 of Salzman's 'English Life in the Middle Ages', Oxford, 1926. This is said to belong to a series 'The Four Estates of the Realm', but it is almost certainly another Holy Family, with the Virgin Mary spinning from a distaff, the Holy Child busy collecting chips and shavings off the floor and putting them in a basket, and Joseph himself working at the bench. He is using a tryplane (Fig. 66*a*) with a stock 28–30 in. long, the middle section being made deeper to give extra strength. The fore end is fitted with an upright, curved handle for the left hand, while the back of the stock is flat. The cross-rivet for the wedge is a conspicuous feature. Among the other tools on the cabinet he is making, fitted with linenfold panels, is a shorter plane of a similar shape with a scroll handle in the front (Fig. 66*b*). Here again the middle part of the stock is made deeper to support the iron, and the cross-rivet is particularly clear.

The first half of the 15th century was not only a period of cultural and religious ferment, but was also marked by technological advances in many fields. It is not surprising that about this time the traditional way of holding the plane iron by means of a wedge driven tight against a cross-bar, which had been in use since Roman times, was superseded by the now almost universal grooved wedge. The new method had several advantages. The effective bedding area for the wedge was much larger, in some cases almost doubled, while the holes to take the cross-rivet, always a weakness, as they come in the thinnest part of the stock, were eliminated. The middle part of the thin end of the wedge could also be cut away, giving more room for the shaving to emerge.

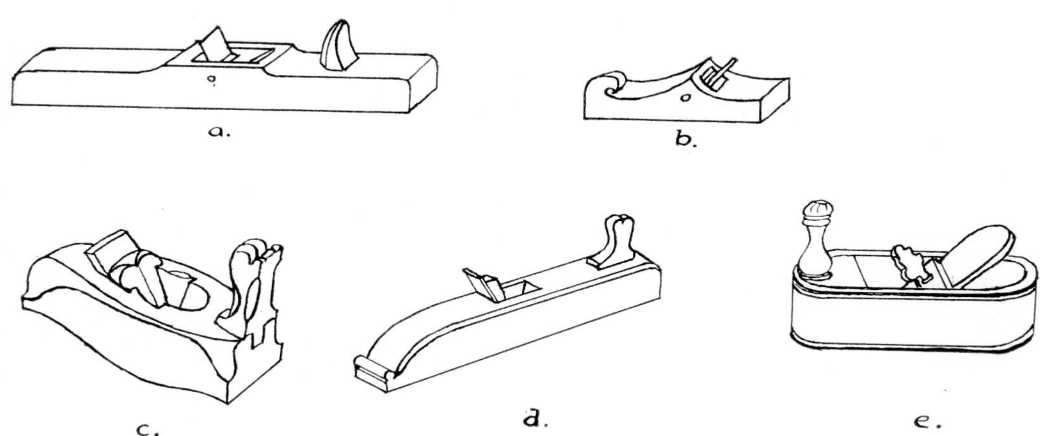

66. (*a*) 16th-century Tryplane, Bourdichon, Paris, *c.* 1510. (*b*) 16th-century Smoother, Bourdichon, Paris, *c.* 1510. (*c*) Smoothing Plane, Durer's 'Melancholia', 1514. (*d*) Early 17th-century Tryplane, Saenredam, 'Holy Family'. (*e*) Iron Block Plane, *c.* 1570, *Historical Museum, Dresden*

Greber cites an early example of this type, a square block of beech with an iron sole, carved with late Gothic tracery along the sides. It is in a private collection at Munich, and dates from about 1500. In discussing this tool, Herr Greber points out that the man who made it had not completely solved the problems of the new method, as the wedge is much too thick, and consequently the mouth opening too narrow.

The first accurately dated example of the new pattern occurs in Dürer's engraving 'Melancholia', dated 1514. The smoothing plane shown in the foreground (Fig. 66*c*) still has a rather small mouth opening, while the grooves for the wedges are comparatively deep. It was probably to allow for this that the sides of the stock were made with a pronounced bulge, a feature standardised in this country in the coffin plane. Another new departure, the stopped chamfers along the top edge, gave a more comfortable grip, and has been retained to this day. In fact, except for the tall front grip or 'toat' this smoothing plane has a very modern look about it.

A very similar tool is shown in use by one of the joiners in Jost Ammann's woodcut of the cabinet-maker's shop of about the middle of the 16th century. The other tools on the bench include a tryplane and a plough. Up to now most of the examples given have come from France or South Germany, but a Flemish jack plane of about 1625 is shown in use by Joseph's assistant, probably Jesus himself as a youth, in a 'Holy Family' by the Haarlem artist Saenredam. This plane (Fig. 66*d*) is typical in the absence of a grip for the right hand, and the prominent 'toat' at the fore end.

An entirely different type of small smoothing plane, which from the number of surviving examples must have been widely used, gives further evidence of the urge for experiment in new methods by the craftsmen of the 16th century. It is essentially a small block plane, made of iron, with the ends bent round in a semi-circle, and a turned upright handle at the fore end (Fig. 66*e*). The iron is secured by a small thumbscrew threaded through a bar across the mouth, the forerunner of the modern adjusting screw. Two of these planes, 5 in. long and 2 in. wide, were in the collection of the Elector August of Saxony at Dresden, dating from about 1570. A third plane of the same pattern, but slightly larger, about 5½ in. long, with a wedge instead of a thumbscrew, is in the Arts and Crafts Museum at Vienna. All three are very beautifully etched with floral designs (not attempted in the sketch), while one of the Dresden planes shows a hunting scene, with hart and hound and huntsman. A fourth plane of this pattern is shown in a portrait of the Nuremberg cabinet-maker Friedrich Finkhauer (died 2nd December, 1571) at work at the bench, a miniature in the cartulary of Landauer Abbey, now in the Nurem-

67. 16th-century Smoothing Plane, Novaya Zemlya Expedition, 1596 *Rijksmuseum, Amsterdam*

berg Municipal Libary. This picture is notable in giving a named portrait of a master craftsman of the 16th century.

Finally there is the Novaya Zemlya smoothing plane (Fig. 67). By a lucky chance, this can be fairly accurately dated. In 1596 a Dutch expedition under the command of Jacob van Heemskerck and Willem Barentz sailed for China via the North-east Passage. The intention was to avoid the Portuguese, Spanish, and English pirates in the Atlantic and round the Cape. On reaching Novaya Zemlya they were wrecked and forced to winter on the ice, returning to Holland in the spring of 1597. Some of the stores they left behind were found in 1871 and 1875, including this plane, obviously home-made and little the worse for wear, and a number of plane irons, some with square cutting edges and others for rounding planes, and all tapered back in width from the cutting edge. With regard to the plane itself, it is of beech, $6\frac{3}{4}$ in. long and $2\frac{1}{2}$ in. wide, with the iron set at an angle of 45 degrees. Its shape suggests that it is a transitional form between the medieval block planes (Figs. 61 and 65) and one of the two standard types of 18th-century Dutch smoothing planes. In any case it is one of the oldest surviving planes in Northern Europe since Roman times.

5: Trying Planes and Jack Planes, 1600–1800

From the craftsman's point of view these two centuries may be described as the 'Golden Age' of woodwork. Most of the work done previously had been strictly utilitarian in character and crude in construction, although this had been frequently masked by the richness of the applied ornament, usually in the form of carving. But with the rising standards of domestic comfort and amenity, culminating in the Baroque period towards the end of the 18th century in luxury and often sheer ostentation, the work that the cabinet-makers and joiners were called upon to do, all of it entirely by hand, demanded the utmost skill and a wide range of special tools. Besides this, the opening up of the New World and the Far East by the merchant adventurers brought new varieties of rare and exotic timbers, replacing the coarse, home-grown oaks, walnuts, and softwoods. As this new material was comparatively expensive, the arts of veneering and inlaying, known in one form or another since Egyptian times, were further refined, and used extensively to bring out the beauty of the new materials. The higher standard of work demanded better tools to do it with, and this period shows a rapid evolution of new types, and the improvement in detail of the standard tools.

Fortunately for the historian the surviving material from this period is so plentiful as to be embarrassing; it is hard to decide what to leave out. The principle adopted here is to stress the practical features of the new developments, for although each craftsman spent much time and loving care on the embellishment of his tools, this must not distract our attention from the main trends of evolution. No doubt many of the surviving tools owe their preservation as much to their carved decoration as to anything else, and it is

68. Title-page 'The Childhood of Jesus', Hieronymus Wierix, Antwerp, 1550–1617 *'The Times' and the British Museum*

noticeable that the illustrations of tools in the technical manuals of the period are often much simpler and plainer than the corresponding museum specimens, which are often almost minor works of art.

Taking the large planes first, the main line of development turns on the improvement of the handles. As we have already noted, the craftsmen of Southern Europe developed the hollowed-out grips of Roman times to the point of providing an applied handle like that on an old-fashioned flat-iron, while the fore end was usually left plain. In the north, however, an upright grip at the front was almost universal, while the heel of the stock was simply shaped or chamfered to give a more comfortable grip. At the beginning of the 17th century there seems to have been a fusion of the two traditions, at least as far as the larger planes were concerned, and during the period under consideration, with one or two exceptions most of them show handles both fore and aft. The earliest example known at present to the writer (one has to be cautious, as new material on this subject is constantly cropping up) occurs on the title-page of a 'Childhood of Jesus' series of engravings, by the Dutch artist Hieronymus Wierix, who flourished in Amsterdam at the turn of the 16th and 17th centuries (Fig. 68). The two long planes under the bench have two handles, but as they are drawn end-on, their actual shape is not very clear. Judging from the other engravings in the same series where planes are shown, the front 'toat' or upright handle took the form of a scroll curved towards the toe, while the handle for the right hand was shaped something like that of a flat-iron.

Before discussing these two-handled planes in detail it would be as well to dispose of a sizeable group of jack and trying planes of the 17th–18th centuries which have no handles at all. It may be significant that they appear to be commonest in Austria, South Germany, and Switzerland, i.e., in the no-man's-land between the two traditions, although this same Wierix engraving shows two jack planes of this type. The large plane from Trier (Fig. 69) is a typical example. It is about 35 in. long and 3½ in. wide in the middle

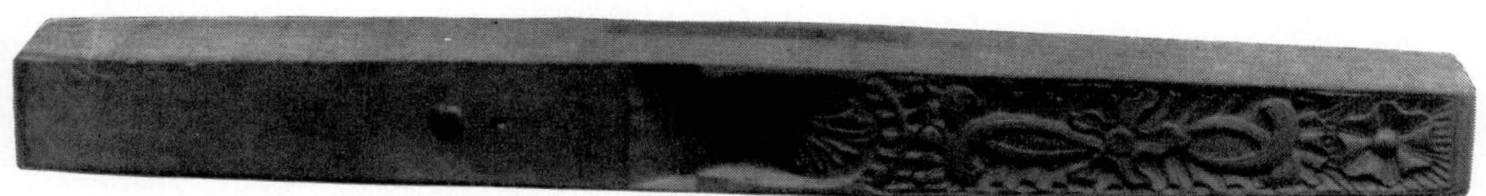

69. 'Langhobel', 18th Century *Stadtischesmuseum, Trier*

with both ends gradually tapered to a smooth curve. It is carved with a simple design in low relief. Similar planes, some of them much more elaborately decorated, are in the Tyrolean Folk Museum at Innsbruck and in the Historical Museum at Berne. Another is shown on a carved shop sign of an early 18th-century master joiner in the Musée des Arts Décoratifs, Paris (Fig. 135). From various sources the total number of planes of this type amounts to over twenty, dating from 1650 to 1750. Some of the Tyrolean planes have leather straps nailed to the stock behind the iron, while another in the National Museum, Prague, dated 1696, has two strips of wood nailed across the top. A similar tryplane, dated 1723, carved with floral and star designs, the owner's name: BARTEL BRUNER IHIWM, and the motto: 'ALLES MIT GOT ANGEFANGEN—WIRD ZUM GUTEN END

GELANGEN', is in the town museum at Hagenau, in Alsace, and has both a leather strap and a hole about $\frac{3}{4}$ in. diameter to take a handle. Another carved plane with no handles is in the Sheffield City Museum. It is $28\frac{1}{4}$ in. long, and probably came from Germany. In most of the plain handleless jack and trying planes the stock is the same section from end to end.

To return to the large planes with two handles, a good indication of the shapes preferred in the 17th and 18th centuries is given in one of the earliest illustrated technical manuals, Félibien's 'Principes de l'Architecture, etc.', Paris, 1676 (Fig. 70). André

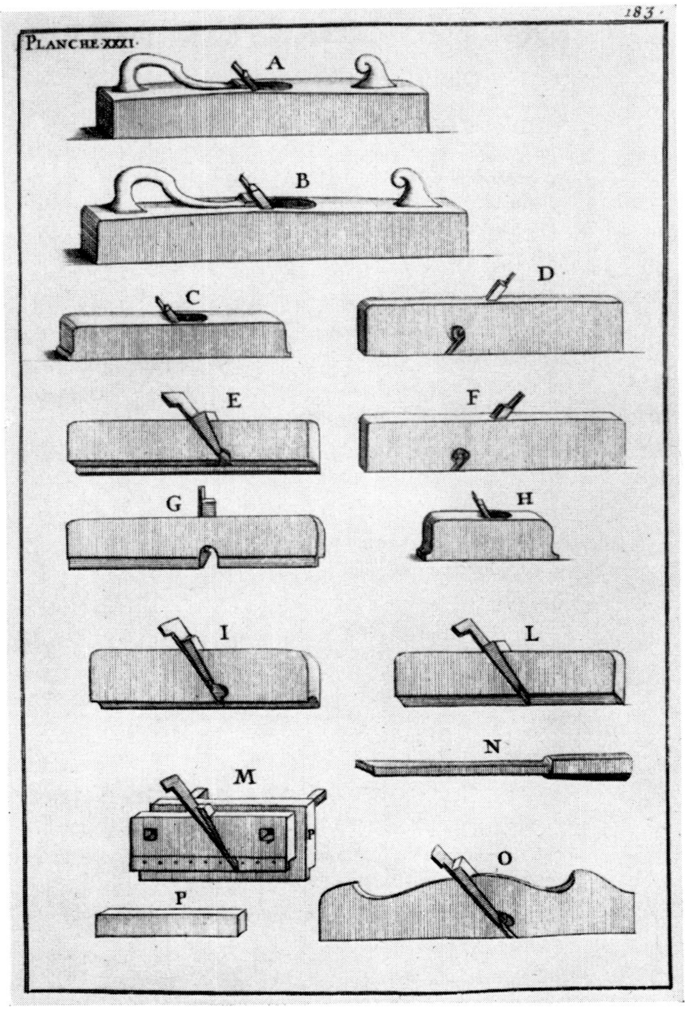

70. 17th-century Joiners' Planes *Félibien, 'Principes de l'Architecture', Paris, 1676*

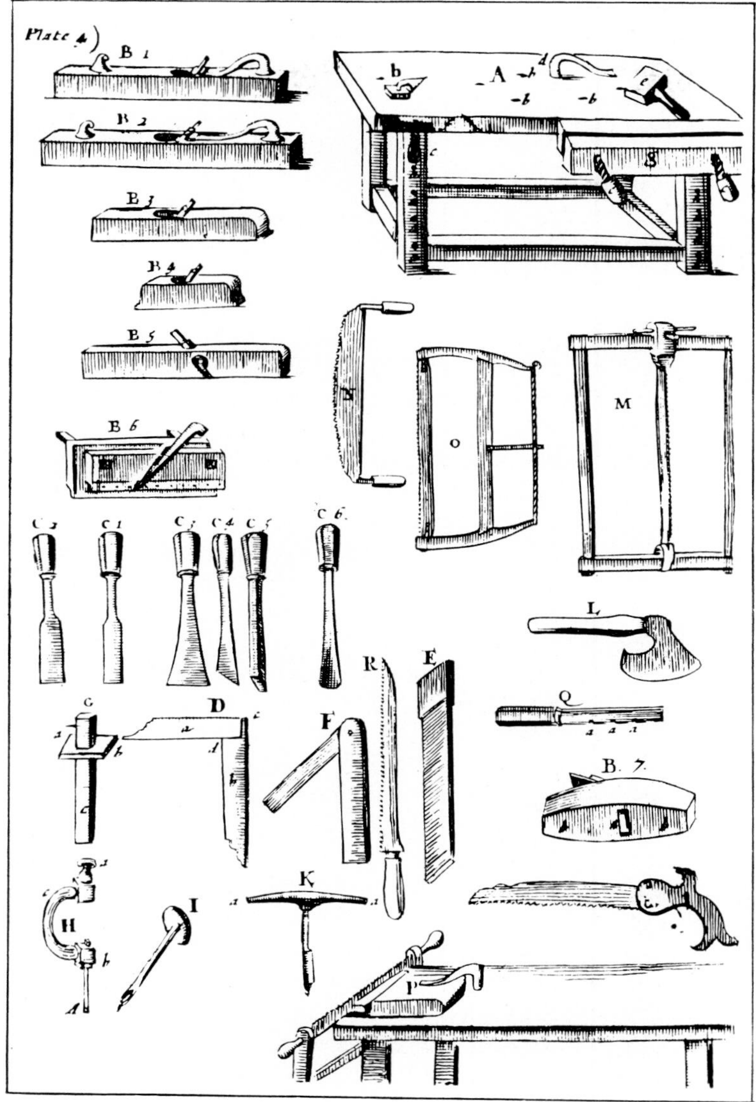

71. Joiners' Tools *Joseph Moxon, 1683*

Félibien (1619–1695) was an architect and art historian, and his illustrations of joiners' and other building craftsmen's tools were slavishly copied during the following century by other French and English writers. In particular, Joseph Moxon lifted most of this plate for his page of joiners' tools in 'Mechanick Exercises, or the Doctrine of Handy-works', London, 1683 (Fig. 71), the first systematic account in English of the tools and methods of the craftsmen of the period. Joseph Moxon is described on the title-page as a Fellow of the Royal Society and Hydrographer to the late King Charles (II). He was a printer and map-maker, a Yorkshireman, and a friend of Samuel Pepys, who records in his diary buying a pair of globes from him.

The plane at the top of Fig. 70 is described as the *riflard*. Moxon calls it the 'Fore plaine, because it is used before you come to work with the Smooth plaine or the Joynter'. In another passage he says that 'this tool is called the Jack plaine by carpenters, but it is indeed the same that Joyners call the Fore plaine'. He adds: 'the iron hath a concave arch on it, and is set ranker than the edge of the Smooth plaine or Joynter, taking off not Gutters, but little hollow Dawks'. The amount of set he advocates is the thickness of an old shilling for softwoods, but for hard, curly, or knotty woods the thickness of an old groat. The plane below it, known in French as the *varlope*, of which there are different sizes, is exactly the same shape as the *riflard*, with a scroll-shaped grip at the front and the main handle shaped like the end of a shepherd's crook. This is Moxon's 'Joynter', which he specifies as being longer than the Fore plaine, but gives no sizes. In copying Félibien's planes the English engraver missed one point; the stock is shown the same depth all along, whereas on the French original the top of the stock tapers gradually both ways from the highest point just behind the iron.

Although this shepherd's-crook handle seems highly improbable to us nowadays, it appears on a large plane in the Musée des Arts Décoratifs, in the Palais du Louvre, Paris. Traces of a broken front grip can also be seen in front of the mouth. The stock of this tool, which is 30 in. long and about 2¼ in. wide, made of pear or apple, with a sole of hornbeam, tapers distinctly from a point immediately behind the iron towards both ends. Extra support for the iron itself is afforded by a scroll-like projection recalling the Bourdichon plane of 1510. Another example of this shepherd's-crook handle occurs on a large tryplane in the Historisches Museum at Basel; the front grip in this case is carved in the shape of a dog's head. Another known to the writer is in the Rhaetisches Museum at Chur, Graubunden, Switzerland. None of these planes is dated, but they may be safely attributed to the late 17th or early 18th century.

A tryplane in Roubo's 'L'art du menuisier', Paris, 1769–75 also has the top of the stock tapered both ways from the middle, and the iron is bedded against an additional projection carried right across the top. The scroll of the front grip is twisted away from the operator. The *varlope* in Diderot's 'Encyclopédie' (1765) is a much simpler tool: the stock is merely tapered both ways as before, but the handle, like Roubo's, is more like the Italian flat-iron shape. In his text Diderot speaks of larger and smaller *varlopes*, and of the *riflard*, which was a roughing jack plane similar to Moxon's 'Fore plaine', but he gives no details of their size, except that the largest were about 3 ft. long.

Regarding the word *varlope*, the authorities appear to be rather doubtful about its derivation. Littré quotes the Limousin word *garlopo* and the Spanish and Portuguese *garlopa*, a long plane, said by Diez to come from a Dutch word *weerloop*; *weer*, backwards, and *loop*, to run. Littré seems uncertain whether there is such a word. Larousse, on the other hand, derives *varlope* direct from *voorlooper*. The only common factor in all this is the suggestion of a Dutch origin. We have already seen that one of the earliest examples of the two-handled plane occurs in an engraving by a Dutch artist of about 1600. Although the modern word for tryplane in Dutch is *reisschaaf*, the term *voorlooper* is also sometimes used. It is very likely that the French joiners, as well as adopting the extra handle, took over and modified the name of the tool as well.

How these planes developed in Holland is another and very interesting story, which demands a chapter to itself.

6: Dutch Standard Tryplanes, 1700–1800

The standard Dutch tryplane or *reisschaaf* of the 18th century, of which a typical example from Leeuwarden, in almost mint condition, is shown in Fig. 72, together with the smoothing and other planes which show similar features, such as carved and dated mouth openings, offer some interesting problems to the technological historian. In the first place they were probably the first attempt to standardise the design of a commonly used tool such as the plane. Previous to this, as many surviving examples show, they had always been made by the craftsmen themselves, and purposely made different to one another. These Dutch planes, however, are all virtually identical, except for variations in length. For this and other reasons, which will be considered later, it is almost certain that they were all made to a standard pattern in small family workshops, and sold over the counter to the various tradesmen. No doubt some of them are copies made by a workman who may not have been able to afford to buy a standard model, as some of the carving is distinctly crude in execution, but there are too many of them, and they are all too much alike, to be explained away as merely a fashion.

72. Standard Dutch Tryplane, dated 1748 — *Fries Museum, Leeuwarden*

For convenience a list of all the planes of this type known up to the time of writing has been drawn up in Table III. This shows the number of each type for each decade, the pattern of the mouth carving, and the present whereabouts of the tool. From this it is clear that the design seems to have originated before 1700, and lasted just over a hundred years, remaining more or less unchanged in all essentials throughout this period. As far as the tryplanes were concerned, the new design was a great advance on anything which had gone before, and for a long time they had a sort of international reputation something like that of the Stanley planes of today. This alone would have a restraining influence on any attempts at improvement or variation, quite apart from the usual inertia of woodworkers generally with regard to their tools. The result was that towards the end of this period they were some years out of date, and their disappearance, when it came, was rapid and complete.

TABLE III

DUTCH STANDARD PLANES

	Type of Plane			*Mouth Carving*					*Distribution*						*Total*
Date	*R*	*B*	*S*	*a*	*b*	*c*	*d*	*e*	*Hol.*	*G.B.*	*B.*	*G.*	*S.*	*U.S.*	
To 1700	1			1									1		1
1701–10	1*				1					1					1
1711–20	1				1				1						1
1721–30	1	7	2	4	2	2		2	6	3	1				10
1731–40	1	12	4	1	1	10		5	11	3	3				17
1741–50	1	5			2	4			4	2					6
1751–60	4	9				11		2	10	2	1				13
1761–70	3	10	3			12		4	9	5	1	1			16
1771–80	2	4	1			5		2	3	4					7
1781–90	6	3		1		6	1	1	7	2					9
1791–1800	2	6	1				7	2	6	3					9
1801–10	1	1					1	1	2						2
No date	1							1						1	1
Totals	25	57	11	7	7	50	9								
				73				20	59	25	6	1	1	1	93

R=*reisschaaf*=tryplane or jointer; *B*=*blokschaaf* or smoother; *S*=*schaaf* or smoother.
For mouth carvings see Fig. 73.

From the column showing the distribution it can be seen that the centre of production must have been Holland, as nearly two-thirds of the surviving planes are still there. The next largest group consists of those in the English collections, which can be accounted for by the better opportunities for tracing them here. Half a dozen are known for Belgium, but no doubt further enquiry there would unearth a few more. There is at least one in a private German collection, and one each in Sweden and the U.S.A. Two small *schaven*, adapted for use as hollows and rounds, were taken from Holland by workmen engaged by Peter I after his visit to the Haarlem shipyards, but they are not included in the above list, as the photograph supplied by the Hermitage Museum, Leningrad, does not show the mouth opening or whether it carries a date. In spite of repeated enquiries, no examples are known from France, Denmark, or Norway.

This theory of a Dutch origin for these planes is confirmed by a picture which used to belong to the Haarlem Carpenters' Guild, dated 1629, and is now in the Haarlem Museum. The subject of the painting is the 'Flight to Egypt', and the central oval is surrounded by a group of tools, among which there is a very fine example of a tryplane. This is identical in almost every respect with those now under discussion, except that the mouth opening is carried across square, with small spirals in the corners, and there is no date. The general shape of the large handle is also very similar, but the decorative carved scrolls are absent. This tool must have been the prototype on which the design of the standard tryplane of the following century was based.

Taking the tryplanes first, the 1748 Leeuwarden plane has already been mentioned. From the illustration it will be seen that the stock of these planes, almost square in section at its highest point just behind the iron, tapers gradually towards each end. The elaborately shaped and carved handle is fitted off centre by means of two dovetails, which can be clearly seen in the Leeuwarden picture. This type of handle was a great improvement on the earlier flat-iron or shepherd's-crook types, as it directed the pressure down towards the cutting edge of the iron. Both wedge and iron have a semi-circular top, while the front grip, placed centrally on a wide square base tenoned and pinned to the stock, carries spiral and rosette designs like those on the handle and wedge. A large nail is provided at the fore end to protect the stock when removing or adjusting the iron.

Of the twenty-five long planes in Table III, the second, marked with an asterisk, is unique in being the only known example the length of a modern jack plane. It is a round-soled plane, 14 in. long, with a type (*b*) mouth carving enclosing the date 1706, and a very crude handle, and is now in the Science Museum, South Kensington. All the others vary in length from 24½ in. to 33 in. and 36 in., with correspondingly wider and thicker stocks. Where the wood is known, they are of beech. Why there should be no jack planes of this or a similar pattern is so far a complete mystery.

73. Mouth Carvings on Standard Dutch Planes

Perhaps the most striking and characteristic feature of these planes is the carved design enclosing the date. Some of the commoner variations are shown in Fig. 73. There are two main groups; in one, the scrolls at the corners of the mouth are connected with a double curve, in the other by a straight line. The latter design, type (*e*), remained more or less constant throughout the period, the first examples occurring about 1730, and they are fairly evenly distributed in each succeeding decade. The line of the scrolls is carried round to frame the date, ending in two opposing spirals meeting on the centre line.

The other group, however, shows considerable development during the period. In its earliest form (Fig. 73*a*) the two curves meet in a point, while the frame enclosing the date is a simple incised semi-circle. This design was current during the 1720's and 1730's; the single case in the list for 1781–90 is a sport, a tryplane in the Openlucht-museum at Arnhem, dated 1785, with the rare inclusion of initials, in this case ITZ, in addition to the date. Later [type (*b*)] the point where the two curves met was elaborated, while the sides of the frame round the date were emphasised by a row of gouge cuts, ending in two rudimentary spirals. The gap between them was filled by a small humped curve. This design occurs sporadically up to 1747. About 1725 the outer spirals were fully developed [type (*c*)], and the space between them embellished with two others of opposite hand, making four in all. This is the commonest design of them all, and was current till the 1790's, when it was superseded by type (*d*). In this variation, the gouge-cuts start half-way round the curve, instead of in the corners, the outer spirals are diminished and the inner pair enlarged. The whole design is better proportioned and more elegant, especially the figures of the date. The designs with the double curve *a–d* comprise about four-fifths of the known examples, the remaining fifth being type (*e*).

74. Tryplane dated 1668 *Nordiska Museet, Stockholm*

Taking the planes in Table III in detail, the earliest dated example (Fig. 74) is clearly of the same pattern as the Leeuwarden plane, except that the middle scroll of the handle has at some time or other broken off. The carved decoration is much simpler, however, and the whole plane bears the impression of being a local Swedish copy of a Dutch original, the only debatable feature being the date itself. This is enclosed in the semi-circular frame of the primitive type (*a*), and is at least forty-eight years earlier than the next dated tryplane on the list, the Arnhem example dated 1716. But since this type of tryplane was known as early as 1629, according to the Haarlem guild picture, the apparently early date of 1668 may well be authentic.

The plane in Fig. 75 is rather a problem. It is described by the museum authorities as a 'Carpenter's Plane, Italian, early XVIIth century. Carved Florentine plane with emblem of Florentine lily (?).' The question mark is theirs. It forms part of the Dudley P. Allen Collection, which includes some smaller tools which very probably are Italian. It is clear, however, that the Cleveland plane reproduces all the essential features of the Dutch tools we are considering: the tapering stock, the square-based front grip, and the mouth opening, similar to type (*e*) with two rosettes instead of spirals. The date, if it ever existed, has been obliterated. The shape of the main handle is also identical, with the rosette in the centre of the larger element. The so-called Florentine lily replaces the other rosette in the central section of the handle, and is repeated on the upper face of the front grip, but to the writer it does not look much like the usual Florentine lily, which is generally shown as a *fleur-de-lis* with buds between the petals. If this plane did come from Italy, it may be an Italian copy of an 18th-century Dutch original. One other point which suggests a late date; the mouth has been slotted to received the nut of a double iron. From considerations which will be outlined later, this cannot have been done much before 1785–90. The only other case of this being done to a plane of this type is one in the Science Museum (Inv. No. 1953, 429) dated 1792.

75. Early 17th-century Italian (?) Tryplane *Cleveland Museum of Art, Cleveland, Ohio, U.S.A.*

The tryplane in the Musée de la Byloke, Ghent, whose mouth opening has been taken as typical of the earlier design (Fig. 72*a*) is described as a 'Rabot de luxe, provenant de la corporation de Menuisiers'. It is a very long plane, and was possibly the property of the Guild, as it also has the emblem of the Guild with a large 'G' for Ghent carved on the stock behind the handle. It may have been lent out from time to time to members for special jobs.

The plane in the Victoria and Albert Museum (Fig. 72*e*) is illustrated in E. H. Pinto's book, 'Treen', Batsford, London, 1949, Pl. III. It is a particularly well-preserved example of the standard pattern, with the type (*e*) mouth design.

There is little to remark about the rest of the planes on the list, as they are all more or less identical, but a Leiden plane of 1763, one of a group of three, is of some interest. At some time or other the handle of the standard type, which, although very beautiful in appearance, must have been rather uncomfortable to use for any length of time, was replaced by a simpler and more functional pattern, shown in Fig. 76*a*.

A rather more precise date for the introduction of this new type of handle is given by the trade card of John Jennion, of the 'Three Plains' in Queen Street, Cheapside, illustrated in Sir Ambrose Heal's 'Signboards of Old London Shops', Batsford, 1947, p. 170. The date suggested in this work is *c.* 1730. The librarian of the Guildhall Library of the City of London, Mr. A. H. Hall, has kindly searched the records of the Joiners' Company for this period, and found that John Jennion, after completing his apprenticeship, was admitted to the freedom of the Company on 6th May, 1732. The earliest quarterage book of 1737 gives his address as Queen Street, and this was unchanged until in the last quarter of 1756/57 payment was made by Ann Jennion, widow. Jennion, then, appears to have been a master joiner, flourishing about 1735–57, who adopted for his sign a picture of three contemporary tryplanes. All three have a tapered stock, as in the Dutch and French planes, but no front grip. It was probably found that the new handle, shown to a larger scale at Fig. 76*b*, being more effective than the old, made a a front grip unnecessary.

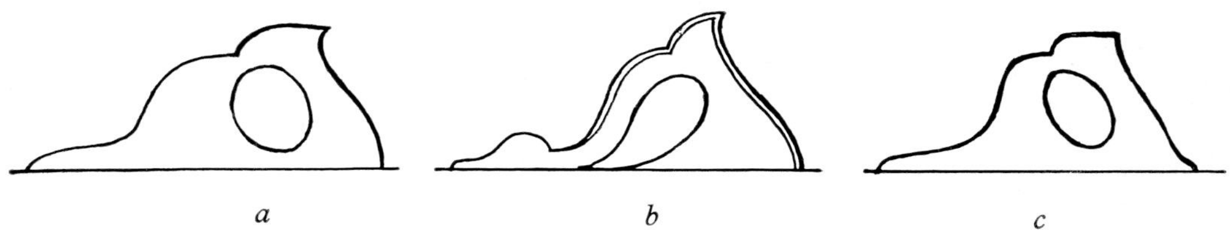

a *b* *c*

76. Tryplane Handles, 18th Century: (*a*) Lakenhal, Leiden, 1763; (*b*) Jennion Trade Card, *c.* 1750; (*c*) Wollin, Pomerania, *c.* 1800

The actual process of experiment on these lines, which must have been going on all over Europe in the second half of the 18th century, can be seen by comparing three planes in the Nordiska Museet, Stockholm. They originally belonged to the Crown Prince Adolf Frederik, Duke of Holstein-Gottorp, who became King of Sweden in 1751, and reigned until 1771. According to Larousse, he was not a particularly energetic ruler, but his interest for us lies in his addiction to the hobby of woodwork. The planes were evidently made for him before he was overtaken by the affairs of state; they are beautifully carved with the Prince's monogram and crown, and various floral motives, and the dates 1748 and 1749. The first, dated 1748, is very well known, and has been illustrated many times, but it is essentially a survival of the medieval plane of the northern tradition, with a grip, carved in the shape of a bird's head, at the fore end. It may be compared directly with the plane on the Saenredam engraving (Fig. 66*d*). The second plane is of a similar pattern, with rather simpler carving on the sides of the stock, while the front grip, with a plain knob at the end, has been turned at right angles, bringing the knob horizontal. The third plane, however, is of great interest. It is dated 1749, and the front grip is missing altogether, although the dovetail socket into which it fitted still remains. At the back a closed handle, similar to those on the Leiden and Jennion planes, has been fitted later, the carved design being partly obliterated by it. How long after 1749 this was done it is impossible to say, but this plane has also been fitted with a double iron, which shows that it was in use at least until the last quarter of the 18th century.

A tryplane very similar to those shown in the Jennion trade card is found on the sculptured footstone to the grave of Mark Sharp, a local carpenter (Fig. 151), in the churchyard at Lewes, dated 1747. The handle is almost identical, and also appears to be set off centre. In his 'Geschichte des Hobels' J. M. Greber gives a tryplane from a private collection in Wollin, Pomerania, with a similar grip (Fig. 76*c*) at the back, and no grip at the front. The stock is carved with the figure of a man with a staff in his hand (Daedalus ?). Greber dates this tool to about 1800.

It is interesting to note that at about the same time, i.e., early in the second half of the 18th century, similar changes were taking place in the shape of the handles of saws. Previously hand-saws had been provided with straight or pistol-shaped handles, but about half-way through the century both hand- and tenon-saws had adopted a new pattern similar to that of the plane handle. The earliest actual example of this occurs in the Mark Sharp footstone mentioned above. The reason for this was exactly the same in both cases; the need to get the pressure down to the cutting edge of the tools. There is not at present enough evidence to decide which came first, but in German-speaking countries both the new pattern of plane handle and the hand-saws with similarly shaped grips are known as *Fuchsschwanze* (Fox's brush), so it seems likely that both improvements came at about the same time.

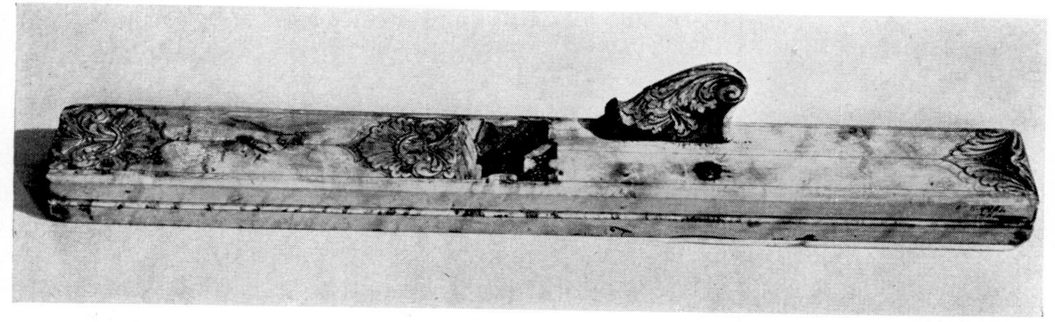

77. Long Plane from Gulbrandsdalen, *c.* 1800 — *De Sandvigske Samlinger, Lillehammer*

As a matter of interest, an unusual plane from Gulbrandsdalen, dated to about 1800, is shown in Fig. 77. This is reproduced by courtesy of Dr. Sigurd Grieg, curator of the Sandvigske Samlinger, Lillehammer, Norway. The handle of this plane is a very curious shape, quite out of the run of anything we have been considering here, but it is also set off centre, like most 18th-century planes. There is no grip at the front, and the mouth is cut for a double iron. An almost identical tool, owned by the celebrated wood-carver Erik Hellelokken (1824–1904), is in the same museum, and is illustrated in G. A. Norman's 'History of the Plane'.

It now appears that John Jennion was a plane maker. In 1724 he was put to Robert Wooding and admitted to the Joiners' Company in 1732. In 1736 a Robert Fitkin was put to Anne Wooding, Robert's widow, and the family can be traced to John Fitkin of Finsbury in 1826. In 1739 Jennion took Geo. Sampson as an apprentice. Planes with all these names on them have been found in public and private collections. Robert Wooding was himself apprenticed in 1693.

7: Smoothing Planes, 1600–1800

In spite of the variety of pattern displayed by 17th- and 18th-century smoothing planes, it is possible to separate out five main types, each, to borrow a term from biology, with a well-defined habitat, which in most cases has persisted to the present day. In fact the study of any modern tool catalogue from Scandinavia, Germany, or Switzerland will reveal types of planes almost unknown in this country, and vice versa. This is not surprising when we realise that the period saw the final collapse of the international feudal system and the rise of national groupings which discouraged the free interchange of ideas, especially at the artisan level. The wide-ranging migrations of the master-masons and master-carpenters of the Middle Ages, such as Villard de Honnecourt, were over, and although it was customary for the better type of craftsman, after completing his apprenticeship, to treat himself to a *Wanderjahr*, he rarely left his own cultural environment. This led to a certain amount of in-breeding, the results of which may be seen in the following pages.

The simplest type of smoothing plane is a square block about 8–8½ in. long, with or without a front grip, or 'Nase', as the Germans call it. A 15th-century example has been shown in Fig. 59*b*, and the small plane lying on the ground in the 1600 Wierix engraving is of the same pattern. The *Schlichthobel* or smoothing plane in Comenius's 'Orbis Pictus', an illustrated dictionary in four languages published in 1666, is a similar tool, with the top of the grip rounded off. Moxon (1683), Roubo (1769), and Diderot (1765), in the works previously cited, give square blocks without the 'Nase'. Both ends of Moxon's smoother are shaped with an ogee curve, while Roubo's is simply chamfered along the top edges. The tool survives in the present-day French workshop as the *rabot ordinaire* with a single iron 1½–1¾ in. wide (Heurtematte, 'Cours de Technologie du Bois', Paris, 1948). Very few tools of this type have found their way into the museums, they were too plain and common.

A similar square block with the sides shaped to a curve, to allow for a wider iron and deeper groove for the wedges, is the most obvious variation on the above. We have already encountered a tool of this kind in the 1514 Dürer engraving. Moxon gives a drawing of this type in his plate of joiners' tools (Fig. 71), but there is no reference to it in the text, although this was one of the few additions he made to Félibien's original 1676 engraving. This suggests that it had already become a typical English pattern, and it survives to this day in the form of the 'coffin' plane. It appears, however, to be unknown in the Low Countries, North Germany, or Scandinavia, but it turns up again in South Germany and Austria, where it seems to have always been popular. Fig. 78 shows a group of planes from the Tyrol. They have clearly been preserved because of the neatness of the chip-carved decoration, and several have the bulging stock. Some of them are further distinguished by a feature unknown elsewhere: the wedge and iron are let into the stock near the heel, while the opening for the shavings is entirely separate. It would be interesting to know how this worked, and if it did, why nobody else ever tried it.

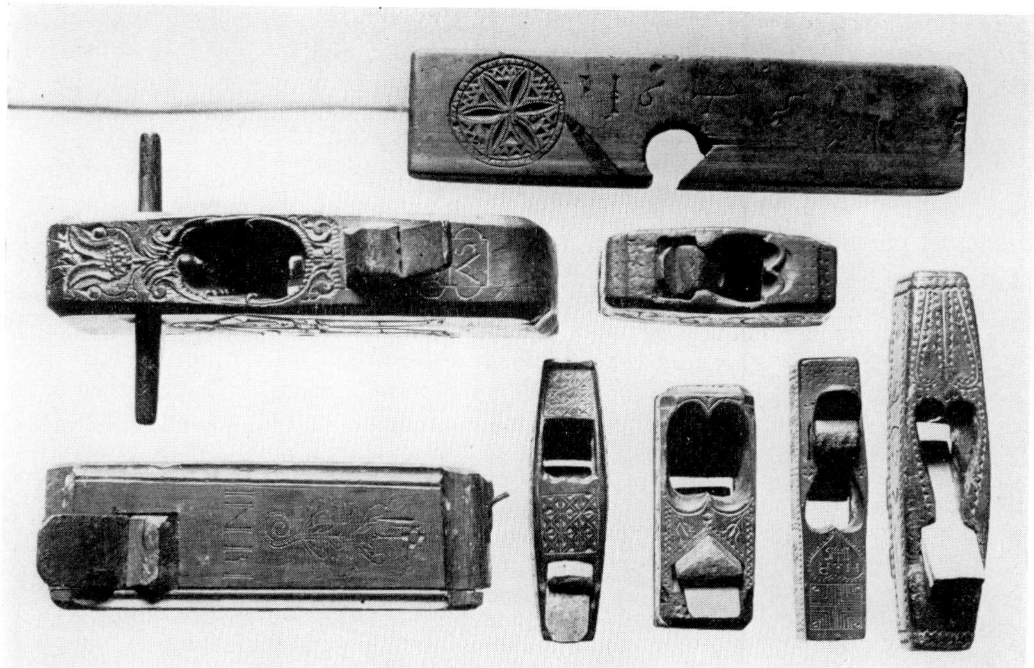

78. Tyrolean Smoothing and Moulding Planes *Tiroler Volkskunstmuseum, Innsbruck*

79. 18th-century Smoothing Planes *Haslemere Educational Museum*

The Swiss-German-Scandinavian smoothing plane of the 17th–18th centuries is a more complicated pattern, but although it is still listed in the present-day catalogues in those countries, it is almost unknown here. Messrs. A. B. Salmen's Successors, Ltd., Edmonton, London, N.18, have been making planes of this type for some years, under the name of the 'Continental' plane, and in some circles it is known as the 'Bismark' plane, owing, presumably, to its German associations. In these planes the stock is square and parallel, while the front of the sole projects forward beyond the upright front grip. A characteristic feature is the fluting carried round the sides of the stock at the level of the top of the step. The plane in the background of Fig. 79, said to have come from Scandinavia, is a good example of the type, with the characteristic fluting along the sides, and a delicately executed relief in front of the mouth opening. A rare French version of this pattern is shown in Fig. 80, very chastely decorated with zig-zag cords and tassels, and various floral designs. This plane has a slightly bulging plan, but the front projection is well emphasised, and carved with the initials C.A.D., probably the owner and maker.

80. 18th-century Smoothing Plane
Musée des Arts Decoratifs, Paris

81. 20th-century Smoothing Plane
Lachappelle A.G. Luzern, Switzerland

The 'Record Fausthobel', by Lachappelle A.G., Kriens, Lucerne, Switzerland (Fig. 81) may be included here to show the survival of this type to modern times. The design has been reduced to its essentials, but the fluting along the sides remains in vestigial form as a narrow V, while a shaped block has been provided to give additional support for the iron and a more comfortable grip. These planes are usually in hornbeam, but more expensive models are listed with soles of lignum vitae or evergreen oak (*chène verte*). The fixing of the wedge against a cross-bar of brass is a reversion to the old Roman and medieval practice. Similar smoothing planes to this may be obtained in any tool shop in Europe east of the Rhine, and they are also popular as far south as Greece and Crete.

Another entirely distinct pattern, equally unknown here, but apparently very popular since the 17th century in Scandinavia and the Low Countries, is the *schaaf*, as it is known in Holland, and with a variation in spelling but a similar sound, the *skav* in Denmark. One of the earliest representations of the type occurs on the seal of the Kolding Joiners'

Guild, dated 1683 (Fig. 82). Typical features are the curved sides, narrowing towards the front, the volute-shaped front grip carved out of the solid, and the echoing spiral at the back of the stock, which is made higher to form a bed for the iron. A simplified version is shown in the smaller of the two planes on Fig. 83, dated 1618. A similar pair from Liège are illustrated in Fig. 84, and are said to have belonged to a lute-maker of that town. The smaller plane shows all the typical features, including the ogee pattern of the mouth carving, of the numerous examples of this type in the Swedish and Danish

82. Seal of Kolding Joiners' Guild, 1683
G. A. Norman, Lillehammer, Norway

83. Schaaf-type Smoothing Planes, dated 1618 and 1727 *Fries Museum, Leeuwarden*

museums. These, however, are rarely dated, but a small oak plane of the *schaaf* pattern, with the mouth carved to this ogee design, and dated 1692, is in the Salisbury, Wilts, Museum.

84. Smoothing Planes, one dated 1738 *Musée de la Vie Wallonne, Liège*

The popularity of this *schaaf* is emphasised by its adoption by the makers of the carved and dated Dutch planes of the 18th century. The larger tools in both Figs. 83 and 84 are very good examples, indeed the 1727 Leeuwarden plane is the earliest of the eleven listed in Table III. The latest, also in the Fries Museum, is dated 1792. The only standard *schaaf* known to be in this country is in the private collection of Mr. T. W. Bagshawe, F.S.A., F.R.Hist.S., at Luton, a very well-preserved example dated 1774. The mouth carvings of these planes are evenly distributed, five being of type (*c*) and six of type (*e*), but sometimes the execution appears much cruder than usual (the Liège plane, Fig. 84, is an example of this) which suggests that they may have been home-made copies of the standard commercial article. The *schaaf* was also very suitable for use as a compass plane, and several cases of this are known. The two examples in the Hermitage Museum at Leningrad, adapted for use as a pair of hollows and rounds, have already been mentioned.

A smoothing plane of a totally different pattern is shown in the foreground of Fig. 79. The stock is rectangular in cross-section, with straight sides, while the top slopes down in a smooth curve to form a projecting step at the front. The upright grip is carved with a grotesque head turned to the left, while the sides are carved in low relief with a leaf design, and a shield on the flat part of the top. This plane is said to have come from Flanders, but although nothing definite is known about it, the slot in the bed for the screw of a double iron suggests a date in the early 19th century. There is a similar plane, 10 in. long, the grip carved with a negro's head turned to the right, in the Werdenfelser Museum at Garmisch-Partenkirchen in Bavaria, dated 1838. The only other example of this pattern known to the writer occurs in the Dudley P. Allen Collection at Cleveland, Ohio (Fig. 85, right). It is described by the museum authorities as: 'Italian, late 17th-

85. 16th- and 17th-century Planes *Cleveland Museum of Art, Cleveland, Ohio, U.S.A.*

century, 11½ in. long. Boxwood and ebony inlay, handle terminating in carved lion holding mitre, the emblem of the city of Venice and of cabinet-makers'. Except that the 'lion' looks more like a dog with human arms, and the 'mitre' is almost certainly a try-square, this may pass; but it is curious how rare inlaid planes are. One other plane, in the Musée des Arts Decoratifs in Paris, has some of the characteristics of this *schaaf* variation. It is illustrated in Hooper's 'Handicraft in Wood', Batsford, 1952, and has a high back and volute front grip, beautifully carved in the Louis Quinze style. Perhaps the Novaya Zemlya plane (Fig. 67) was a forerunner of these unusual, but probably useful little tools.

The other tool on the left of Fig. 85 almost evades classification altogether. It is said to be late 16th-century Italian, and is carved with portrait heads and ornament, including a rigged ship, treated in colour. The position of the front grip is most unusual, while the wedge, apparently later than the rest of the tool, seems to be set in backwards to hold what looks like a double iron.

Coming at last to the standard Dutch version of the square block smoothing plane, this is known variously as the *blokschaaf* or *bossingblok*. Incidentally, the term *blokschaaf* is possibly linguistic evidence for the priority of the *schaaf* type above, as it must have been already in existence before the square block type was introduced. A well-preserved example, showing all the typical features, is illustrated in Fig. 86. The beech stock, $7\frac{1}{2}$–$8\frac{1}{2}$ in. long, is rectangular in plan, with a flat top slightly higher in the middle and sloping down towards each end, and a groove around all four sides. The top of the wedge is usually semi-circular, and decorated either with plain concentric circles, as here, or with a rosette design, as on the tryplane handles. The mouth carvings are similar to those on the other planes, except that in rather more than half the known examples, twenty-eight out of fifty-two, the iron is set on the skew, and the scrolls of the mouth carving, and sometimes the entire design, is skewed to match. This skewing of the iron, which is always to the right, is a unique feature of these planes, while the planes themselves are native to Holland, and unknown elsewhere.

Another unusual point is that most or all of these planes have the stock cut away on the off side, with the side of the iron projecting, as in a rebate or shoulder plane. As this corner is often rounded as well, the tool is frequently described as a moulding or rebate plane. The Rijksmuseum tool in Fig. 86 has a rebate on both sides, and conse-

86. Skewed *Blokschaaf*, dated 1755 *Rijksmuseum, Amsterdam*

quently Greber (*op. cit.*) calls it an *Abplatthobel*.* In the Pinto private collection a skewed *blokschaaf* dated 1764 has been fitted with an adjustable fence and turned into a sash fillister. Another in the Victoria and Albert Museum has a fixed iron fence in the middle of the sole, and can be used for rebating on either hand.

* Equivalent to our Dado plane.

A large number of these *blokschaaf* planes have small stamps usually impressed in threes on both ends of the stock. These stamps take various forms: some have a pair of initials separated by a *fleur-de-lis*; in others the initials are surmounted by a crown; one has the figure of a man with a staff (Daedalus ?); another looks like a Cupid with a bow and arrow.

Details of these stamps are only available for about half the planes listed on Table III, but it is possible to separate out several groups of identical stamps, each with a fairly well-defined date range. The earliest group consists of four planes stamped with the initials M and R. They are all in England, two in the Science Museum, dated 1723 and 1733; one in the Victoria and Albert Museum, dated 1734, and the fourth, dated 1731, was purchased by the writer in an antique shop in Delft some years ago. The 1723 plane is a skewed *blokschaaf* with a type (*b*) mouth carving, while the other three are all square *blokschaven* of type (*e*).

A second, more numerous group of eight have the letters F M with a *fleur-de-lis* between them. The date range of these is longer, from 1747 to 1783. All but one are *blokschaven* of type (*c*) mouth pattern, the other being a tryplane, also type (*c*). A plough dated 1771 carries the same stamp.

Most of the stamps with the crown have different initials, but there is a group of three with the initials IVD (Jan van Delft or van Dyck) in copperplate with the crown above. They are all skewed *blokschaven* with type (*d*) mouth carvings, and they are all in this country: one in the Science Museum dated 1782, one at Cardiff dated 1791, and one at Haslemere dated 1794. Since these stamps occur in groups on the same type of plane with similar decoration, it seems reasonable to suggest that they were the makers', and research is going forward in Holland to see whether it can be established who the makers were and where they worked.

Besides the stamps described above, many planes have groups of larger initials, sometimes roughly carved or impressed over them. These are all different, and were probably the owners'. Sometimes there is more than one group on the same plane, showing how the tool had passed from hand to hand.

One curious point about these carved and dated planes is that when they died out the custom of dating tools seems to have died out at the same time. This occurred early in the 19th century, and was probably due to the increasing commercial mass production of the tools themselves. In any case the conditions of work during the early stages of the Industrial Revolution left apprentices and craftsmen with neither the leisure nor the inclination to embellish their tools in the old manner.

There are two other types of plane which differ in several ways from the general run, and as they are usually used for smoothing and the like, they may as well be dealt with here. Mr. E. H. Pinto, of the Pinto Collection of Wooden Bygones, Northwood, Middlesex, on a visit to Naples, came across a Holy Family picture by a rare artist, Bartolomeo Schidone, in the Palazzo Reale, showing among other tools a plane almost identical with one in his collection (Fig. 87*a*). He had provisionally labelled his plane as 'Korean type but probably of European manufacture'. A similar plane with two cross-handles occurs in one of the intarsia panels of tools in San Petronio at Bologna, where it is shown hanging up in the rack with the sole facing outwards (Fig. 87*b*). Greber, who illustrates the panel on Fig. 58*b* of his book, calls it a *Zweimannshobel* or *Ketschhobel* (two-man or drag plane). He also shows a 17th–18th-century grooving plane from

Switzerland, and a plane from Kassel for moulding sash-bars, both of which have two rounded grips projecting on both sides before and behind the iron. A similar tool, with one cross-handle *in front of the iron*, is shown with the Tyrolean planes in Fig. 78. Planes with two cross-handles are still in use today, and they are shown in the catalogues of F. Ott & Co., of Ochsenfurt-on-Main, and the Lachappelle A.G., of Lucerne, Switzerland, both being about 12 in. long with a double iron $2\frac{3}{8}$ in. in width. These are in the section dealing with carpenters' tools. The Swiss firm, as usual, give the French name as well: *rabot galère avec manches* (galley plane with handles), an allusion to the hard work, as of galley slaves, entailed in their use, which is similar to the sense of the German dialect word *Ketsch* in *Ketschhobel*. The German makers further describe these planes as being of 'South-German type'.

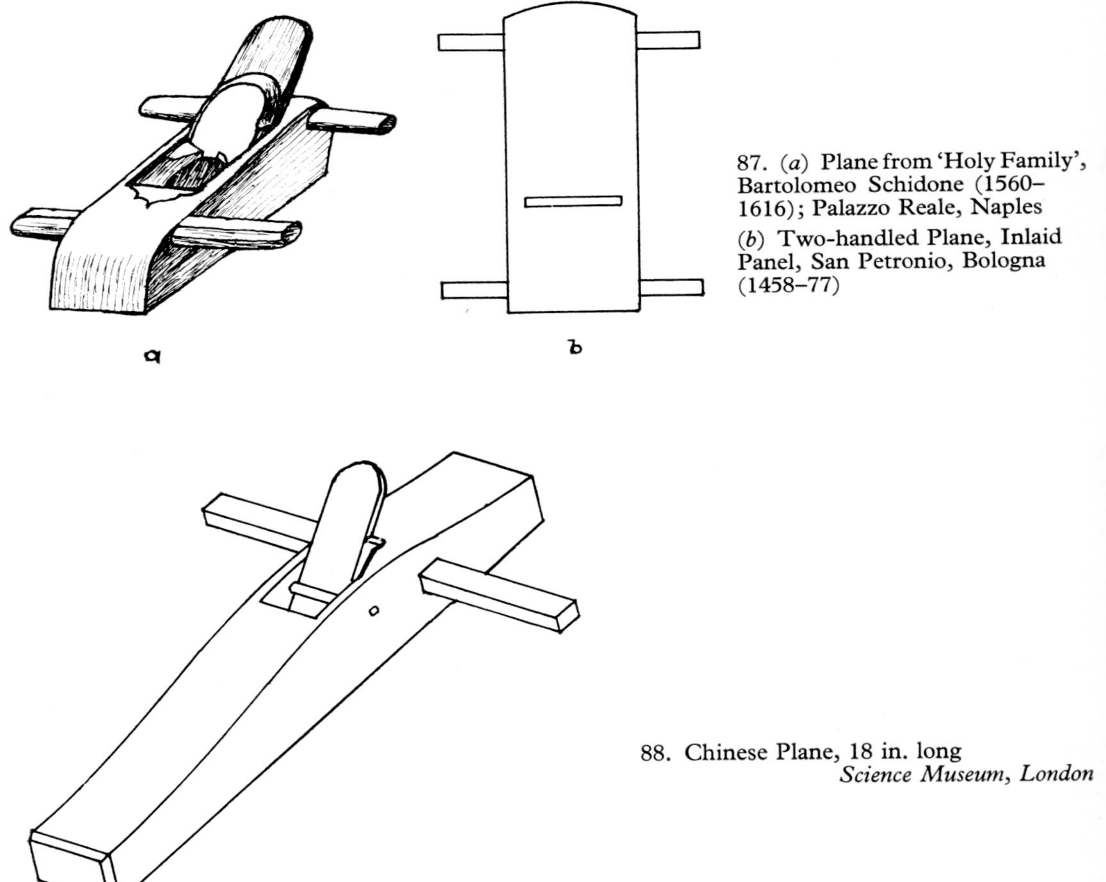

87. (*a*) Plane from 'Holy Family', Bartolomeo Schidone (1560–1616); Palazzo Reale, Naples
(*b*) Two-handled Plane, Inlaid Panel, San Petronio, Bologna (1458–77)

88. Chinese Plane, 18 in. long
Science Museum, London

Comparing these with the Korean planes in Mercer's 'Ancient Carpenters' Tools' (p. 118, Fig. 113), the Chinese planes in Greber, and a Chinese plane in the Science Museum (Fig. 88), it will be seen that although there is a superficial resemblance between them, there are fundamental differences. While most of the Italian and South-German planes have two grips, those with only one have it in front of the iron, whereas the Oriental tools are invariably shown with one grip only, *behind the iron.* This is sometimes explained by the oft-reiterated statement that the Chinese and Japanese pull their planes, just as they do their saws, a custom said to be due to some anatomical peculiarity of the Oriental wrist. It is true that east of Suez, and even in those parts of Europe formerly occupied by the Turks, such as Albania and Greece, pull-saws are still in common use, but this does not apply to planes. In fact on p. 241 of 'China at Work' by Rudolf P. Hommel, John Day Co., N.Y., U.S.A., the very opposite is stated: 'All Chinese planes are pushed away from the body'. Another cherished illusion gone. Actually the 'drag-planes' of Southern Europe were worked by two men, one pushing and the other pulling. The Lachappelle firm list among their coopers' tools a plane about 11 in. long, with one cross-grip behind the iron, similar to the 'Cooper's Short Jointer' illustrated by Mercer in Fig. 114. Mercer's description of the way this tool is used is rather confusing; in any case the Lachappelle plane is specifically described as an *Einmannshobel* or one-man plane, and is used for smoothing the bottoms of deep casks.

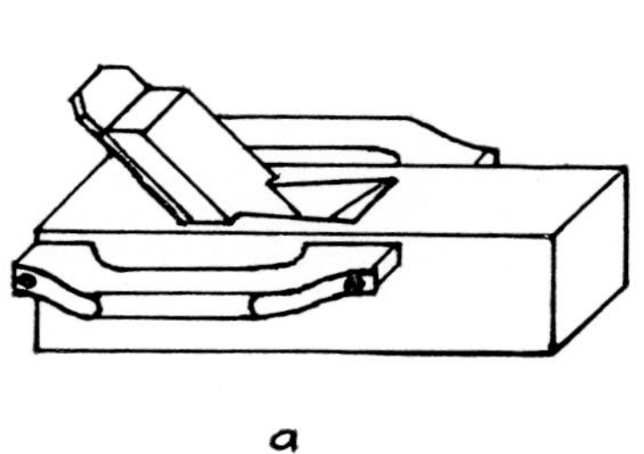

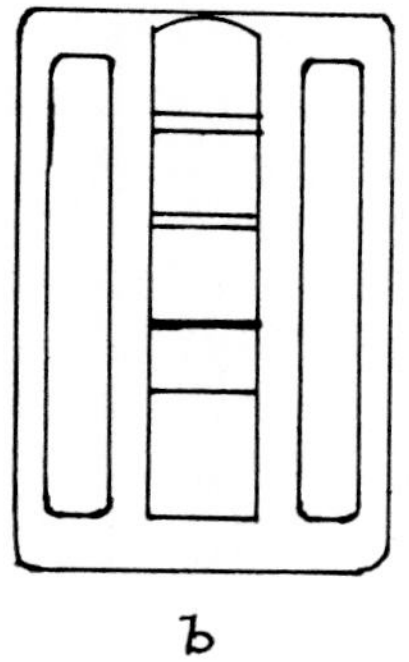

89

(*a*) 'Ketschhobel', 1952 Catalogue, Lachappelle A.G., Luzern, Switzerland

(*b*) Plane with Side Handles, Inlaid Panel, San Petronio, Bologna, 1468–77

Another *rabot galère* illustrated in the current Lachappelle catalogue (Fig. 89*a*) is also a curious survival from the Middle Ages, and being almost as unknown in this country as the others, merits a short discussion. The earliest appearance of the type is in the same fresco in the Campo Santo at Pisa from which the long tryplane was taken, and a similar tool is shown in the Bologna inlaid panels (Fig. 89*b*). Here the additional grips are on each side of the stock, with their centre line just behind the plane iron, thus achieving the same result as the cross-handle. This type of *rabot-galère* could, at a pinch, be either pushed or pulled, but although they could be quite effective for surfacing large or recalcitrant timbers, they never seem to have found much favour north of the Alps.

8: 1800 to the Present Day

Before proceeding to the development of the plane itself during the 19th century there is one point which must be dealt with first, as it affects planes of all, or nearly all types. This is the introduction of the double iron, which seems to have been invented, probably by an Englishman, some time in the last quarter of the 18th century. The first documentary evidence of this major improvement so far encountered comes from an invoice, dated 1787, from one Joseph Parks, of Sheffield, to a Mr. A. Hildick, also of Sheffield, for 'top and cut irons'. The writer is indebted to Mr. T. A. Seed, of Samuel Osborne and Co. Ltd., for the news of this highly interesting document.

This date is further confirmed by the discovery by J. M. Greber of an inventory of tools belonging at one time to the celebrated German cabinet-maker David Roentgen (1743–1807). The inventory was made in 1798, some four years after the Roentgen business in Neuwied was wound up. It mentions both German and English tryplanes and smoothing planes, but only the English tools have the additional description 'with double irons'. Herr Greber suggests that they were probably bought by Roentgen in England during a comparatively prosperous period of the firm's existence, some time in the middle 1780's.

The probable English origin of the double iron is also suggested by the fact that the earliest description and illustration of the device occurs in Peter Nicholson's 'Mechanical Exercises, or the Elements and Practice of Carpentry, Joinery, etc.', London, 1812. As the title shows, this book was based on Moxon's, in fact it was the first illustrated treatise on the practical arts for over a hundred years. Nicholson describes his jack plane as having a single iron, but notes in a later passage that 'to prevent the iron from tearing the wood a cover is used with a reversed basil (i.e., bevel)'. His illustration is shown at Fig. 90, and it will be noted that both cap and cutter have the usual 18th-century curved ends.

A much clearer illustration of the double iron is found in one of the plates from Smith's 'Key to the Manufactories of Sheffield', published there in 1816 (Fig. 91). It is interesting to note that although some of the irons shown have rounded ends, the 'double iron' itself has the modern square-topped cap iron and cutter, and the typical 'English' square nut for the screw. This 'Key' of Smith's may be considered as the first illustrated catalogue of tools ever published in England, but it was hardly a catalogue in the modern sense of the word, as the tools and garden implements shown were not the products of a single manufacturer. It is probable that the comparatively small family firms of Sheffield tool-makers did not at that time have the resources to issue their own lists, so Smith's compilation served a very useful purpose as a reference book for travellers, retail ironmongers, and so on, and is today an invaluable source of information for the historian of tools.

A French book of the same date, the second edition of Hamelin Bergeron's 'Manuel du Tourneur', Paris, 1816, also shows a double iron (Fig. 92). Comparing this with Smith's or Nicholson's, it will be noted that the tops of both irons are rounded, but the cap iron is slotted and the cutter tapped to take the screw, exactly the reverse of the modern practice. Reference to the planes shown on the same plate is not very helpful, as they are all strict copies of those in Diderot's 'Encylopédie' of fifty years earlier, and as we have already seen, these were a hundred years out of date even then.

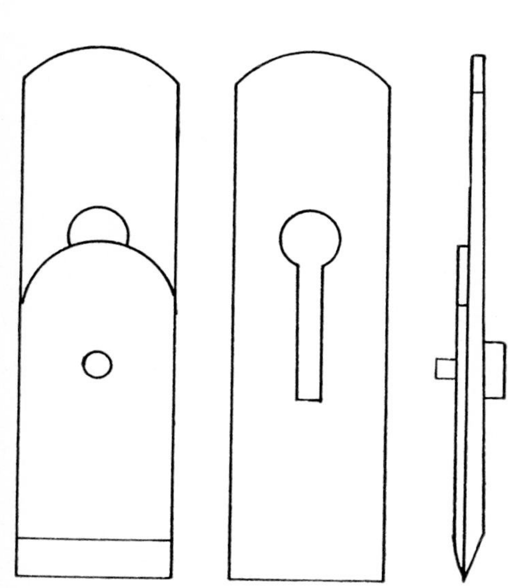

90. Double Iron
Peter Nicholson, 'Mechanical Exercises', 1812

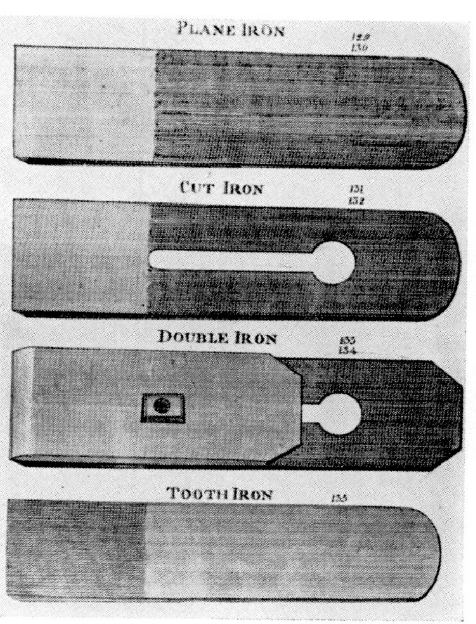

91. Double Iron and Cut Iron
Smith, 'Key to the Manufactories of Sheffield', 1816

92. Double Iron *Bergeron, 'Manuel du Tourneur', 1816*

It is more than likely, however, that we have here, fossilised in Bergeron's book, one of the early stages in the evolution of the double iron. The original genius who first saw the possibilities of the cap iron probably placed it loose on the cutter, holding both in position while driving the wedge home, a somewhat tricky procedure. Indeed M. Jacques Heurtematte, in his 'Cours de Technologie du Bois', Paris, 1949, describes a cap iron of this type, but remarks on the difficulty and the time taken to adjust it properly. The next stage was to screw the cap iron to the cutter, but it was found that after the iron had been ground once or twice, the cap iron had to be moved further up. To effect this, the cap iron was made with a slot, with a large hole at one end to admit the head of the screw. This is the position as we see it in the Bergeron double iron.

There were two objections to this arrangement: the wedge had to be cut away a good deal to clear the screw head, while the long slot weakened the cap iron so that after a time the pressure near the cutting edge was reduced, giving rise to chatter. Killing two birds with one stone, the slot was cut in the cutting iron, the screw reversed, and the groove for its head cut in the bed of the stock, leaving the wedge almost intact.

Another method of ensuring a constant clearance between cap iron and cutting edge, without actually screwing the two irons together, and avoiding too much insult both to stock and wedge, is by means of the 'Long screw', one form of which is shown in Fig. 93,

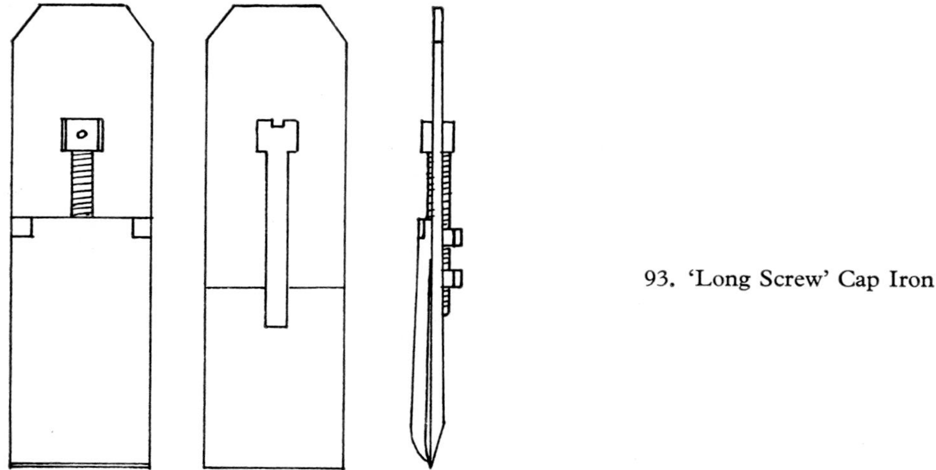

93. 'Long Screw' Cap Iron

drawn from examples in Greber and Heurtematte. In the Goldenberg catalogue of 1875 this form is described as the 'Bavarian' pattern, and other forms of long screw differing according to the shape of the head of the screw, known as the 'French', 'Austrian', and 'Alsatian' are also shown. In all cases the screw is threaded through two bosses attached to the under surface of the cap iron, adjusted to give the requisite clearance, and both cap iron and cutter held in place by the wedge. This device saves having to unscrew the cap iron every time the cutter is sharpened, but it was never very popular in this country or in Northern Europe generally, being confined almost entirely to Austria,

Switzerland, and France, where it survives to this day in some of the catalogues, for use in special coachbuilder's planes and the cooper's long jointer or *colombe*.

To bring this account of the double iron up to date, there has recently appeared on planes of the Stanley type a cap iron the lower end of which is separate, and fits loosely to the fixed portion by means of two small pins. The idea is that this may be removed and the burr taken off after honing the cutter, without having to touch the screw. The writer himself finds that this detachable piece usually falls off when removing the iron, and the time that in theory should be saved is wasted by fishing around under the bench for the missing part. This, however, may be merely another instance of the inveterate conservatism of woodworkers in respect to their tools, which has been remarked on earlier in these pages.

Coming to the planes themselves, the group of tools in Smith's 'Key' (Fig. **94**) shows the final stage in the evolution of the wooden plane in Northern Europe. These planes

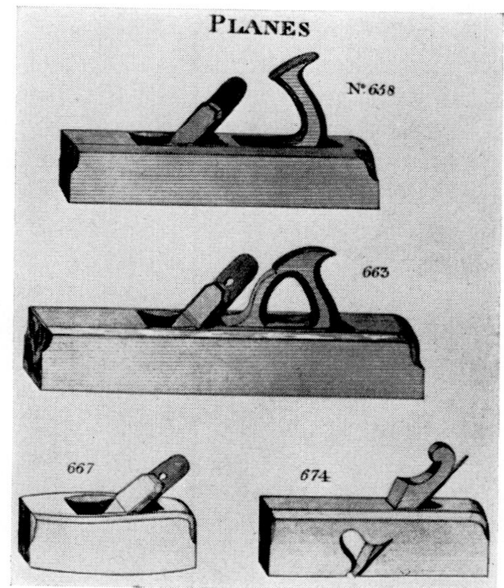

94. Bench Planes *Smith, 'Key to the Manufactories of Sheffield', 1816*

are practically identical with those illustrated in Peter Nicholson's book of four years earlier, and little different, in fact, from those in use today. Both jack and tryplanes are somewhat out of drawing, but it is clear from the illustration that the jack plane has a single iron with the open form of handle, while the tryplane has a double iron, with a closed handle fitted in the centre of the stock, the front grip having by now disappeared for good. All the continental makers have adopted these originally English types for jack and tryplanes, although the Dutch still taper the top of the stock down from the back of the iron to the heel in the traditional manner.

The 'coffin plane' type of smoother shown, common in England since Moxon's time, is confined in the present-day catalogues to this country, Holland, and France, while in the current list of the West German firm of E. C. Emmerich a plane of this type is described as 'English pattern'. In other parts of Europe: Scandinavia, Germany,

Switzerland, Austria, Greece and the Balkans, and the Slavonic countries, the smoothing planes follow the 18th-century Northern European tradition of the parallel-sided stock with the projecting sole, and an upright 'Nase' or toat in the front, as illustrated on Figs. 79 and 81. As has been mentioned earlier, an English maker has recently tried to introduce this type of plane here, but although it has advantages over the ordinary wooden smoother, it is perhaps too late now to overcome the modern preference for the Stanley-type metal smoothing plane.

The further evolution of the plane during the 19th century is concerned very largely with the design of tools with metal stocks fitted with screw- or cam-actuated clamps or lever caps, and various methods of adjusting the iron without using a hammer. This line of progress seems to have been confined to this country and the United States; the continental makers generally were, and still are, content to retain and improve the wooden planes of the traditional pattern. These improvements take the form of using harder woods such as hornbeam for the stock itself, with the sole in lignum vitae or *chène verte* (evergreen oak), and various ingenious ways of jointing these together are adopted.

As we have already seen, planes with metal soles and side plates were standard types in Roman times, and during the Dark Ages and right through the Middle Ages small block planes were frequently made with a metal sole and a bone or wooden core. These small block planes were very useful to violin and other musical-instrument makers. There is an interesting set of six, four of iron and two of brass, in the Stradivarius Museum at Cremona. They are all about 4½ in. long and from 1½ to 2 in. wide, and are thus too small to have a wooden core. They were used by the master between 1666 and 1737.

But it was only in the 19th century, with the improvements in metallurgy and machine tools, that real progress was made in the design and mass production of larger planes mainly in metal. The early stages of this development are obscure, but it is clear that the English and American plane-makers who applied themselves to this problem worked on quite different lines. Generally speaking the English makers concentrated on developing the stock as a hollow metal box filled in with wood, while the Americans, after experimenting with various forms of metal casting screwed to a wooden stock, finally dispensed with the wood altogether (except for the handles, of course), and produced the first all-metal planes.

95. Mitre Plane, *c.* 1820
Lent to the Science Museum, London, by Messrs. Buck & Ryan, of London

There is reason to believe that the English developments, in which the names of Spiers of Ayr and Norris of London figure prominently, took as their starting-point the mitre plane of the pattern shown in Fig. 95. This is clearly the lineal descendant of the medieval block plane or *Vergatthobel* (Figs. 65 and 66*e*). The plane shown in the figure is inscribed R. NELSON, 122 Edgware Road, and is said to date from about 1820, but according to information kindly supplied by Mr. F. N. Macdonald, the Paddington Borough Librarian, the Nelson business at that address was taken over by Geo. Hy. Buck in 1852 or 1853, so the plane may be a few years later. It is in effect an open-topped steel box, square in front and rounded to a semi-circle at the back. The sides are dovetailed to the sole, which projects at both ends, with an overall length of 7½ in. and width of 2 in. The box is filled in with hardwood, the iron being bedded with a flat angle against the back section, and wedged against a bar across the mouth. Mr. R. A. Salaman has two planes of this type in his collection, one with a steel sole 10½ in. by 2¾ in. and rosewood core, the other with a steel sole 10½ in. by 2½ in. dovetailed to brass sides, again with a rosewood core. Both these planes are similar to that in the Science Museum in having the sole projecting at both ends.

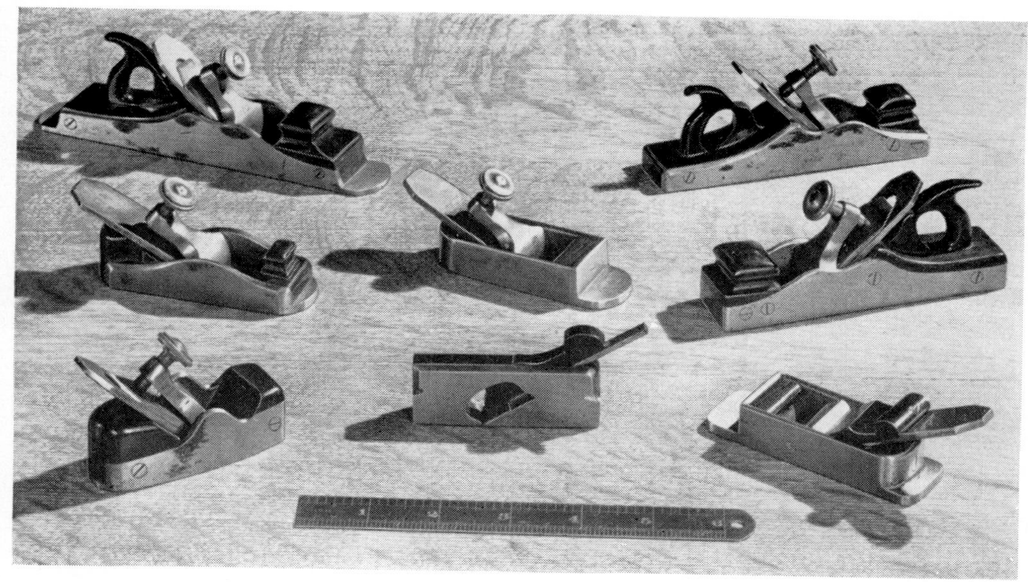

96. Models of Stewart Spiers Planes *Ayr Carnegie Library. Courtesy R. A. Salaman, Esq.*

A much larger plane of this type was purchased in Somerset recently by Mr. E. E. Fleetwood, a friend of the writer, and presented to the Blaise Castle Folk Museum, Bristol. This tool is 12⅝ in. long, 3⅛ in. wide, and 2½ in. high, and with the rosewood core, is extremely heavy. Two other planes of this pattern form part of a kit of tools in the Scarborough Museum, formerly belonging to the late Mr. Nutley, at one time foreman in the cabinet-making department of J. Tonks & Sons (Scarborough) Ltd. They were illustrated in 'The Ironmonger' of 18th August, 1956, and are dated to about a hundred years ago. In these three provincial examples the sole projects at the front only, in contrast to the London tools described above.

A very similar tool is shown at bottom right in Fig. 96, a group of models of the planes made by the celebrated Stewart Spiers of Ayr. According to an obituary notice of his daughter, the late Miss M. Spiers, who carried on the business until 1920, from the 'Ayrshire Post' of 21st May, 1937, kindly communicated to the writer by Mr. J. W. Forsyth, of the Ayr Carnegie Library, the Spiers family had been prominent in the Ould Toon for close on two hundred years. Stewart, one of six brothers, was apprenticed like them to the family cabinet-making business, but about 1840, while on a visit to Edinburgh, he came across a rough casting for an iron plane which so attracted him that he bought it for 1s. 6d., and after finishing it himself, managed to sell it for 18s. 6d. This seemed a much more profitable line of business than cabinet-making, and soon afterwards he left the family concern and set up as a full-time plane-maker. In the 1909 catalogue of the firm, one of the very few extant, there is a rubber stamp inscribed 'Stewart Spiers, Ayr, Iron Plane Manufacturer' and in the centre of the design one of these identical mitre planes, in all probability the original pattern with which he had started his career nearly seventy years before. It is also on record that Mr. Spiers visited the Great Exhibition of 1851 and found a number of his planes there. They had apparently come from America, whither he had already been sending his products; which shows the progress his business had made in the meantime.

The other mitre plane in the group (centre top, Fig. 96), shows the next development, the adoption of a gunmetal lever cap with a knurled screw, replacing the wooden wedge. It will be noticed that this mitre plane has the sole projecting in the front only. In connection with this Holtzapfel, in 'Turning and Mechanical Manipulations', London, 1846, has an interesting passage. On p. 498 he mentions: 'a plane patented in America in 1832, with the bottom or cutting iron made as usual, but without any mortice; the top iron has a thumbscrew at its upper end, and moves on two lateral pins or fulcrums $\frac{3}{4}$ in. from its lower edge; the pins fit into two grooved pieces of metal let into the sides of the plane; the lengths of the grooves exactly determine the situation of the top iron. When . . . the cutter is placed in position . . . and the thumbscrew turned, it bears on the upper part of the cutter, and tilts the top iron, until its lower edge also bears hard against the lower part of the cutter, and thereby fixes it without a wedge.' He adds that this device had not been generally adopted because of the expense, but it is clear that he was not describing a top iron at all, but the screwed lever cap which was later used by Spiers and other English makers for both wood and metal planes. In Germany planes fitted with this type of fastening are known as *Reformhobeln*, and are usually wooden smoothers.

Spiers then modified this metal box by using a U-shaped casting or forging for the sole and side plates, or by dovetailing them as in the Science Museum plane (Fig. 95). The models in Fig. 96 are all screwed, but this is probably owing to their small scale. On all the full-size planes shown in the 1909 catalogue there is no sign of screws on the side plates. The new pattern is shown by the third mitre plane at middle left, with the small cushion-shaped front grip which is such a characteristic feature of the Spiers planes, and the rounded back. For larger planes, listed as 'panel' planes from $13\frac{1}{2}$ in. to $17\frac{1}{2}$ in. long, and as 'joining' planes from $20\frac{1}{2}$ in. to $27\frac{1}{2}$ in. long (the word 'jack' was not used), all with $2\frac{1}{2}$ in. irons, it was easy to adapt this U-shaped casting, with a double-hump curve to the side plates (Fig. 96, top and middle right). The wooden core finished flush with the metal at both ends, and followed the curve of the sides, with a square front grip and a closed handle immediately behind the iron. Extra length in the 'joining' planes was provided by making the sole project about $2\frac{1}{2}$ in. at both ends (Fig. 96, top left).

Two types of smoothing planes, $7\frac{1}{2}$ or $8\frac{1}{2}$ in. long, with $2\frac{1}{8}$ in. irons, were listed, each size with either parallel or rounded sides. One type, shown bottom left in Fig. 96, has the rounded back of the mitre plane just above it in the group, with a plain rounded grip in front. This smoother has rounded sides. The other type was provided with an open handle of the jack-plane pattern (Fig. 97), and is an example of the parallel-sided variation. The man who made the model planes in Fig. 96 knew what he was about, as with the exception of the tool in Fig. 97, he shows the complete range of Spiers planes, and in addition, by accident or design, the actual development from the open-box mitre plane to the final version and its derivatives.

As late as 1909 there was no provision in any of these planes for vertical or lateral adjustment of the iron. The cheaper planes were made of wrought iron, but the majority were of steel, and occasionally gunmetal. The core was of rosewood with gunmetal lever caps and screws.

97. Spiers Handled Smooth Plane
Ayr Carnegie Library

98. Steel Dovetailed Smoothing Plane by Norris
S. Tyzack & Sons, 1935

The introduction to the 1909 Spiers catalogue mentions 'the numerous *imitations* [their italics] of these planes now before the public'. Among these imitations perhaps the best known were those made by Norris of London, although Mr. R. A. Salaman, to whom the writer is indebted for much of the information given above, once heard the late Mr. A. Collier, of the Brixton firm, state that Slater of Clerkenwell was making these planes long before Norris. The 1914 catalogue of the Norris firm, from Mr. Salaman's collection, shows a number of planes almost identical with those of Stewart Spiers, the only apparent difference being the smaller knurled screw to the lever cap. Norris included an 'Improved Steel Smoothing Plane' with a closed handle. All these planes are described as 'Dovetailed', referring to the way the iron sole was jointed to the side plates, but in addition, Norris listed similar planes in malleable iron, working out at about 10% cheaper, with the side plates screwed to the core.

The same 1914 catalogue lists jack planes and smoothers of both types, incorporating the adjusting device patented by Norris in 1913. Both the vertical setting and the lateral adjustment of the cutter were achieved with a single operating knob, which makes this device unique of its kind, as in all the others known to the writer the two controls were kept separate. This patent is included in the 'Steel Dovetailed Smoothing Plane' with closed handle, shown in the pre-war catalogue of S. Tyzack & Son, Ltd. (Fig. 98).

The writer remembers using a plane of this pattern as an apprentice some forty years ago, and how beautifully it did its job. But it is not too much to say that they have practically disappeared from the workshops today. The reason is not perhaps far to seek. The plane shown in Fig. 98, with a $2\frac{1}{4}$ in. iron and $7\frac{3}{4}$ in. long, was priced at 48s. 6d. In the same catalogue a Stanley or Record No. $4\frac{1}{2}$, 10 in. long with a $2\frac{3}{8}$ iron, was listed at 15s. 6d., less than a third of the price for a larger plane. One could, in fact, get a whole set of Stanley planes: No. 3 smoother, No. 5 jack, and No. 7 jointer, for 52s. 9d. altogether, or just a few shillings more than a single Norris smoother. The dovetailed jointer planes $28\frac{1}{2}$ in. long with $2\frac{1}{2}$ in. irons were priced at 99s. 0d. each, nearly two weeks' wages for the average joiner of those days.

The Norris screwed lever cap and patent adjusting device were also fitted to conventional smoothing, jack, and trying plane stocks (Fig. 99). This combined the hammerless adjustment of the iron with the advantages, mainly lightness and sweetness of action, of the wooden planes. Even so they were nearly three times as expensive as their ordinary counterparts, which probably accounts for their comparative rarity in the workshops.

The German and Swiss wooden smoothers using the screwed lever cap instead of a wedge, known as *Reformhobeln*, have already been mentioned. In these tools the regulation of shaving thickness is effected indirectly by adjusting the mouth.

The story of the gradual evolution of American planes of the Stanley type is a rather tangled skein, and although we have fairly adequate records in the shape of catalogues and patent specifications, these are not always very helpful. Some of the most vital improvements were not made the subject of patents at all, while some of the ideas it was desired to protect were frequently dropped and played no part in the final result.

99. Wooden Trying Plane with Norris Patent Adjustable Iron
S. Tyzack & Son, 1935

100. Knowles Patent Iron Plane, 1827
Stanley Tools, Chart No. 131

According to 'The Story of the Plane', issued as Chart No. 131 by Stanley Tools, of New Britain, Conn., and other information kindly supplied to the writer by Mr. Austin L. Stowell, Chief Product Engineer of the firm, the main lines of the story are as follows. In 1827 a patent was taken out by H. Knowles for a plane with a cast-iron sole (Fig. 100). This appears to be a jack plane with a flat sole and side plates, rising to their maximum height about one-third of their length from the front. They were provided with two ribs on the inside, forming a groove to take the single iron and the wedge. A closed handle was fitted at the back, and a turned knob in front. This rather crude arrangement must have been very tricky to adjust, and in 1843 a W. Foster patented an improvement to regulate the thickness of the shaving without using a hammer, by means of a square block let into the sole just in front of the cutter, and adjusted vertically with a screw. This device is sometimes met with on continental planes today, but it has never been very popular with our craftsmen, as it reduces the effective area of the sole in contact with the wood.

In 1854 this same cast-iron stock, with slightly curved side plates more like those of the later Stanley planes, was the basis for the introduction by W. S. Loughborough of a screwed clamp instead of the wedge to secure the iron. This again is not the invention of 1832 mentioned by Holtzapfel, as the clamp itself fitted in the groove previously used for the wedge, and was not pivoted on pins or trunnions.

This was the position when Leonard Bailey, of Boston, Mass., who was later to make such outstanding contributions to the development of the plane, first appeared on the scene. His earliest efforts were, however, applied to planes with wooden soles. His first patent, No. 20615, taken out on 22nd June, 1858, was concerned with a 'friction plate' device for the vertical adjustment of the cutting iron of a joiner's plane (Fig. 101).

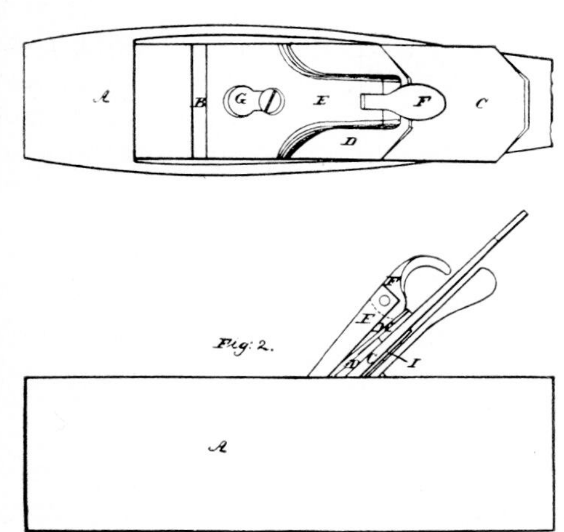

101. Leonard Bailey's First Patent, 1858
Stanley Tools, New Britain, Conn.

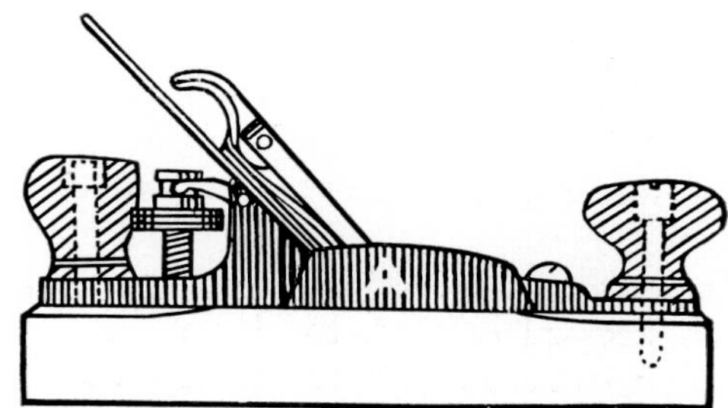

102. Bailey Bench Plane, 1867
Stanley Tools

A careful reading of the specification and scrutiny of the accompanying drawings shows this to have been a singularly complicated and ineffective arrangement, but as nothing more was ever heard of it, there is little point in describing it here. If this had been the only new feature of this patent it might have had some historical interest; the really remarkable thing is that the drawings show the cammed lever cap with a spring at the back, which has since been a feature of all the later Bailey and Stanley planes, and has been retained to this day. Yet this is not mentioned at all in the specifications! Bailey's next patent, No. 21311, of August, 1858, specifically concerned with this lever cap, shows in fact a much cruder version, with no spring at the back, while the thumb cam is turned upwards instead of downwards, a much less effective arrangement. This confusion may have arisen in the Patent Office itself; what is notable is that both were applied to ordinary wooden smoothers with bulging sides, but no grooves to the throat. Since the screw to hold the new lever cap was apparently threaded direct into the wooden bed, it was bound to wear loose in a very short time, and the whole problem had to be thought out afresh and on different lines.

The progress which Bailey had made in the next nine years is shown by the patent No. 67398, taken out in August, 1867, and described quite simply as a 'bench plane' (Fig. 102). A wooden stock is still used, but a shallow boat-shaped casting is screwed to the top, providing a solid bed for the iron, and also a metal seating for the screw securing the cammed lever cap, which was the only feature retained from the previous designs. The spring at the back of this lever cap, shown earlier in No. 20615, is here expressly mentioned in the specification as one of the innovations! The ostensible subject of this patent was the vertical nut and forked lever engaging with a slot in the cap iron, providing a positive vertical adjustment for the cutter. Two knobs were screwed to the casting for handles back and front, and the wooden stock was chamfered along the top and rounded at both ends.

One of the most important features of this model, and indeed one of Bailey's major contributions to progress, is again not mentioned in the specification, and appears to have been taken for granted. This is the comparatively thin cutter with parallel faces. All the cutters used in the previous models had been standard jack- or smoothing-plane irons, tapering back in thickness appreciably from the cutting edge. A thin parallel iron was a great improvement on this, as it saved a lot of time in grinding and could be honed at the same angle, which could thus be kept more constant and made the tool less subject to chatter.

Shortly after this the adjusting nut was turned through 90 degrees to the horizontal position, and the forked lever turned the other way to suit. In the earlier pattern the knob had to be cut away to make room for the nut; when it was turned the other way there was even less clearance, so the back knob was dispensed with altogether, the end of the casting being rounded to make a comfortable grip. Bailey also provided a handled smoother 9–10 in. long, and a 'jenny' plane 13 in. long, with a jack-plane handle bedded on a stepped casting, to give more room for adjusting the nut. The term 'jenny' is curious, but the writer's surmise is that being slightly shorter than a 'jack', it was naturally called a 'jenny', mules being much commoner animals a hundred years ago than they are now. The jack, fore, and jointer planes had a flat casting screwed to a long, parallel-sided stock, with an open grip and a turned knob for the left hand. These three planes also show in rudimentary form another important feature of Bailey's tools, which was to loom very large in their subsequent development, and helped to account for their popularity, the partial standarisation of the components. Apart from the stocks themselves, and the corresponding castings, all the parts, for the various sizes of cutter used, were identical and interchangeable.

This process of standardisation was carried further still in the all-metal planes introduced about this time. The earlier Knowles cast-metal sole was slightly modified and provided with a separate bed or frog, which could be adjusted to vary the mouth opening. All the other standard components, such as the lever cap and the forked vertical adjusting lever, developed on the previous wooden stocks, were incorporated in the new design, which apart from one feature added some years later, is very much like the final version of the plane made today.

At this time Bailey was engaged in the manufacture of his planes in a small way in Boston, Mass., but in 1869 he sold his business and most of his patent rights to the Stanley Rule & Level Co., of New Britain, Conn. He was then appointed head of their plane department, and the first catalogue of the company, issued in 1870, gives illustrations of his new designs.

In 1871 G. A. Warren, with his patent No. 111,890, attempted to solve the problem of lateral adjustment of the cutter by means of an eccentric plate working in the slot of the iron, turned by another knurled nut under the frog. This made the space under the iron rather congested, and the device itself was never really effective, and was soon dropped. Warren, however, improved the general balance of the tool by careful spacing and shaping of the handle and knob, and his general design is retained to this day.

Before discussing the final stages in the development of the Stanley planes, there appears to have been another line of progress which was later abandoned, so that it is not mentioned in the official history (Chart No. 131) referred to above. In 'Every Man His Own Mechanic', by Francis Young, London, 1882, the author describes on pp. 90–92 the new American planes which were just then becoming available in this country. He first discusses the 'Bailey's Adjustable' smooth and jack planes of 1870, referred to above, and then goes on to describe the 'Stanley Adjustable' planes, which have *wrought steel* stocks, instead of the iron used in the Bailey planes, and are 'adjusted by the use of a

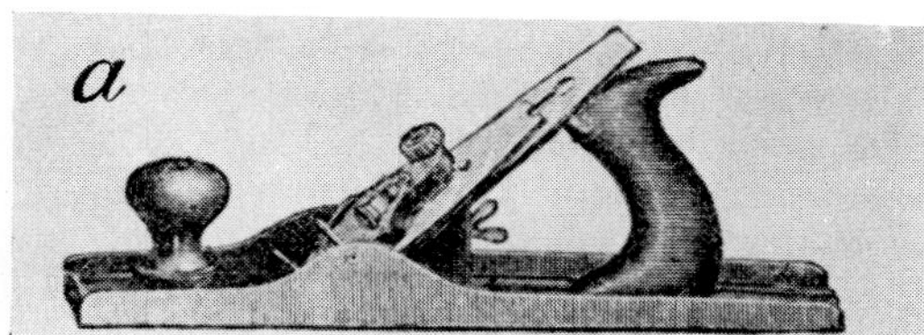

103. Stanley Planes, 1877 — *'Every Man His Own Mechanic', Francis Young, 1882*

compound lever'. The jack plane, 14 in. long, has the all-metal sole of the 1870 pattern (Fig. 103*a*), and he also illustrates a smoother, identical except for length and width of iron. In addition to this (Fig. 103*b*), there is a modified version of the smoother of Fig. 102, and another jack (Fig. 103*c*) with a similar casting screwed to a square-sectioned wooden stock. The striking feature about all these planes is the screwed lever cap like that on the Spiers planes from Scotland, working against a bar across the mouth, instead of the usual cammed lever of the Bailey planes, and what appears to be a thumbscrew behind the iron. In addition, the lever cap itself carries the design of a bell. This was so different to the usual run of Stanley-Bailey planes that one suspected a mistaken attribution on the part of the author of the book, but an enquiry directed to Mr. Stowell in New Britain, Conn., brought a reply which completely solved the mystery. He was good enough to send photostat copies of the pages in the 1877 catalogue of the Stanley Rule & Level Co. showing these planes, and explained that the cutter adjustment which appears in the illustrations to be a butterfly nut is actually a lever with two prongs at the end for finger adjustment. The action is compounded through another lever engaging with the cutter, which gives the vertical setting for the iron. This device was patented by J. A. Traut and H. Richards, employees of the company, in April, 1876. The bell with the numerals 76 cast on the cap iron commemorates the hundredth anniversary of the ringing of the Liberty Bell declaring the independence of the United States on 4th July, 1776. This was evidently an attempt to combine the advantages of the Spiers lever cap with the other Bailey innovations, but apparently it did not meet with the approval of the customers, and the later Stanley planes reverted to the springed-cam lever cap and the vertical adjustment device.

In July, 1888, J. A. Traut took out a further patent which finally solved the problem of lateral adjustment of the iron (Fig. 104). The device consists of a narrow lever pivoted on the upper face of the frog and projecting above the cutter, carrying a circular disc engaging in the slot of the iron. This method is still used in the present-day Stanley planes.

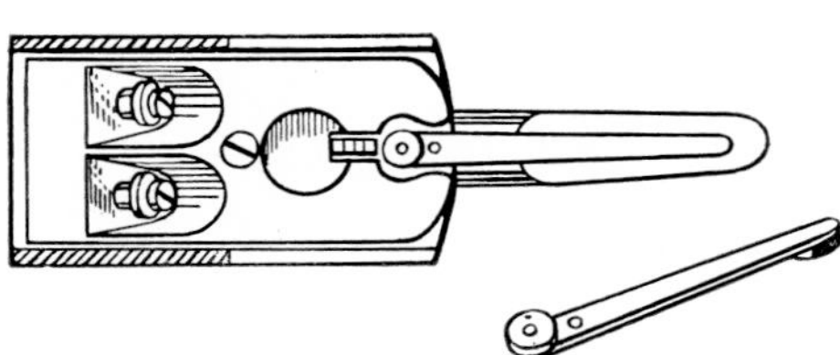

104. Traut Patent Lateral Adjustment
Stanley Tools Chart No. 131

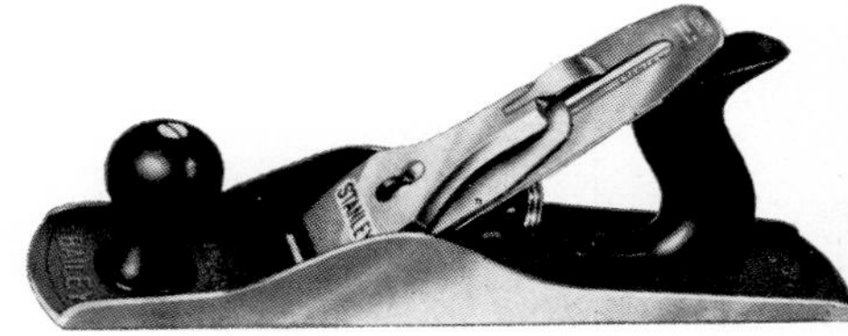

105. Stanley Plane, 1958
Stanley Works (G.B.) Ltd, Sheffield

Later improvements include a firmer seating for the frog itself and the provision of a raised ring on the casting to secure the base of the knob. These were added in the early years of the present century, and the final result (Fig. 105) has succeeded in ousting most of its rivals in America itself and in this country, while it is also very popular on the continent of Europe. Being less bulky than its wooden counterpart, it is easier to handle, and the effective pressure on handle and front knob is close to the actual cutting edge. The screw and lever adjustments make sharpening and setting comparatively easy, indeed the latter can be done without loosening the iron at all. The Stanley-type plane may be described, in fact, as the Ford of woodworking tools. Mass produced for a world-wide market, it is consequently cheaper or offers a better product for the same price, with a full range of completely interchangeable spare parts, and since the expiration of the patents the pattern has been copied almost everywhere.

To complete the story of the American developments, mention must be made of the tools listed in the 1920 catalogue of Sargent and Company, of New Haven, Conn. These include a full range of 'Iron and Wood Bottom Planes', most of them in all respects identical with the Stanley types. In addition, there is a set of metal planes, of which the fore and tryplanes are of the type shown in Fig. 106, patented on 12th January, 1915.

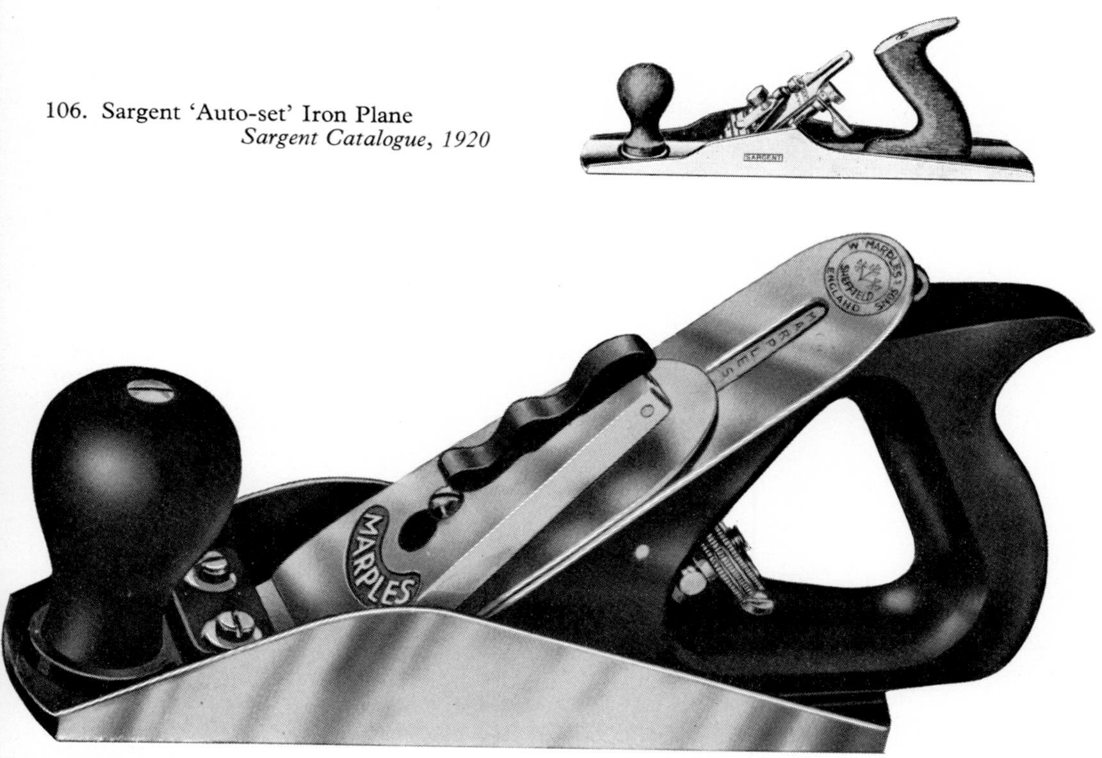

106. Sargent 'Auto-set' Iron Plane
Sargent Catalogue, 1920

107. Marples X4 Smoother, 1958 *William Marples & Sons, Ltd., Sheffield, England*

The fastening and adjustment of the iron is on an entirely different principle to that of the Stanley or any other pattern. The lever cap also fulfils the function of cap iron, and the two screws shown are respectively the fixing screw and a setting screw for the cap iron similar to that on the 'long-screw' type of loose cap iron shown in Fig. 93. The thickness of the shaving is regulated by the large knurled screw behind the iron itself, and lateral adjustment by the winged lever below it. Although there are actually fewer moving parts, this arrangement is much more complicated than the Stanley device, and as none of the parts are interchangeable with Stanley components, this pattern does not appear to have found much favour outside the United States.

Before concluding this study of the history of the bench plane mention must be made of a new design sponsored by the old-established British firm of William Marples & Sons of Sheffield. This is a definite attempt to improve on the normal American pattern, the main features of which, as has already been shown in these pages, have altered little since about 1870. Many craftsmen, especially in this country, have been feeling for a long time that a better quality smoothing plane was called for, and the high prices that many of them are prepared to pay for second-hand Spiers or Norris planes gives point to this demand.

The new X4 plane (Fig. 107) has a cast steel sole similar to that of the Stanley types, but much stouter and about 8% heavier. The frog which supports the iron follows the English tradition of the Spiers and Norris planes in being of wood, and is in one piece with the handle. These features, together with the more robust design of the clamp and cam-lever securing the cutter, reduce the tendency to chatter. As the frog is fixed, the mouth of the plane is varied by means of an adjustable plate, fixed in position by screws on the top of the casting, so that the size of the opening can be altered without dismantling the plane. The top of the cutter is rounded; another reversion to earlier practice (cf. Figs. 65, 90, and 91). There is, in fact, no point in having a square-topped iron in a metal plane adjusted with screws, and the latest Stanley plane irons have the corners rounded off. The sides of the Marples cutters are also bevelled, and this, with the rounded top, allows the iron to sit more comfortably in the hand when sharpening.

Before leaving the bench planes, it may be of interest to compare the variations in their common names, as set out in Table IV. The first column is largely guess-work, as Moxon does not give any sizes, merely saying that the 'fore plain' and 'strike block'

TABLE IV

COMMON NAMES OF PLANES

Length, in.	*Moxon 1683*	*Nicholson 1812*	*Birmingham 1871*	*Stanley 1870*	*Spiers 1909*	*Norris 1914*	*Stanley 1958*
30		Jointer	Jointer	Jointer			
28	Joynter	,,	,,	,,	Joining	Jointing	
26		Long	Long	,,	,,	,,	
24				,,	,,	,,	
22		Trying	Trying	,,	,,	,,	Jointer 7
20				Fore	,,	,,	
18				,,	Panel	Panel	Fore 6
16	Fore, Jack	Jack	Jack	Jack	,,	,,	,, 5½
14		,,	,,	,,	,,	,,	Jack 5
12	Strike Block			Jenny	,,	,,	
10				Smooth			Smooth 4½
9				,,		Smoothing	,, 4
8	Smoothing	Smooth	Smooth	,,	Smooth	,,	,, 3
7		,,	,,	,,	,,		

are smaller than the 'joynter'. Nicholson in 1812 gives the full range, which is identical with a list of planes by Birmingham makers of 1871. With the exception of the 'long' plane, which has been merged in the tryplanes, these are the names usual in this country at the present time. Both the Stanley and the Sargent catalogues retain Moxon's 'fore' plane, distinguishing it from the slightly shorter jack. This is an instance of the survival in the United States of 17th- and 18th-century words which have since become obsolete in the homeland, such as 'fall' for autumn, and so on. The term 'jenny' in the Stanley list has already been discussed. The names of the Spiers planes are quite different, showing the usage across the Border. From 20 in. upwards they are known as 'joining' planes; below, down to 12 in., as 'panel' planes; the terms try and jack are not used. Norris not only copied the planes, but adopted the same names, except for replacing the missing 't' in 'jointing'. One point brought out by this list is the gradual reduction in the number of sizes listed. Since 1870 the Stanley range has come down from fourteen to seven different sizes, rising after No. 4½ by 4 in. at a time, except for No. 5½ between jack and fore plane.

It may also be instructive to compare the different names for planes in various European languages, as shown in Table V, compiled from present-day catalogues or technical handbooks. The top line gives the word in common use for plane generally. The table brings out several interesting points which have been hinted at in the foregoing pages. In the first place, only the English list gives the full range from jointer through try- and jack planes, from 30 in. down to 14 in., with only one gap at 18 in. The others have the equivalent of a jointer plane 24–26 in. long (the *Fugbank* of the

TABLE V

NAMES OF PLANES IN VARIOUS EUROPEAN LANGUAGES

Length in.	*English* Plane	*French* Rabot	*Dutch* Schaaf	*German* Hobel	*Swedish* Hyvlar	*Russian* Rubnaok
30	Jointer			Fugbank		Fuganok
28	,,					
26	,,	Varlope	Voorloper			
24	,,			Rauhbank	Rubankar	Rubanok
22	Trying					
20	,,				,,	
18				Halblang-hobel	,,	
16	Jack	Riflard				
14			Roffel			
12						
10						
9	Smoothing	Rabot	Blokschaaf	Schropphobel	Skrubhyvlar	Rubanok
8	,,	,,	,,	Schlicht-hobel	Putshyvlar	Shlikhtubel
7	,,		,,	Putzhobel	,,	Shlikhtik

German list, and the corresponding Russian *fuganok* are now practically obsolete); and then nothing till we come to the smoothing planes at 9–8 in. In the German list (E. C. Emmerich, of Remscheid-Hasten) the *halblanghobeln* (half-long planes) are for export only, in other words they are not commonly met with in German workshops. The Dutch *rijschaaf* and *voorloper* (C. G. Sieben & Co., Amsterdam) from 24 in. down to 16 in. are imported Stanley-type metal planes, as are the *rubankar* of the Swedish list (Wolrath & Co., Uppsala). The *riflard* of the French list (Féron et Cie, Paris) and the corresponding *roffel* among the Dutch wooden planes are single-iron roughing planes not normally used by joiners. This lack of what we call the jack plane because to us it is the commonest and most frequently used of all has been previously noted in connection with the list of 18th-century carved Dutch planes in Table III; out of the ninety-three planes there listed only one falls between the tryplanes of 23 in. and upwards, and the smoothers of 8½ in. or less, and this is a special plane with a round sole about 14 in. long. It is also notable in this connection that the sets of tools for use in school or technical college workshops illustrated in the catalogues of F. Ott & Co., of Ochsenfurt a. Main, and the Lachappelle A.G. of Lucerne in Switzerland, and other continental manufacturers, similarly have nothing between the tryplane about 24 in. long and a range of smoothers about 8–9 in. This seems to indicate that Swiss and German craftsmen get on very well without a jack plane at all! Indeed in the description of planing in 'Holzarbeiten' or 'Travaux sur Bois', a textbook for use in Swiss school workshops, it is expressly stated that the wood is planed first with the *Schlichthobel* or smoother, and then trued up with the *Rauhbank*. Similarly a German textbook 'An der Hobelbank ('At the Bench') by Karl Bieler only mentions the *Schropphobel* or scrubbing plane and the tryplane for preparing the material. According to Heurtematte's 'Cours de Technologie du Bois' the French workers take the rough off with the *riflard*, a single-iron plane about 22 in. long, and then true the wood up with a *varlope*.

Now in thirty years of teaching in a woodwork shop the writer has never seen a boy use a jack plane if he can help it. In other words, the instincts of the average English schoolboy appear to coincide with general workshop practice abroad. Yet it is not too much to say that about one-third of the time in the first half-dozen lessons in the usual school handicraft scheme is taken up with learning how to use this very difficult instrument, which is too big to be handled at all comfortably by the average boy, and too short to get a really true surface except in very skilled hands. It is not that the writer is preparing a campaign with the slogan 'Down with jack-planes!', the point is simply mentioned as it has emerged from the evidence, and offered as a possible topic for discussion among practising teachers.

Quite apart from this, the Table has several features of interest from a linguistic point of view. The English names are quite distinct from all the others, but there is an obvious connection between the French *varlope* and the Dutch *voorloper*. It seems at first glance that there might be a similar connection between the Dutch *roffel* and the French *riflard*, but on the authority of Dr. J. C. Daan, of the Royal Academy of Science of Amsterdam, kindly passed on by Dr. J. M. G. van der Poel, of Wageningen, there is no relation between them. The Swedish names for tryplane, roughing plane, and smoother (*rubankar*, *skrubhyvlar*, and *putshyvlar* respectively) are clearly related to the corresponding German terms, but this is only to be expected, as the two languages have close family ties. On the other hand, the Russian use of *rubanok* for *Rauhbank*, and the Slavonic form *fuganok* for *Fugbank* show that when they first began to use these tools (not commonly before the 16th century) they had no native words to identify them with, and were obliged to use the terms used by their German instructors. The word *shlikhtubel* is a direct transliteration of *Schlichthobel*, but in common speech this has been further Russified into *shlikhtik*, i.e., 'little smoother'.

9: Special Planes, Ploughs, Fillisters, etc

In addition to the usual bench planes for smoothing and preparing the timber to size, and finishing the completed work, from earliest times woodworkers of all trades have used special tools of the plane type for cutting rebates, grooves, and mouldings of various shapes. Owing to the wide range of work done with these tools, and their immense variety of pattern, it would be impossible to describe them all in detail, and what follows is a rapid survey of the main lines of development.

We have already seen from the evidence of the surviving irons (Figs. 52 and 53) and completed joiner's work that the Romans employed a wide selection of such special planes, including ploughs, rabbet planes, hollows and rounds, and other moulding planes, but the only stock which has come down to us is the one in the Cairo Museum from Kom Washim.

Tools of this type are never depicted in the medieval illustrations, but although during this period the emphasis was on carved decoration, a good deal of the work has obviously been shaped with some kind of moulding plane, while the linen-fold panels which were so popular in the 15th and 16th centuries must have been worked with sets of hollows and rounds, and the panels themselves let into ploughed grooves or rebates. Among the tools depicted on the inlaid choir stalls of San Petronio, Bologna, there is a fillister with the iron let into the side of the stock, and also what looks very much like a shoulder rabbet plane. On the sacristy door of another large church at Bologna, that of San Domenico, there is an inlaid panel showing some woodworking tools, executed by Fra Damian about 1564. One of these is a narrow moulding or shoulder plane, almost a replica of the Kom Washim plane, with the iron let into the side of the stock. One of the tools in the well-known woodcut of a 16th-century joiner's shop by Jost Ammann resembles an adjustable plough or fillister, with the fence attached to the stock by two staves. Under the bench in the Wierix title-page (Fig. 68) there is a group of narrow planes, some of which may be shoulder planes or perhaps hollows and rounds, and a similar group is shown lying on the shelf in St. Joseph's workshop in another engraving in the same series, entitled 'Bulles de Savon', with the Holy Children blowing bubbles in the foreground. Some of the irons found with the Novaya Zemlya plane are clearly for hollows and rounds.

In his 'Geschichte des Hobels' J. M. Greber illustrates three ploughs from the collection of the Elector of Saxony, formed in 1570, some of which still survive in the Dresden Historical Museum, showing three different and very advanced methods of securing the adjustable fence to the stock. The simplest has two square staves fixed with thumbscrews tapped into the top of the stock. Another tool has three screwed staves with wooden nuts, one of which is missing, while the third plough has four stems in pairs, one pair plain and the other screwed. Another illustration in the same book shows a very interesting plough from Burg Kreuzenstein near Vienna, the stock of which is dated 1688, while the fence is marked 1578. There are two screwed stems going right through the stock, with square wooden nuts, and between them two spacing stems tapped into the fence and securing the whole assembly. The iron of this plough is 4 mm. wide, a not unusual size for panels at the present time.

After such elaborate and no doubt highly efficient German tools, it is rather surprising to find in Félibien's 'Principes' (Fig. 70), dated about a hundred years later, a crude adjustable 'bouvet' or plough plane, with apparently no fastening for the stems at all. Moxon's engraver copied this illustration directly on to his plate (Fig. 71), with the result that in the 'Doctrine of Handyworks' the picture is a mirror image of the original, with the fence on the near or right-hand side!* In Moxon's text the 'Plow' is described as follows: '. . . a narrow Rabbet plain with some additions to it, viz. two square staves marked a, a, (they are not so marked, as it happens) . . . These staves are let stiff through two square Mortesses in the stock . . . and are about 7 or 8 inches long . . . and the Fence (as workmen call it) which comes close under the wooden sole, and reaches about half an inch below. An iron plate the same thickness as the plow iron is nailed to the stock . . . Joyners have several plows for several widths of grooves.' This probably means complete tools for each size, and not interchangeable irons, as at the present time. He adds the curious remark: 'If the Staves go not stiff enough in the Mortesses of the stock you must stiffen them by knocking in a little wooden wedge between the Staves and their Mortesses.' This indicates that the wedges were an additional refinement (they are not shown on the engraving).

Félibien's plate gives several types of *guillaume* or rabbet plane, including a *guillaume debout* or side-rabbet, a *guillaume à platte-bande* or dado grooving plane, and a *feuilleret* or shoulder plane. In addition he shows a *mouchette* or bead, and a *mouchette à grain d'orge*' (barley-corn), a kind of reeding plane.

Moxon's rabbet plane was also copied from Félibien's *guillaume à éboucher*, and he describes it as being used for '. . . plaining a lapped or Rabbetted joynt, and also to strike a Facia [*sic*] in a piece of moulding. The sides of the iron are not enclosed, and it delivers its shaving at the side.' By 'Facia' he probably means the square member of a composite moulding, nowadays usually described as a fillet. He does not illustrate any 'Molding Plains', but lists the following: Round, Hollow, Ogee, and Snipe's Bill. The last-named was a narrow hollow or throating plane.

During the 17th and 18th centuries it was not unusual for ordinary bench planes to be modified for use as ploughs or fillisters. Sometimes a tryplane stock would be adapted for cutting the tongues and grooves in long planks for jointing, as was the case with the plane, 33 in. long, dated 1672, and probably of German origin, from the style of the carving, now in the Hove Museum. Similar tools are illustrated in Greber from Germany and Switzerland. These planes could only cut a specific size of tongue or groove, and were not adjustable. Another solution of this problem was to make one tool do the

* Although some modern catalogues list 'left-handed' ploughs and fillisters.

work of two, as in the combined tongue and groove plane from Holland (Fig. 108), with two cutters facing in opposite directions, and a fence on the sole common to both. Sets of tools of this type would be very convenient for working standard thicknesses of boarding.

108. Combined Tongue and Groove Plane, 18th Century

Friesmuseum, Leeuwarden

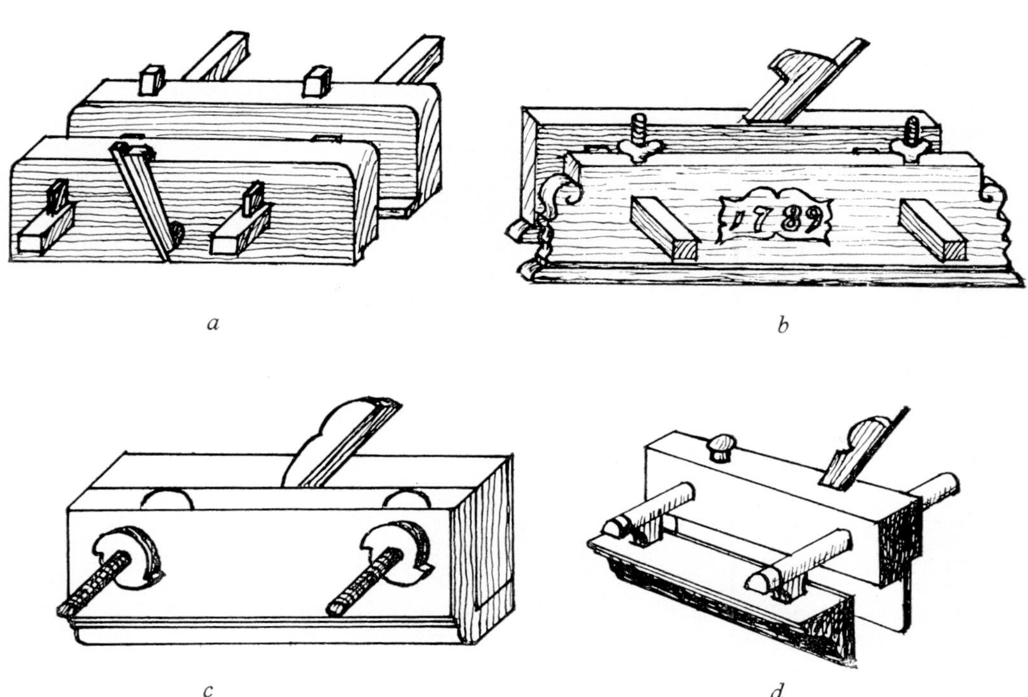

109. 18th–19th-century Ploughs: (*a*) Diderot, 'Encyclopedie', 1765; (*b*) Dutch Plough, dated 1789; (*c*) Bergeron, 'L'Art du Tourneur', 1816; (*d*) Nicholson, 'Mechanical Exercises', 1812

In the Pinto Collection there is a skewed *blokschaaf* of the standard pattern, dated 1764, which has been adapted for use as a sash fillister. Two square staves are let right through and fixed to the plane stock, while the fence is rather crudely secured with vertical wedges. This tool is illustrated in E. H. Pinto's 'Treen', Fig. 110. The stock of an almost identical *blokschaaf*, dated some three years later, now in the Horniman Museum in South London, has holes in the stock to take similar staves. The Dutch plane-makers of the 18th century also made and marketed a specially designed plough, with elaborately carved and decorated fences, the square staves of which are secured by metal thumbscrews let into the top of the fence (Fig. 109*b*). There are a number of these planes in the Fries Museum at Leeuwarden and the Openluchtmuseum at Arnhem, and a particularly well-preserved specimen, dated 1743, in the Science Museum at South Kensington.

One remarkable difference between the English and continental adjustable ploughs and fillisters is that in the former the staves are fixed to the fence and pass more or less freely through the stock, while in the latter the staves, whether square or screwed, are fixed to the stock and pass through the fence. Consequently, in all foreign tools of this type, right up to the present day, the fence is slightly deeper than the stock itself, being flush at the top and projecting about $\frac{1}{2}$ in. below the cutter. Moxon's 'plow', copied from Félibien's French book, is a case in point. A later French plough, from Diderot's 'Encyclopédie' (Fig. 109*a*), shows this deep fence, fixed with vertical wedges driven down through the top. Roubo, in 'L'Art du Menuisier', Paris, 1769, shows a similar arrangement. The use by the Dutch of metal or wooden thumbscrews has already been noted (Fig. 109*b*).

Another method of fixing this deep fence was by means of screwed staves with wooden nuts, mentioned previously in connection with the 16th-century ploughs at Dresden. The survival of this method in France is clearly shown by the rather crude engraving of the *bouvet universel* (sash fillister) in Bergeron's 'Manuel du Tourneur', Paris, 1812 (Fig. 109*c*). The two nuts on the outside are clear enough, but the corresponding screws inside the fence are merely indicated by curved lines. A much better illustration of this type is the coachbuilder's plough from the Reid bequest in the Science Museum (Fig. 110), dated to about 1850, and bearing the maker's name, 'Gautier et Baillet, Aux Mines de Suède, rue Lamartine 6, Paris'. The spacing of the fence is regulated by the two cogged nuts inside, and fastened tight by the two collars on the outside. Ploughs and fillisters of this pattern are listed in all the present-day catalogues of the continental makers, and are used as far east as Poland and Russia.

We have already noted Moxon's suggestion that when the staves work loose in the stock, as they inevitably do, they should be fixed with small wedges. This had to be done through the thickness of the stock, as vertical wedges such as those in the Diderot and Roubo tools would interfere with the setting of the iron. Such horizontal wedges would, however, prevent any close setting of the fence, so the English makers adopted a shallow fence, screwing or riveting the staves to spacing pieces which allowed easy access to the wedges. This is first shown on the plough illustrated on Plate 4 of Nicholson's book (Fig. 109*d*), but unfortunately his engraver left the wedges out! This method resulted in a saving of weight and bulk, with the additional advantage that there was a certain amount of play when the staves were knocked alternately into position. This became the accepted English practice, and the tools shown in the Marples 1864 catalogue (Fig. 111) are in all respects identical with those in common use today. It is curious, in this connection, that the better-class ploughs and fillisters with the screwed staves of Fig. 110, listed in Buck and Hickman's 1953 catalogue, Figs. 5083 and 5085, although in this respect similar to the corresponding foreign tools, have the same shallow fence and spacing pieces of the English wedged types.

110. Coachbuilder's Plough, *c.* 1850
Reid Bequest, Science Museum, London

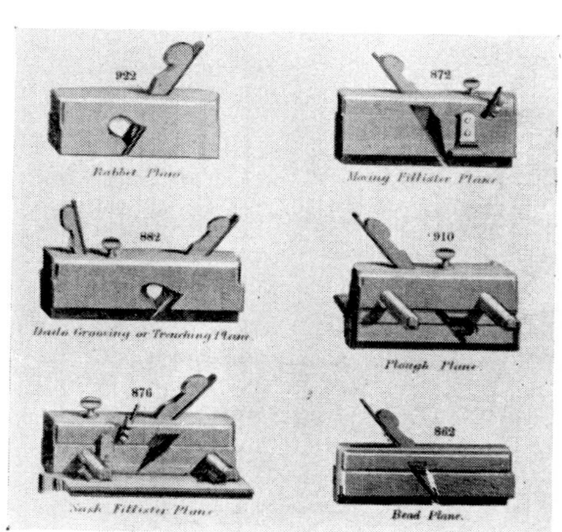

111. Ploughs, Fillisters, etc.
William Marples & Sons, 1864

Samuel Carruthers, of Philadelphia, in an advertisement in the Pennsylvania Chronicle, Mar. 6th, 1767, mentions 'double-iron'd planes of a late construction . . . for cross-grained or curled stuff.' Charles F. Hummel, 'English Tools in America', Winterthur Portfolio, 1965, Vol. II, p. 28.

The irons for these planes were almost certainly imported from Sheffield, England.

SECTION III

THE SAW

1: The Bronze Age

IT HAS been suggested that the invention of the saw may be dated right back to Neolithic times, but although a number of flint tools with a serrated edge have survived from Palestine, Egypt, and North-west Europe, the consensus of opinion seems to be that they were either knives or a primitive form of scythe. Indeed when the writer approached Prof. Dr. E. Vogt, the Director of the Schweizerischer Landesmuseum at Zürich, for photographs of some of the implements of this type found at Swiss lake-village sites, he replied that he would let me have them by all means, but that in his opinion they were not really effective (*wirkliche*) saws at all, but probably used as knives. Under such primitive conditions the distinction cannot have been clear, but their peculiar shape, and the fact that as often as not they were backed with a wooden handle, precluded them from being used to cut right through a piece of wood like an ordinary saw. They could have been used to cut all round a bone, or a branch of a sapling, which is of a similar hollow cylindrical form, but anything more ambitious than this would have been beyond their scope. Some of the Scandinavian flint 'saws' are

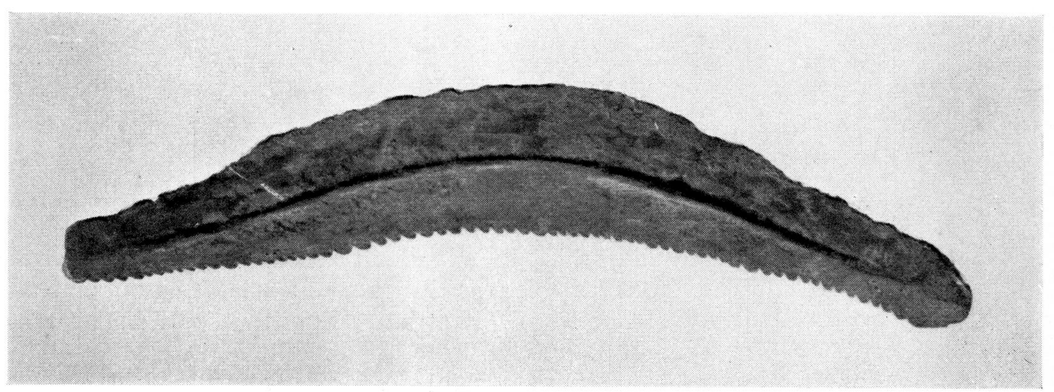

112. Late Bronze Age Saw *Nationalmuseet, Copenhagen*

described as 'semi-lunate', from their shape like a half-moon, and it is curious that the bronze implement from Denmark shown in Fig. 112 seems to be a copy in bronze of this type of saw. Here again the rib down the middle would prevent it from being used as a normal saw.

It is, in fact, fairly obvious that only a metal saw would have any advantage in working life and economy of material over the existing stone axes and other cutting tools, and consequently the first real saws in the modern sense were developed in the Copper or Early Bronze Age. Two copper saws from Egypt, dating from the XVIIIth Dynasty (*c.* 1490 B.C.) are shown in Fig. 113. The large blade is nearly 20 in. long, and is pro-

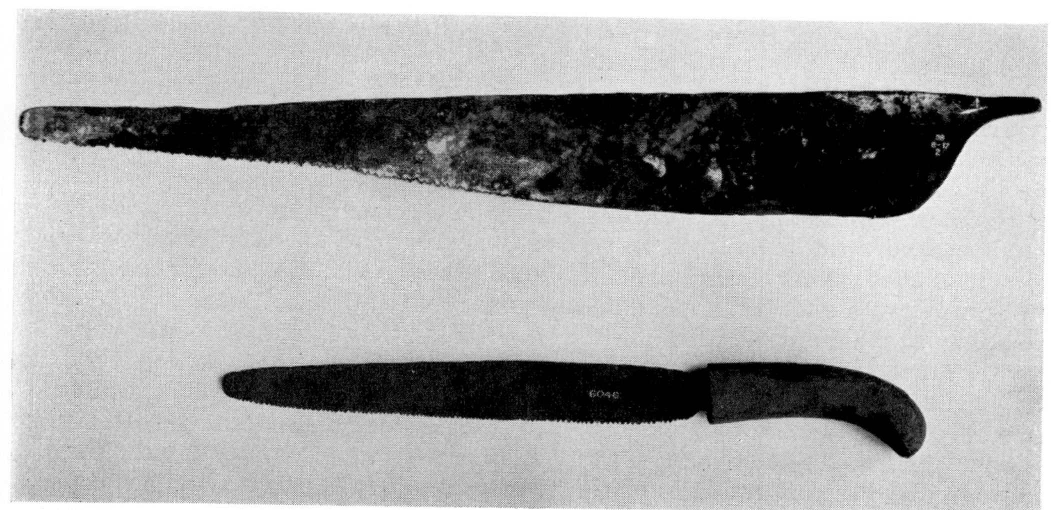

113. Egyptian Copper Saws, *c.* 1490 B.C. *Trustees of the British Museum*

vided with a tang which fitted into a wooden handle similar to that shown in the smaller tool below. This latter is very much like the saw in the Sopi coffin frieze (Fig. 7), in fact this was the standard shape for Egyptian hand-saws for nearly 2,000 years. The teeth of the larger saw are cut very irregularly and only extend about half-way along the blade. It is clear that both these tools were used with a pulling action, as the hook on the teeth, where appreciable, points towards the tang. The modern pushing stroke would have caused these comparatively soft blades to buckle, and even nowadays fret and coping saws are mounted in the same way for this reason. How these Egyptian saws were used is shown very clearly on numerous tomb reliefs and frescoes from the IIIrd Dynasty onwards, and particularly clearly in the well-known model of the carpenters' shop of 2000 B.C. in the museum at Cairo, a picture of which is reproduced in John Hooper's 'Handcraft in Wood', Batsford, 1952. The piece to be sawn was lashed to an upright post fixed firmly in the ground. This is, in fact, the only possible method with a pull-saw; the modern practice of cutting a plank with the wood laid on a trestle or sawing horse is obviously out of the question.

The teeth of these copper, and later bronze saws had no set, and were very irregular in shape and size; they must have been very slow and laborious in action. Flinders Petrie, in his description of the excavations at Tarkhan I, a Ist Dynasty site, mentions a piece of hardwood found there, still bearing the marks of the saw on it, showing how the workman had started his cut from all four corners of the block in turn. It must have taken him hours, if not days, sawing away under the hot Egyptian sun, for the wood appears to have the texture of teak or greenheart. Looking at the photograph of this lump of wood, one cannot help feeling a pang of sympathy for the poor fellow, although he has been dead and forgotten these 5,000 years.

The Minoans of the Bronze Age made considerable advances in the design of the saw, as shown by the three large blades, dating from the Neopalatial period (1700–1400 B.C., roughly corresponding to Evans's Late Minoan I) in the museum at Heraklion in Crete. The largest of these, No. 701, came from the royal villa at Haghia Triada, and is about 5 ft. 6 in. long and 5 in. wide, tapering slightly at one end. There are three circular holes ⅜ in. in diameter arranged in a triangle at one end, and two more of the same size, spaced rather wider apart, at the other. The wooden handles have disappeared, so it is impossible to say what shape they were, but it is likely that the saw was used both as a cross-cut and as a rip-saw. The teeth are cut uniformly along the whole length of the blade, with four to five points to the inch. The saw from Knossos, No. 2053, is 5 ft. 2 in. long, and varies in width from 6 in. at the square end to 7 and 8 in. in the middle, tapering to about 4 in. There are three holes arranged like those in the Haghia Triada saw at the square end, but no sign of any at the other. The teeth are cut with four to five points to the inch along most of the length of the blade, but nearer the narrow end they are much smaller, with eight points to the inch. The third saw of this type, from Mallia, is very similar: 5 ft. 3 in. long, 5 in. wide at the square end, increasing to 6 in. in the middle, and tapering to about 4½ in. at the rounded end. This saw has five holes to secure the handle, while the teeth vary from seven points to the inch near the square end, to five and then four points per inch along most of the length, with a short section near the toe with about eight to the inch. A very similar, but much shorter blade from Knossos, dating from the Late Minoan I period (1580–1450 B.C.), is in the Ashmolean Museum at Oxford (Fig. 114). This saw is only 16 in. long, 2¾ in. wide at the square

114. Bronze Saw from Knossos, Crete *Ashmolean Museum, Oxford*

end, 4 in. wide in the middle, tapering to about 1½ in. at the toe. The teeth are small and irregular, with about ten to twelve points to the inch, and the toothed edge has a pronounced curve. There are three holes at the square end for fixing a handle, as in the

Heraklion saws. These tools could have been used for sawing stone (at Knossos this is comparatively soft) or wood indifferently.

One of the showcases in Room Z at Heraklion contains some small bronze tools from Eastern Crete. Of particular interest are five thin bronze plates from the settlement of Apodhoulou at Amari, all identical in size, about 1 in. long and ¾ in. wide. One end has a slight curve, while the other is rounded more distinctly, and both are cut with small teeth about twelve points to the inch. These blades may have been mounted close together in a wooden handle in some way, in order to cut the teeth of wooden or ivory combs.

Two small bronze saws from the lake villages of Switzerland are shown in Fig. 115. The upper example is about 9 in. long and just over 1 in. wide, and if the hole at the right-hand end was provided with a rivet to fix the handle, it was clearly used with a pulling action. The smaller saw from Corcelettes must have been fixed in some kind of frame, or possibly to a bow-shaped piece of springy wood to keep the blade taut.

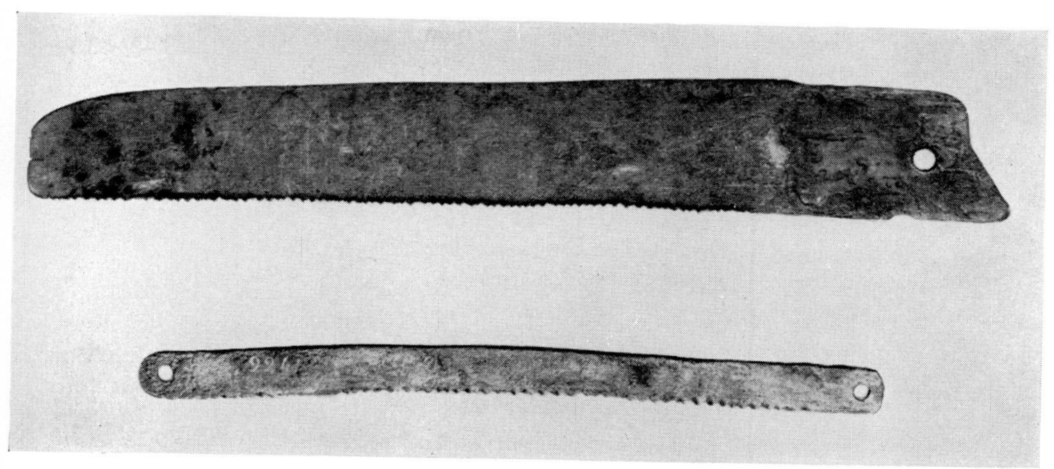

115. Late Bronze Age Saws: (*a*) Moerigen, Bielersee; (*b*) Corcelettes, Grandson
Landesmuseum, Zürich

The little bronze saw from Monkton, Pembrokeshire (Fig. 116) has a much more complicated design, but its manner of use is problematical. The blade is about 6½ in. long by ¾ in. wide, with a very slight hollow curve, one end being turned over to form a loop, the other bored to admit a spirally fluted ring, now broken, which was originally attached to the blade. Although the little loop at the end is now crushed flat, a piece of wood could have been passed through it to form a handle, the other end going through the ring to keep the blade strained; in short a primitive and rather ingenious frame saw. Mr. Smallcombe, the former Director of Reading Museum, has suggested, however, that the ring may have served to attach the tool to the workman's belt or girdle.

Remarkably few saws are known from the Etruscan bronze period; those that are being usually fragments of small frame-saws similar to the foregoing. The museum at Bologna possesses eight fragments of varying width, from ¾ in. to 1½ in., all about 1½ in.

long, with about twelve teeth to the inch; one of these fragments has a small hole near one end. The Pigorini Museum at Rome shows two fragments of a similar saw from the Ripostiglio di Galuzzo at Chiusi, both pieces being about 3½ in. long and ¾ in. wide. One piece has a curious knob at one end, which may have served the same purpose as the cross-rivets on a modern coping saw, for straining the blade in a frame. The same collection contains two other similar fragments of a thin bronze saw from Modicea, near Ragusa in Sicily, the larger of which, 4 in. long and ¾ in. wide, has a small fixing hole near one end. The small size of these fragments throws into sharper relief the relatively enormous dimensions of the Minoan bronze saws described above; much larger than any tools of the kind up to as late as the 17th century. They also give some idea of the technological background to the tremendous artistic achievements of the prehistoric peoples of Crete.

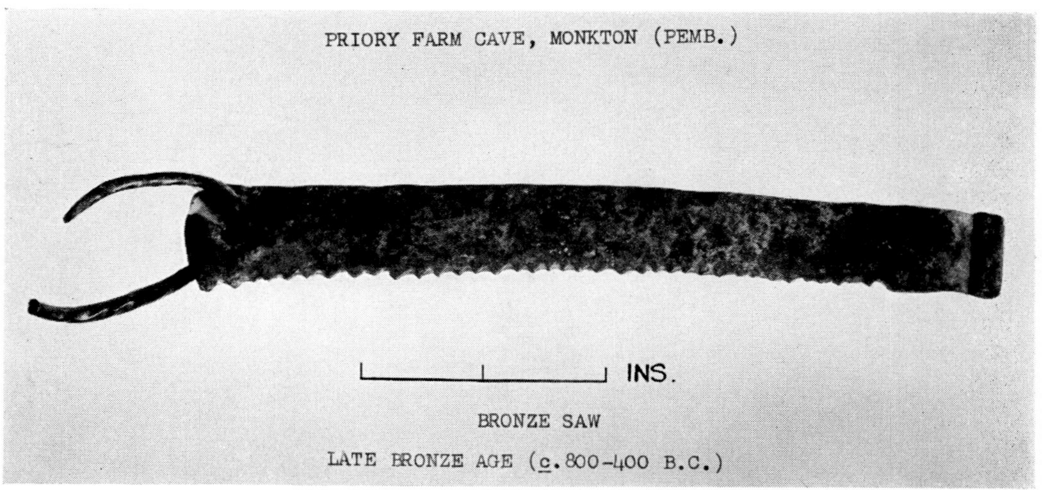

116. Late Bronze Age Saw, *c.* 800–400 B.C.

By permission of the National Museum of Wales, Cardiff

117. Socketed Bronze Saw, Tagar Culture, 6th–3rd Centuries B.C.

Minusinsk Museum, Krasnoyar, Siberia, U.S.S.R.

A bronze saw of a somewhat later period, but of a totally different and indeed unique type, is shown in Fig. 117, reproduced by permission of Mme. V. P. Levasheva, of the Historical Museum at Moscow, and formerly for many years at Minusinsk in Central

Siberia. It was found with a hoard of bronze woodworking tools, including socketed axes, chisels, and gouges, belonging to the Tagar culture, which flourished in the basin of the Yenesei river near Krasnoyar from about the 6th to the 3rd century B.C. The blade of the saw is about 7 in. long by 1½ in. wide, and is serrated on both edges. The unique feature is the socketed handle, set centrally on the blade. Such sockets are common enough on chisels and gouges, in fact the Minusinsk gouges are identical with some found in a similar hoard at Llynfawr, Glamorgan, several thousand miles to the west, but this is the only case known of such a method of hafting a saw.

2: The Early Iron Age and Roman Period

The use of iron instead of bronze brought with it many improvements in the design of the saw, but owing to the weakness of his material the craftsman was still obliged to retain the comparatively narrow blades, used with the same pulling action, as his Bronze Age predecessor. Sir Flinders Petrie illustrates three iron saws from the find of the Assyrian armourer's tools from Thebes (*c.* 660 B.C.) on Pl. L of his 'Tools and Weapons'. These are possibly the earliest iron saws known; one of the three is narrow and double-edged, and was probably part of a framed saw, the other two blades have a decided rake to the teeth, and both were pull-saws.

Two saws from the La Tène site near the Bielersee in Kanton Neuarberg, Switzerland, are typical of the Early Iron Age in Europe, especially in the hollow curve of the cutting edge, and the method of fixing the handle, of wood or horn, with rivets to a long tang. One of these is in an excellent state of preservation, and it is clear that the very accurately cut teeth, about ten to the inch, are hooked towards the handle. This saw is about 13¼ in. long overall, of which 4¾ in. is accounted for by the carved handle. The second saw from the same site is smaller, about 7½ in. long, with a more obvious sickle-like shape, and although the teeth are more worn and corroded, it is still clear that they are hooked towards the heel. These tools are in the Landesmuseum, Zürich.

One of the saws from the Late La Tène (*c.* 200 B.C.) lake dwelling at Glastonbury (Fig. 118) is also well preserved (when the writer saw it last, in a bottle of what looked very much like Somerset rough cider). The teeth are somewhat irregular, but there is a distinct backward hook to them, while the scroll-shaped wooden handle is remarkable in being if anything rather longer than the saw itself. This blade also has the concave cutting edge of the Swiss La Tène saws, and the handle is fixed to the tang with two rivets in exactly the same manner. Other fragments of saws found at Glastonbury include a short end of a simple tanged blade with half a dozen teeth, and the tang part of another blade similar to Fig. 118, with two rivet holes. Another wooden handle with a similar scroll at the end, but bent at a much sharper angle (very helpful in using a pull-saw), was no doubt intended for another blade.

Another well-preserved example of a Late Iron Age (150–100 B.C.) saw from an English source is the one found at Barley, Herts, and now in the Archaeological Museum of

Cambridge University. It is similar in shape to the Glastonbury saw above, with a slighter curve to the serrated edge. The blade is $10\frac{3}{4}$ in. long and $1\frac{1}{2}$ in. wide, tapering almost to a point, with six to seven well-cut teeth to the inch, hooked distinctly towards the handle. One rivet is still in place on the tang, and there are holes for three others.

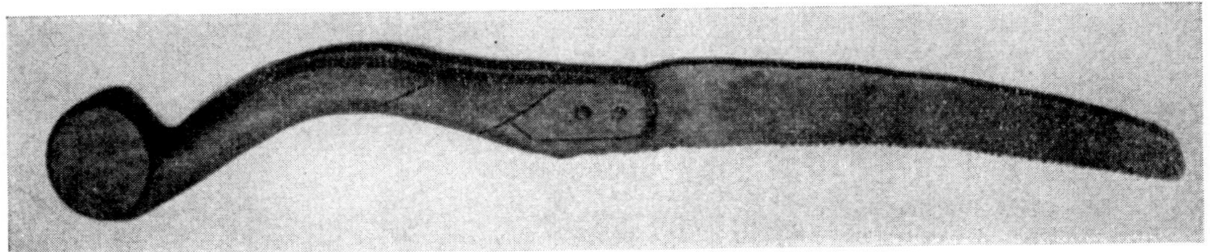

118. Early Iron Age Saw *Glastonbury Museum*

The Romans took over these simple hand-saws and rudimentary frame-saws, and introduced many important improvements in their design. Whether they invented the device of setting the teeth or not, the first literary allusion to it occurs in Pliny ('Nat. Hist.', XVI, 83): 'The green woods, with the exception of the robur (a kind of oak) and the box offer a more obstinate resistance, filling the intervals between the teeth with saw-dust, and making its edge uniform and inert; it is for this reason that the teeth are often made to project right and left in turn, a method by which the sawdust is discharged.' This is only part of the story; if Pliny had been a practical craftsman he would have realised that the main purpose of setting the teeth in this manner is to ensure that the saw-kerf is wider than the thickness of the blade, thus providing for its freer passage through the wood. As a consequence there is less strain on the blade, and the saw could be pushed instead of pulled, without so much tendency to buckle. The pushing stroke increases the efficiency of the tool considerably, as the timber to be cut need not be fixed to the bench or a post, but held firmly on a stool by the workman's hand or knee. A minor improvement was that the cutting edge could then be made straight instead of concave, giving much more accuracy in use.

119. Roman Handsaw, Hohenrain-Ottenhausen
Historisches Museum, Rathaus, Luzern, Switzerland

All these features are illustrated in the saw from Hohenrain-Ottenhausen (Fig. 119). The shape is similar to that of the preceding La Tène saws, but the cutting edge is practically straight and the teeth not only show traces of set but point towards the front. This saw is about 13 in. long overall with about 8 in. of blade carrying the teeth, spaced at about seven to eight to the inch. The handle has not survived, but two rivets, about $1\frac{3}{4}$ in. long by $\frac{3}{16}$ in. in diameter, are still in the rather worn holes in the tang. Two similar blades, one about the same length with a pierced iron handle instead of a tang, the other about 6 in. long, with rather crudely cut teeth about six to the inch, from another Roman station at Seeb, are in the Landesmuseum at Zürich.

In 'Tools and Weapons' Pl. L, No. 34, Sir Flinders Petrie illustrates a hand-saw from Pompeii with part of the tang missing, but enough of the blade survives to show that the cutting edge was practically straight, and that the teeth were hooked towards the front, so that this saw must also have been used with a push stroke.

Some of the smaller saws found on many Roman sites, such as those illustrated on Pl. XXXVI of 'London in Roman Times', and the small handled 'saw' from Newstead in Scotland appear to be little more than knives with a serrated edge. In fact one of these tools found recently in the City of London and exhibited in the Guildhall Museum at the Royal Exchange is described as a pruning saw, a very plausible suggestion, which takes them, however, rather outside the scope of this study. The Newstead saw, for good measure, has both edges supplied with teeth, the lower edge having about eight, and the upper edge about twelve points to the inch. This tool gives the impression that the maker took a piece of old saw-blade and fitted the handle to it, as the teeth continue into the slot in the grip, where they are practically useless. It is also notable in being a reversion to the older pulling type.

With the materials at their disposal the Romans could have made little advance beyond this narrow knife- or sword-like blade, for any tool of hammered iron as long or as wide as the modern hand-saw would have buckled under the slightest pressure. One solution which was tried was to extend the handle along the top of the blade, thus anticipating the modern backed saws. This appears to have been the original form of the saw blade from the Gaulish camp at Mont Auxois (Fig. 120) now in the museum at

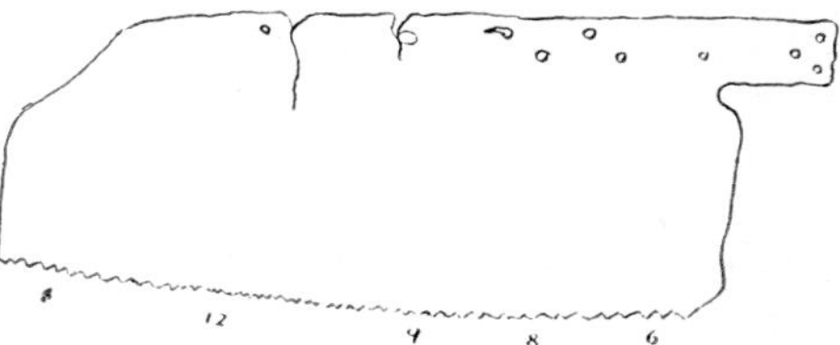

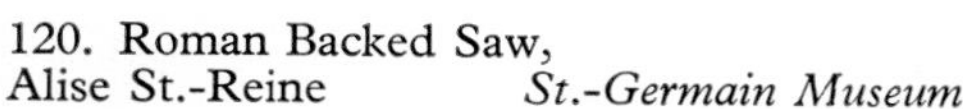

120. Roman Backed Saw,
Alise St.-Reine *St.-Germain Museum*

Saint-Germain. This is described in the catalogue of the museum as a *scie à chevilles* (dowel saw), but this is because it resembles the modern French saw of that name; it was not necessarily used as such by the pre-Roman Celts. The blade is about 8½ in. long by 4 in. wide; the handle is missing, but there is a group of three rivet holes in the tang and a row of holes along the upper edge of the blade, indicating how the handle was probably fixed. Even so the blade has cracked and buckled in one or two places, and one of the rivets has apparently been torn out of position. The teeth are cut in a curious manner, shown by the small figures (of points to the inch) below the cutting edge, which is slightly convex. With the exception of the first inch or so they are cut progressively larger towards the heel, a remarkable anticipation of the large modern saws cut in this way, and known from one end of Europe to the other as 'Spanish' pit-saws. These two features: the backed blade and the variably cut teeth, are as far as is known unique in saws of the Roman period.

The only other way to mount a narrow blade to prevent it from buckling is to strain it in some kind of frame, and there is plenty of evidence to show that the Romans were acquainted with several types of framed saw, from the small hand-saw for bench work

121. Fragment of Roman Saw-blade; Small Backed Saw *Landesmuseum, Zürich*

122. Roman Framed Saw *'Antichi Monumenti', Florence*

to the large two-man cross-cut and pit-saws. The fragment from Albisreiden in Fig. 121 is probably part of the blade of a large saw of this type. It is just over 12 in. long by 2¼ in. wide, with about four to six teeth to the inch; there are a number of 'cows and calves', but the set can be clearly distinguished. Two Roman (or Etruscan) workmen using a saw of this kind are shown in a detail from a relief figured in 'Antichi Monumenti', Florence, 1810, Pl. XI (Fig. 122). The blade is strained in a crude wooden frame, while the plank being cut is propped against a sawing horse, and further supported by an upright strut; the 'top sawyer' standing on the foot of the sloping plank, with the 'pitman' on the ground. This seems to have been a fairly common method of rip-sawing in Roman times, and a one-man variation of it is shown in the picture of one of the shipwrights on the Catacombs gold-glass vessel (Fig. 123). On the other hand the Romans also used high trestles with the top sawyer standing on the plank laid flat across them, as in the detail from an Etruscan painted bowl (Fig. 124), and the relief from Deneuvre in the Musée Historique de Lorrain, Nancy.

123. Roman Shipwright with Saw, Catacombs Gold-glass Vessel *Vatican Museum*

124. Etruscan Sawyers on Painted Bowl

Another large but rather primitive type of frame-saw, the direct successor of similar Bronze Age tools, is illustrated in Fig. 125. The original saw came from the Fayoum, Egypt, and is now in the University College Museum, London, but there is a copy in the Science Museum at South Kensington. The frame consists of a single piece of wood, oval in section, bent into a semi-circle. The iron blade, 2½ in. wide and about 2 ft. 6 in. long, with approximately four teeth to the inch, shaped for ripping, is let into saw-kerfs at each end of the bow, clinched round, and fastened with crude spikes. J. M. Greber, in his 'Geschichte des Hobels', makes the plausible suggestion that the Romans introduced this type of saw into Egypt from Greece; it also turns up in 10th-century Russia, probably from the same source.

Evidence for the use of small framed saws is fairly copious. The two objects in the middle of the bronze model tools in the British Museum (Fig. 13) are clearly intended

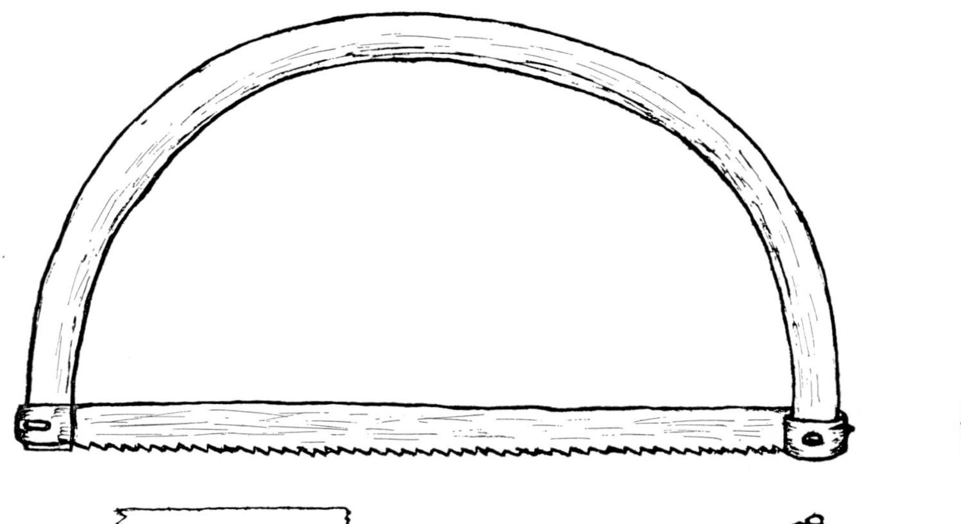

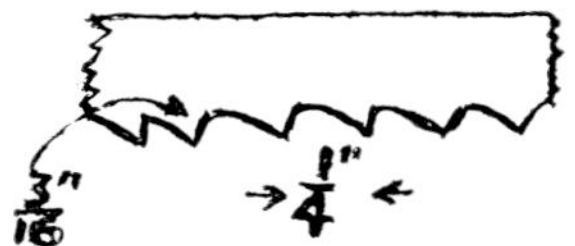

125 (*above*). Saw in Bent Wooden Frame
University College Museum, London

126. Altar to Minerva
Museo Capitolini, Rome

to represent small framed bench-saws, complete with straining-cord and toggle-stick. A stylised version of this is shown on an altar dedicated to Minerva by a college of artisans, now in the Museo Capitolini at Rome (Fig. 126). This relief also illustrates a cross-cut saw with curious slotted handles, something like the handles of Roman planes.

Mercer, in 'Ancient Carpenters' Tools', devoted a good deal of space to discussing whether the small Roman framed saws were provided with toggle-sticks or not, but in his attempts to solve this problem he only succeeded in making confusion worse confounded. He was misled in the first place by basing his argument on an illustration lacking the stick, used by nearly all the authorities, from Rich (p. 559, 'serrula') to Disston 'The Saw in History', 1916, all of whom had copied one another without giving the original source. It is probable that was taken from a relief of Roman chair-makers at work, in the Antiquarium Comunale at Rome (Fig. 127), where a small but very well-defined frame-saw, lacking the stick, is shown hanging on the wall. A much simpler framed saw, with the cord clearly detailed, but no stick, is shown in the Nativity scene of the Milan Dyptich, which according to John Beckwith, 'The Werden Casket Reconsidered', 'The Art Bulletin', March 1958, dates from about the middle of the 6th century. Even larger saws sometimes lack the stick, for example the tool being used by the shipwright on the Catacombs vessel (Fig. 123). It is not necessary to account for these

127. Roman Chair-makers *Antiquarium Comunale, Rome*

discrepancies by saying that the artist did not know his business (the tool in Fig. 127 is quite unambiguous on this point, and was probably copied from an actual saw); it is quite possible that the Romans sometimes used a stick and sometimes not. The cord could have been well damped before straining it on the frame, and on drying it would give sufficient tension to serve their purpose. Eventually, to avoid the necessity of continually re-wetting and tying the cord, the straining-stick method was adopted, with the further advantage that it could be adjusted at will, or slackened off when the saw was not in use.

Pliny's description of the method of setting the saw teeth, which was perhaps the Romans' chief contribution to the development of this tool, is confirmed by the survival of saw-sets and files, sometimes combined in one instrument, at many sites, including Saalburg, Newstead, and Silchester. Mercer also shows (Fig. 248) a two-slotted saw-set from Mainz of a very modern type.

3: The Hand-saw, Medieval to the 18th Century

After the fall of the Roman Empire the drop in the standard of living and the level of culture in Europe was reflected in a similar lowering of technological achievement. We have already noted the scarcity of planes during the Middle Ages, and very much the same is true of saws, in fact the sort of work the craftsman was called upon to do could be done quite adequately with much cruder tools. For example the Bayeux Tapestry, dating from the end of the 11th century, has a fairly long section showing the whole process of felling and preparing timber and building the ships for Duke William's invasion, yet not a single saw is in evidence. The only tools shown are two types of axe, the adze, the hammer or mallet, and a breast auger. What applied to ships would also be true of house-building or furniture-making; indeed up to quite modern times in the more backward areas most of this work was still done with the axe. There was more waste of material, of course, but this hardly mattered as it was plentiful enough.

Of the tools which have survived from the period perhaps the earliest is an iron blade found with other Anglo-Saxon material at Mitchell's Hill, Icklingham, Suffolk, and now in Moyse's Hall Museum, Bury St. Edmunds. The tool is about 11¼ in. long overall, of which 5 in. carries teeth, and 1¼ in. wide. The plain portion of the blade is enclosed in a U-shaped iron sheath which may have originally protected the toothed edge, or may have been a sort of adjustable handle. The saw looks very much like a modern hack-saw, only much thicker and coarser, and it appears to have been used with a pulling action.

The only other tool of this period is a fragment 4½ in. long and 2¾ in. wide from Thetford, now in the Castle Museum at Norwich. This has what looks like two rivet holes near one end, while the blade is serrated on both edges, one having eight points to the inch, the other fourteen. The two edges of the fragment are not exactly parallel, the end opposite the holes being very slightly narrower. This suggests it may be part of a small hand- or dowel-saw, but Group Captain G. M. Knocker, who excavated the site, suggests that it may have been used for cutting combs. It dates from the first half of the 10th century.

A kit of shipbuilder's tools of the Late Viking period (A.D. 950–1000) from Mastermyr in Gotland is shown in Fig. 128. This includes two saws, one of which is an

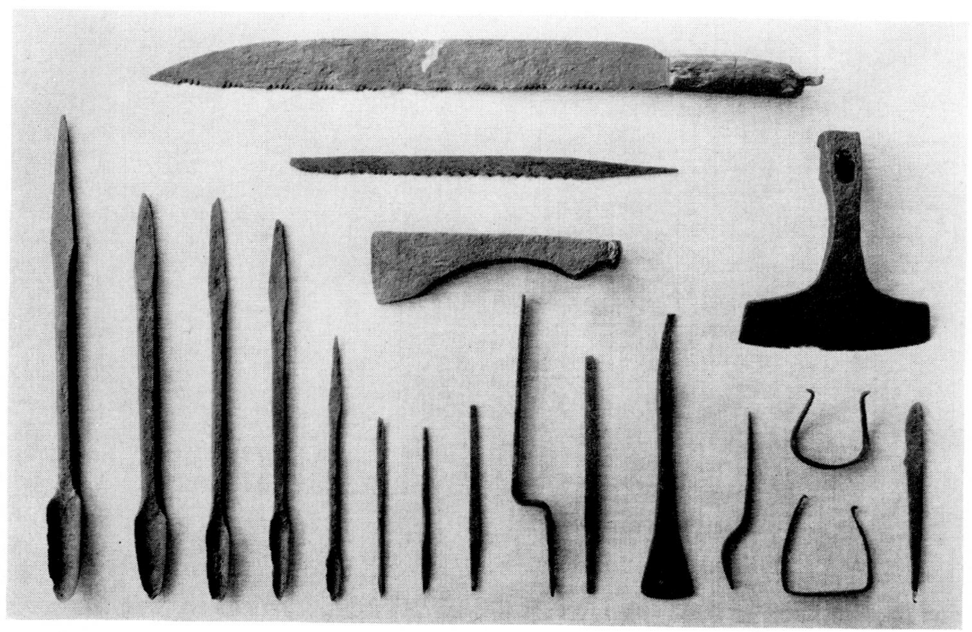

128. Shipbuilders' Tools, Late Viking Period, A.D. 950–1000 — *Statens Historiska Museet, Stockholm*

almost exact replica of the blade of a modern pad-saw. The teeth are very accurately filed and set in the normal manner. The other tool is much longer and wider, with the blade shaped like a bread knife, with a tang running through the wooden handle. The teeth of this saw are filed in groups of five from opposite sides of the blade, making its resemblance to a bread knife even closer. As far as is known at present, this particular method of grouping the teeth is unique.

Two other unusual ways of sharpening and setting saw teeth are shown by tools found when excavating the pre-Mongolian fortified settlements in Northern Russia, dating from the 10th and 11th centuries. They are described in 'Metal-working Technique in Medieval Russia' by B. A. Kolchin, Moscow, 1953. Discussing the general position of the saw in the primitive Russia of this period, Kolchin remarks that they were only used by joiners and cabinet-makers; all tree-felling was done with the axe, and the timber prepared with axe, adze, and a curved draw-knife known as the *skobel*

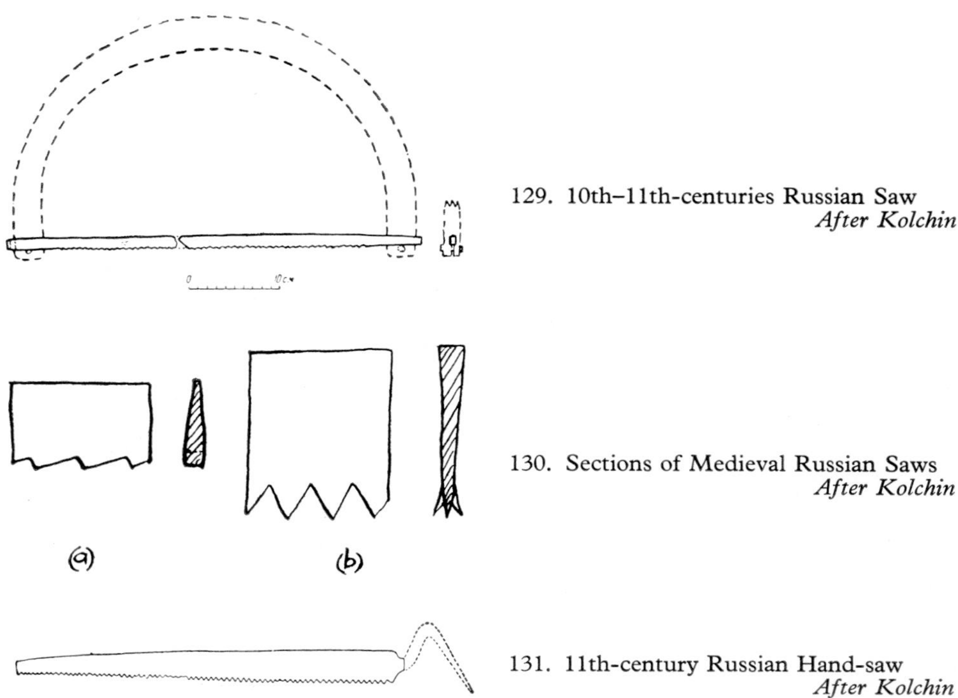

129. 10th–11th-centuries Russian Saw
After Kolchin

130. Sections of Medieval Russian Saws
After Kolchin

131. 11th-century Russian Hand-saw
After Kolchin

(two of which are shown in the bottom right-hand corner of the Mastermyr group, Fig. 128). There were two main types of saw: the *luchkovaya* (bow) saw, with a narrow blade fitted to a semi-circular wooden bow, and a hand-saw known as the *nojhovok* from its shape like a large knife (*nojh*). For the frame Kolchin quotes as his authority a 13th-century ikon of the life of St. George, one scene of which shows the saint being sawn in half with an instrument of this pattern, closely resembling the Greco-Roman saw from Egypt (Fig. 125).

Framed-saw blades were found at various sites, and all were very similar in form. One complete blade from Knyajhnaya Gora is $18\frac{1}{2}$ in. long by $\frac{5}{8}$ in. wide, with the ends bent round to form a socket for the frame (Fig. 129). The profile of the teeth and the section of the blade are shown at Fig. 130*a*. The teeth, with about four points to the inch, were cut with a flat file and have no set, the blade being wedge-shaped in cross-section, with the thick edge downwards, which gave a certain amount of clearance.* Another fragment from Staraya Ryazan about 3 in. long had similar teeth with a cutting angle of about 100 degrees.

The *nojhovok* or hand-saw was made in a different way. An example from Novgorod, dating from the 11th century (Fig. 131), was found entire, except for the tang. The blade is about $15\frac{1}{2}$ in. long, and $1\frac{1}{2}$ in. wide at the handle end, tapering to about $\frac{5}{8}$ in. at the toe. This blade is also wedge-shaped in cross-section (Fig. 130*b*), but the thicker

* Cf. the modern method of swaging.

edge is at the top. The teeth are cut rather larger at the heel, with about 4½ points to the inch, diminishing to about six to the inch at the toe. As may be seen from the cross-section, the teeth are set, but in a very curious manner. The first tooth is flat in the plane of the blade, the second is bent to the right, the third to the left, and the fourth flat again, and so on. In other words, each pair of set teeth is separated by a flat one. The teeth with no set were filed from both sides; those with set from the side opposite the set in the usual way, a three-cornered file having been used. Such a complicated method of setting, combined with the variation in size from heel to toe, shows that 11th-century Russian tool-makers and carpenters could not have been quite so primitive as might be supposed. One other point may be worth mentioning. Although the teeth of this saw are roughly isosceles, it is possible that here we have the forerunner of the M-toothed saw, which appeared some centuries later. It is easy to see that the intermediate teeth with no set, being filed from both sides, would tend to get smaller and smaller, leaving the pairs of set teeth their original size. Eventually it would be found that they could be eliminated altogether, while the gaps thus formed would give a very efficient saw for cutting green or soft timber.

Metallurgical analysis of these Russian saws revealed in one case a structure of sorbite with ferrite, in sharply defined layers, and in another a mixture of pearlite and ferrite. In places the carbon content was as high as 0·7%.

Kolchin's suggestion that the tang of the hand-saw was bent in the manner shown need not necessarily be accepted. The majority of saws of this type shown in medieval pictures have a straight handle, as in Fig. 128.

A similar, but much simpler saw than this was found in a 13th-century midden at Windcliffe, I.O.W., and is now in the Carisbrooke Castle Museum. The blade is about 10 in. long and 3 in. wide, with a straight tang 3 in. long. The few teeth still left on the blade are very irregularly cut to about four points to the inch.

As was noted in the case of the plane, there appear to be no actual saws surviving from the High Middle Ages, or even up to the end of the 16th century, but fortunately the documentary evidence is copious enough. This shows that the four main types of saw in Roman times: the small (sword-like) hand-saw, the small framed saw for bench work, the larger framed saws for ripping timber into boards, and the two-man cross-cut, were retained with only slight improvements in detail. Indeed they persisted throughout the Renaissance period up to the early years of the 18th century. That is why the date at the head of this section, adopted after much thought, appears to ignore the usual historical divisions of Middle Ages, Renaissance, and so on. No radical changes could in fact have been made until a method was found of preparing steel in wide strips, and this had to wait until the dawn of the Industrial Revolution.

The small hand-saws with the straight handles were used by carpenters and boat-builders for general work, and are frequently depicted in the medieval illustrations. Some of them have a distinctly curved, scimitar-like blade (Fig. 132), and quite often, instead of a ferrule, a sort of guard like that on the hilt of a sword. A typical example of this is the saw to the right of the plinth on the Wierix title-page (Fig. 68); there is a very similar tool in the well-known picture of St. Joseph in the 'Annonciation' by the Maître de Flémalle; and many others too numerous to mention here in detail.

Félibien (1676) shows a straight version of this saw with a ferrule, and calls it a 'Scie à main [hand-saw] ou Égohine'. It would be interesting to know the origin of this very un-French-looking word, but so far it has eluded the writer. It is spelt nowadays *égoïne*, and is used in modern French to distinguish the English or American type of hand-saw from the framed saw more often found in continental workshops.

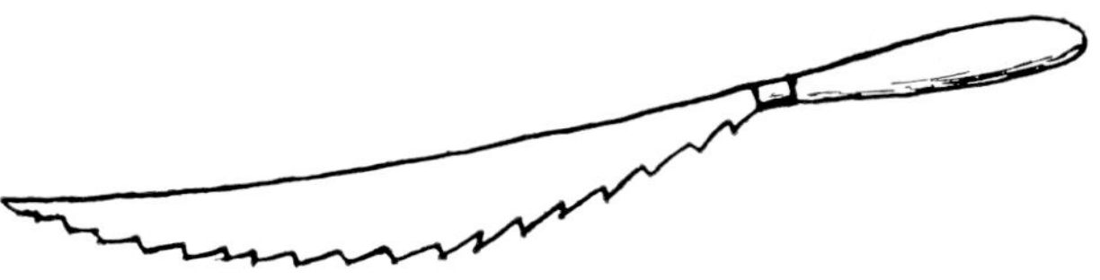

132. Early 15th-century Hand-saw
Bedford Book of Hours, British Museum

133. 17th-century Hand-saws, Dalecarlia *Nordiska Museet, Stockholm*

Moxon copies this drawing of Félibien's, and calls it a compass saw. This, he explains, 'has no set, but the edge is made so broad, and the back so thin, that it may easily follow the broad edge . . . It's Office is to cut a round, or any other Compass kerf.' This appears to be a similar idea to the Russian framed-saw blade in Fig. 130*a*.

This type of saw survived until the latter half of the 18th century in France, judging from the plate of joiners' tools in 'Encyclopédie' of 1765, but there is reason to think that it was getting rather out of date by this time. Occasionally the handle was bent at right angles, as in the saw figuring in the 15th-century misericord from St. Nicholas Chapel, King's Lynn, in the Victoria and Albert Museum. Examples of both patterns of handle are shown in the 17th-century saws from Dalecarlia, Sweden (Fig. 133). One of these is unusual in having the handle longer than the saw itself, and is dated 1633.

The small framed saw is, however, much commoner, especially in the pictures of joiners' and cabinet-makers' workshops. The earlier patterns, including that hung on the wall of the 13th-century joiner's shop in the Chartres Cathedral window (Fig. 134*a*), the saw on the ground in the Bedford Book of Hours picture of Noah's Ark (Fig. 134*b*), and one carried by a tradesman in a Burgundian MS. illustration of the 15th century, showing the Four Estates of the Realm (British Museum Add. MS. 18750, f.3) have the blade riveted to the lower ends of the frame, which was sometimes prolonged to form a handle, like the modern buck saw. Towards the end of the 16th century, particularly in South Germany, more elaborate frames were developed, and the joiner in the Jost Ammann woodcut is using a tool with turned handles like the modern bow-saw. The framed saw in the foreground of the Wierix frontispiece (Fig. 68) has the blade fixed at each end to a short tang, which passes through the frame and ends in a small knob. The blade of these tools may have been capable of being turned, but in actual fact all the illustrations show them with the blade in the same plane as the frame.

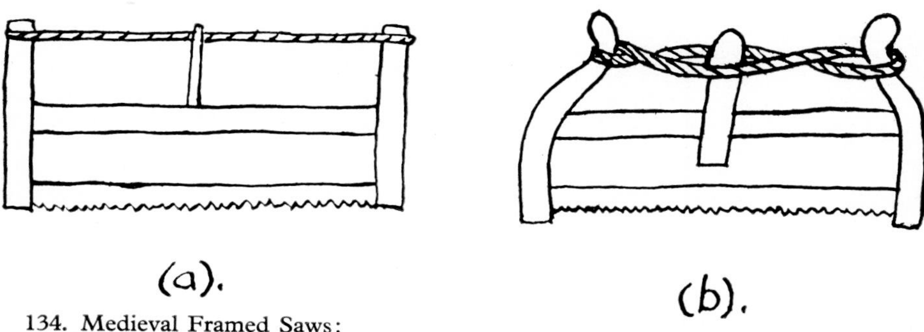

134. Medieval Framed Saws:
(*a*) 13th Century (*Chartres Cathedral*); (*b*) 15th Century (*Bedford Book of Hours*)

Félibien illustrated a small framed saw with a fixed, riveted blade, called a *scie à tenon*. Two rather larger framed saws, with tangs and knobs exactly like the Wierix saw mentioned above, identical except for a slight difference in size, also appear on his plate of 'Tools and other things necessary for Joinery work'. The larger one he calls the *scie à débiter* (literally, the saw for cutting up), the other, the *scie à tourner* (turning saw). Yet, as stated above, the two are identical. Another curious point is that on the same plate he illustrates the set-up for sharpening saws (having no bench screws or vice, they had to wedge the blade in a grooved block secured to the bench with a hold-fast). The saw shown is a framed saw with fairly large turned handles. Moxon's engraver copied this faithfully (Fig. 71) but failed to show that the block was grooved. It seems, however, that by about 1650, or thereabouts, some framed saws were capable of being turned like our modern bow-saw.

Moxon only illustrates one framed saw of the type we are considering, copied direct from Félibien's *scie à débiter*; the tangs and knobs are a trifle sketchy, but the dovetailed joint of the central member of the frame is quite clear. He calls this sometimes a Bow Saw and sometimes a Frame Saw, while in his 'Explanation of terms used in Joynery' he remarks: 'In Pl. 4 O would be a Tennant saw, were the flat of the blade turned to where the edge now stands'. In another passage he states rather cryptically: 'The

Tennant Saw being thin hath a back to keep it from bending.' At first glance this sounds as if he were describing a modern backed tenon-saw, but it is more likely that in his muddle-headed way he was simply referring to the wooden frame. The really exasperating thing about Moxon's Plate 4 is that the only two tools shown as additions to Félibien's plate: the very English-type smoothing plane at B.7, and the saw below it, are not mentioned in the text at all! The signficance of this in the case of the saw will be dealt with later in its proper place.

Discussing saws generally, Moxon remarks that 'the Tennant Saw, Frame-saw, and Bow-saw Kerf is seldom above a half a half-quarter of an inch wide (a rather roundabout way of saying a sixteenth; neither eighths nor sixteenths were marked on the rules of this period). He gives some interesting advice to carpenters and joiners to buy their saws at an ironmonger's shop, especially in Foster-Lane, London, and to 'chuse steel rather than iron'. That this advice is given in respect to saws only seems to suggest that most of the other tools were made by the craftsman himself, the iron parts being supplied by a blacksmith acquaintance, and further, that at that time steel saws were something of a novelty. Reading between the lines, however, it is likely that Moxon was here referring indirectly to the very saw we noted above, as having been introduced among the French tools of Félibien by his English engraver. These new wide blades were the product of the recently introduced water mills for rolling wider steel strip, and would naturally only have been obtainable in an ironmonger's shop.

With reference to the shops in Foster Lane at the turn of the 17th century Sir Ambrose Heal, in his 'Sign-boards of Old London Shops', gives the name of Edward and William Martin, at the White Lion and 3 Flower de Luces, Foster Lane, Cheapside, in 1744. In Price's 'Signs of Old London' ('London Topographical Record', Vol. 4) two more ironmongers of Foster Lane are found: 1694–1705 Henry Perris or Pettis, at the Hare and Buck's Head, and in 1668 Antony Poole, at the Nag's Head. Ward and parish assessments in the Guildhall Records Office include several ironmongers in the Foster Lane area: for instance in the poll-tax of 1692–93 (Aldersgate Within, St. Leonard's Precinct) Thomas Benford or Penford, Lidia Poole, Anthony Lawson, and Mary East are so described, and in St. John Zachary, John Gerrard and Michael Plumber. In a 1694 assessment the name of Benjamin Bound, ironmonger, appears, and in the parish register for St. Michael le Querne his address is given as the 3 Flowers de Luce. This shows that an ironmonger's business was carried on at this address some fifty years before the Martins had it. The writer is indebted to Mr. Raymond Smith, Librarian and Curator of the Guildhall Library, for the above information, and for permission to inspect the series of orphans' inventories in the Guildhall Records Office. These fascinating documents give some idea of the stock-in-trade of a 17th-century ironmonger. Among the tools mentioned in the inventory of Thomas ffowler, dated 14th February, 1665 (Roll 31), a typical example, there are 'chyselles, playning irons, pairs of nippers, carving tooles, iron compasses, steele hamers, hamers, joynt rules, rules. gymblettes, gardner's saws, and saws'. Generally speaking, very few saws are mentioned, and nothing is said about steel ones, although the distinction is made in the case of the 'hamers'. All this, however, is rather earlier than Moxon, and the steel saws may have appeared in the meantime.

Diderot's plate of joiners' tools in the 1765 'Encyclopédie' gives the same series of plain framed saws as his predecessor Félibien of a hundred years earlier; he probably

135. Carved Shop Sign, Early 18th Century *Musée des Arts Decoratifs, Louvre, Paris*

had them copied just as Moxon did before him. The compilers of the reference books of this period were inveterate pirates; there were no laws of international or even national copyright to restrain them, and it was more in keeping with their ideas of scholarship to take the old books down from their shelves and filch the illustrations than go into the workshops and see the actual tools the craftsmen were using. For this reason the elaborate framed saw shown in the carved shop sign from Paris (Fig. 135) may be earlier than it might seem in comparison with Diderot's engravings, perhaps not later than the first quarter of the 18th century. In any case, the tools shown in this carving, and in the very similar group carved on the guild chest of the Corporation of Strasbourg Joiners, dated 1692, in the Musée de l'Œuvre Notre Dame in that city, and the inlaid panel of a similar chest of the Joiners' Guild of Copenhagen, dated 1679 (Fig. 136), are more likely

136. Inlaid Panel, Chest of Copenhagen Joiners' Guild, dated 1679 *Dansk Folkmuseum, Copenhagen*

to be authentic than Moxon's or Diderot's, for the simple reason that they were executed by men who were actually using them every day of their lives. All the saws in these panels have the small tangs of the Wierix framed saw, with rather larger knobs at both ends, and they may easily have been turning saws.

Framed saws like these are still in common use in France, Germany, Italy, Greece, and other parts of Europe at the present day, in preference to the broad-bladed hand-saw of the English or American type, which are still somewhat of a luxury, like Stanley planes. The reason is probably their comparative cheapness; only the narrow steel blade need be purchased; the rest of the tool can be and often is made by the workman himself. Of course they need rather more skill in their use, but this appears to be no handicap to French or German joiners. One rainy afternoon a few summers ago the writer, accompanied by a German friend often mentioned in these pages, Herr J. M. Greber, spent a very profitable hour in the workshop of a carpenter of Bernkastel, in the Moselle district. No English-type hand-saws were seen; all the work was done with various kinds of framed saws, and the foreman carpenter cheerfully demonstrated the different methods used in ripping, cross-cutting, sawing tenons, and so on, with these apparently crude and old-fashioned tools. There was a certain amount of heated argument between the two Germans as to the correct position of the feet when ripping down a plank, but this appeared to be a local variant of the standard method.

4: The 'Pit'-saw, Medieval to the 18th Century

With regard to the large saws for cutting logs into planks or boards, the Roman pattern of framed saw as shown in Figs. 122 and 124 was retained almost unaltered throughout the Middle Ages, and is still in use at the present day in some backward districts. Before discussing this subject in detail there is one point which should be cleared up first. As these saws, and the modern broad-bladed version with the tiller handle, are known in English as 'pit'-saws, from the method of using them with a pit, some misconceptions about medieval sawyers have become current. For example, in the article on 'The Medieval Artisan' on p. 391 of Vol. II of the 'History of Technology', Singer and others, O.U.P., 1956, the writer remarks: 'Large logs were sawn into planks with a pit-saw, as an alternative to bring riven. The log was manœuvred over a large pit in which the lower of the two men worked. In our examples (from the "Livre de Rustican" and a miniature by Tavernier from the "Chroniques et Conquestes de Charlemagne") the log rests on trestles well above the ground, but this may have been due to the exigencies of the situations. The carpenters on the building site in Plate 30B (Rustican) may be a mile or two away from their permanent establishment where most of their wood is sawn; those working under bow-fire in Fig. 350 (Tavernier) might well prefer the security of a saw-pit if they had but the leisure to make one.'

This is a curious piece of special pleading, put forward to explain the use of trestles in the two medieval examples given. The writer has even heard it suggested that a pit discovered during recent excavations at Silchester may have been used by Roman sawyers, but from what follows the reader will appreciate that only the finding of the skeleton of an unfortunate 'pitman' still clutching the remains of a large saw, would provide convincing proof of this. Yet these misconceptions have arisen as a result of a purely linguistic usage. It is only in English that these saws are known as 'pit'-saws. In French they are called *scies à refendre* or *scies de long*; in German *Klob-*, *Langen-*, *Bret*, *Schrot-*, *Spalt-*, or

Dielensagen; in Spanish *serruchos*;* in Russian *prodolnie pili* (length saws); in Swedish *Kran-* or cleaving saws. All these words refer either to the size of the saw itself, or to the fact that it is used for splitting or parting the wood; there is no trace of the idea of 'pit'.

In actual fact, in the forty-five representations of the hand-sawing of logs or large balks by two men known to the present writer, dating from Roman times to the present day, from sources all over Europe and parts of Africa, only eight show a pit in use. Two of these are from the 18th century; the other six are comparatively recent. The remaining thirty-seven show the wood either laid flat on two pairs of trestles or on one trestle with a crutch at the other end, or on one trestle only, the other end of the wood resting on the ground, or in one case secured by a chain, with the wood itself at an angle to the horizontal. The figures are: two trestles—18; one trestle and crutches—7; one trestle with the wood sloping—12; using a pit—8.

There are two Roman examples showing the wood laid flat on two trestles: the Etruscan painted bowl (Fig. 124) depicting two Cupids sawing a balk (only one trestle is visible, but the wood is flat, and the other end must have rested on another), and the relief from Deneuvre in the Nancy Museum, dated to about A.D. 325. In the other Roman pictures of sawyers the wood rests on the ground at one end, and is supported on a strut or trestle at the other: a wall-painting from Pompeii; a mosaic from St. Paul's Basilica, Rome, of about A.D. 400, since destroyed but copied by Gerber in 1637 (both illustrated in Greber, 'Der Werdegang unserer Holzsägen', Fachblatt für Holzarbeiten, Berlin, 1937; IV, Bild 16, and VI; Bild 25); and the engraving in Fig. 122, which shows both trestle and strut. The workman in the Catacombs gold-glass vessel in the Vatican (Fig. 123) who is ripping down a board also has his wood leaning against a sawing horse, with his foot against the lower end, but this example has not been counted in the list above, as he is working single-handed.

This Roman method was retained in Italy down to at least the 17th century. In the mosaic of Noah building the Ark in the cathedral at Monreale near Palermo in Sicily, dating from 1170, the wood is supported at one end by two struts lashed together to form a trestle, the top sawyer standing on the lower end, which is resting on the ground. In the same picture another workman is ripping down a plank with a small framed saw, with one foot on the wood and holding the upper end in his left hand. In the 13th-century mosaic of the same subject in St. Mark's, Venice, the wood rests against a small trestle, with the pitman sitting on the ground under the sloping log. The soffit of the main arch of the same church has a relief in stone of a group of shipbuilders, one pair of whom are ripping down a balk resting in the same manner on a single trestle. This method is also used in the Noah's Ark picture by Pietro de Puccio in the Camposanto at Pisa (1390), a fresco in the church of St. Francis at Assisi, and a mosaic of the same subject in the baptistery at Florence. In all these cases a large wooden-framed saw is being used.

A very interesting example of the use of this method occurs in the famous copy of the 'Decretals of Gregory' from the Priory of St. Bartholemew, London (B.M. Roy. MS. 10. E. IV, F. 99v.), where two workmen, using a cross-cut saw, are ripping down a plank resting at an angle on one trestle. Mr. B. Schofield, of the British Museum, in a written communication, says that 'this MS. was probably written in Italy and illuminated in England'. If so, the picture was evidently copied from an Italian original, as the method

* '*Serrucho braguero*,'—'braced' saw.

is not known north of the Alps. Finally, an engraving on copper by Antonio Tempesta, illustrated in Mercer Fig. 28, and dating to about 1630, shows two sawyers, one standing on the log resting against a crude trestle, the other again sitting on the ground, as in the St. Mark's mosaic. The saw used in this case is a cross-cut with two horizontal tillers.

A very similar method to this appears to be used in the Far East. One of Hokusai's colour prints of the 'Thirty-six Views of Fuji' shows two sawyers ripping down a sloping balk laid on a high trestle at one end, resting on the ground at the other, and supported in between by a shorter trestle. Both are working single-handed, using the broad-bladed Japanese saw with the pistol-shaped handle, one standing on the balk, and the other on the ground under the smaller trestle. One of their mates is sharpening a spare saw fixed upright in a tree-stump. Hokusai was born in 1760 and died in 1849.

Two examples occur from the 15th century of sawyers working on a balk laid flat on two high trestles: the Tavernier picture, dated to 1460, quoted above, and a scene of building work in 'Le Livre du Chastel de Labour', by Jean Bruyant, a manuscript in the Widener Collection, Philadelphia, U.S.A. Other instances of this method are as follows: an engraving entitled 'Prudencia' by the elder Breughel (1530–1600); the painting 'The Carpenters' by Richard Tassel (1580–1660) in the Musée des Beaux Arts at Strasbourg; a picture by Francesco Guardi (1712–1793) 'Workmen tarring a Gondola' in the Ashmolean at Oxford; three engravings in Diderot's 'Encyclopédie' (1762–77), the shipyard, the saw-yard, and the frontispiece of 'Charpente'; a woodcut probably by Oortman in a Dutch children's book *c.* 1820; a painting by J. Maclise, R.A. (*c.* 1860) of Peter I at Deptford (here the wood is laid on a high, flat scaffold); and a painting by Alfred Sisley, at one time in the Petit Pavillon, Paris, of a French roadside scene with sawyers, dating from about 1875. All these are shown using a large framed saw. Further examples, using the modern broad-bladed 'pit'-saw on trestles, occur in a drawing made by J. Knutson at Varberg in 1840, now in the National Museum of Finland; a photograph taken at Nuorgams, Finnish Lapp District, by Ingalill Granlund in 1948 (Dr. Gösta Berg, 'Sawing by Hand of Planks and Boards', Stockholm 1957–58); a photograph taken by J. Paasuke in Esthonia in 1913 (Eesti rahvaparane puutoondus', A. Viires, Tallinn, 1960); and of Danish sawyers at work in the Open-Air Museum of Hjerl Hede, Jutland, by Dr. Erik Andren, of the Nordiska Museet, Stockholm, in 1958.

Returning to the church-building scene in the 'Livre de Rustican', the remark in the article quoted, that 'the carpenters on the building site . . . may be a mile or two away from the permanent establishment where most of their wood is sawn' is itself rather wide of the mark. From evidence to be given later, it is almost certain that these two men were not carpenters at all, but professional sawyers who specialised in rip-sawing, moving from job to job as required, and taking their equipment with them. A close examination of this very fascinating picture, the details of which are so accurate that it must have been painted by someone who had observed closely the building methods of his time, reveals that the balk being sawn rests flat on a pair of stepped trestles at one end, and a pair of crutches at the other. By the side of the top-sawyer there is a long stick resting against the balk (Fig. 137).

All these features are clearly shown in a woodcut of the Ass and the Wolf sawing a balk, with the Ass as top-sawyer, from the first book printed in Sweden, the 'Dialogus Creaturarum Moralizatus', Stockholm, 1483, which is, in fact, a mirror copy of a similar woodcut in a German 'Zwiesprache der Tiere' of 1480 (Fig. 138). The crutch is shown

137. 15th-century Sawyers, Livre de Rustican
British Museum

138. 'Zwiesprache der Tiere', 1480
Courtesy, J. M. Greber

more clearly in these cuts, and the legs of the trestles have two rungs, forming a rough ladder. The long stick at the ass's side is also prominent.

It is therefore very interesting to note, in the engraving 'Les scieurs de long' (Fig. 139), in the Wierix 'Infantia Jesu' series, with the Holy Child as top-sawyer, and St. Joseph as pitman, which is no doubt theologically perfectly sound, the stepped trestles, crutch, and long stick exactly as in the 'Dialogue of the Animals' woodcuts and the Rustican miniature. The trestles and crutch are also shown in detail in the group of tools, etc., on the title-page of the series (Fig. 68), together with the large framed saw.

Confirmation of this use by professional sawyers of the trestle and crutches comes

139. 'Les Scieurs de Long', Hieronymus Wierix, *c.* 1600 *The Trustees of the British Museum*

from the carved wooden *torchère* of the Sawyers' Guild of Ghent, said to date from the middle of the 17th century, and now in the Musée de Folklore there. This consists of a garland, decorated with various tools, including a large framed saw, a trestle, and what looks like a slotted saw-set, surrounding the figures of the Three Wise Men, and two sawyers at work. The log is supported on a crutch in front, but the details of the trestle at the other end are not clear from the photograph, while the saw itself has been damaged, and there is no trace of the long stick. The figures of the two sawyers are jointed like puppets, and were set in motion by a simple mechanism actuated by a string passing down through the hollow shaft. The candle or torch-holder which was fixed to the top is now missing. The *torchère* was carried in procession on the feast day of the Guild, which was under the patronage of St. Corneille.

It is this *torchère* which suggests that the workmen in the 'Rustican' scene were specialist sawyers, members of a separate guild, and using their own equipment. The disadvantage of using two high trestles is the initial difficulty of lifting the heavy balk up on to them. The stepped trestle at one end would make it easier to manœuvre one end of the balk to the top, and the other end could be raised by means of the crutch. The use of a crutch instead of the solid-topped trestle also simplified the process of shifting the support after the initial short length of wood had been sawn, by simply inserting another crutch nearer the end. This also obviated the necessity to remove and dismantle the saw, and of re-inserting it into the kerf on the other side of the trestle. The purpose of the long stick is not clear, but it may have been used by the top-sawyer to retain his balance while these adjustments were being carried out.

Recently the writer was astonished to find that this method is still used by sawyers in the boat-building and repairing yards on the bank of the Nile at Old Cairo. In two cases, where the work was being done in the open air, one end of the log or balk rested on a beam lashed at a convenient height to two palm trees (Fig. 140), with the other

140. Arab Sawyers, Old Cairo, 1961
Photo by Author

supported by a crutch. Another pair of sawyers working in a smoky shed had one end of their log resting on a beam fixed to the walls, and a similar crutch at the front end. The really remarkable thing is that the Arab sawyers are still using a wooden-framed saw almost identical with that depicted on the Roman relief (Fig. 122), and the Wierix engraving, one 2,000 and the other nearly 400 years ago!

Another variation of sawing on trestles, not included in the above list, was encountered recently in the Museo Etnografico Siciliano G. Pitrè, at Favorita, near Palermo. One of the models on exhibition there shows two sawyers ripping a balk laid lengthwise on a single trestle, having a large V-shaped cut at one end to admit the saw, which was of the usual wooden-framed type. This method appears to have been used up to the beginning of the present century.

141. Swiss Sawyers, *c.* 1900 *Courtesy R. A. Salaman, Esq.*

A very interesting method of sawing, which has some affinities with the Roman and medieval Italian method of raising one end of the balk on a single trestle, is shown in a photograph of Swiss sawyers at work (Fig. 141), taken about 1900 by Dr. R. N. Salaman, and kindly communicated to the writer by his son, R. A. Salaman, In this variation the sloping balk is supported near the middle by a sort of tripod, the lower end being held down by a chain anchored to an underground frame on which the tripod is mounted. The top-sawyer stands on the balk in the usual way, with, in this case, two others working below as pitmen. In another picture of the same gang four men are shown working simultaneously in pairs, making two cuts in the same balk, one saw being staggered about 3 ft. further down the wood. One advantage of this method is that a much longer cut can be made without moving the timber; what they probably did was to saw about half-way down, remove the saw, and slew the whole balk round the other way on the tripod, and chain the short end down again. In this case the saw need not be dismantled at all. Discussing these photographs with Mr. Salaman, Mr. Bernard Miles suggested that the timber was intended to 'spring' while being cut, and that it is much easier to saw an unsupported end than wood between two fixed bearers.

From the above it can be seen that over 80% of the examples of ripping down planks from the log or balk, from sources dating from Roman times to the present day, coming from all over Europe and parts of Africa, show the use of trestles in one form or another, while the remaining less than 20% show the use of a pit. According to the 'Shorter Oxford Dictionary', the term 'pit' in connection with sawing dates from the Old English period, i.e., before 1150, but the earliest actual reference in Salzman's 'Building in England' (p. 342) to a 'puttesaw' comes from the Westminster Lodge list of 1444, and mention of the pits themselves no earlier than 1535.* On the other hand the Magdalen College Deeds, in the account for building the 'Bell' at Andover, have an entry for 1534 'for grett naylis to make sawyng trestilles' (*op. cit.*, p. 343).

Dr. Gösta Berg ('Sawing by Hand') suggests that the earliest documentary evidence for the use of pits for sawing in Scandinavia comes from a boundary agreement between two farms in the Ringkobing province of Denmark, dated 1487, while an actual *savgrav* is mentioned at Vejlby Rectory in 1622 in connection with a murder trial. Moxon is rather ambiguous on the subject. He states: 'The Stuff . . . is fastened with wedges over the Pit (if the Joyner be accomodated with a Pit), if he have none, he makes shift with two high frames a little more than a Man high in its stead (called great Trusselles) with four legs spreading outward.' This seems to imply that towards the end of the 17th century in England pits were in fairly common use, especially by professional sawyers, while the odd ripping job was usually done by carpenters using trestles. There is no doubt that for a long run a good deal of manhandling of heavy timbers (which would be resented by skilled men like sawyers) could be avoided by digging a pit, a task which could be done anywhere at any time by comparatively low-paid labourers. The sawyers then need only carry with them their special tools and sharpening equipment from job to job. But there is no evidence available as yet to decide on the priority of the method as between Denmark and England.

What is in fact the earliest representation of a saw-pit in use known to the writer came from an entirely unsuspected source. In reply to a request for material on the

* 'The Merry Wives of Windsor,' Act IV, Sc. IV. 'Let them from forth a sawpit rush at once . . .'

history of woodworking tools, the Director of the Museo Naval at Madrid was good enough to photograph several pages of a manuscript 'Diccionario de Construcción Naval' by the Marquès de la Victoria, dating from the first half of the 18th century, showing the tools and methods used in the Spanish naval dockyards of that period. Page 28 of this work is headed: 'Asierradero a la Inglesa' (English Saw-yard) (Fig. 142).

142. 'English' Saw-yard, 18th-century Spanish MS. 'Diccionario de Construcción Naval'
Museo Naval, Madrid

As the inscription is of considerable interest, it is reproduced in full: 'Asierradero a la Inglesa. Pavage cubierto, donde se asierran la Tablazon y Maderos. La Sierra es un Azerrucho, de dos manos por arriba, y por abajo. La transom de Maderos sin labor, a forma de Reja, sirve de Caballero. Y es debajo de ella que se ponen los hombres, para guyar y ayudar al Asierrador, que manipule el Azerrucho, puesto sobre las Tosas a Maderos.' This may be translated as follows: 'English Saw-yard. Covered enclosure, where the Decking and Timbers are sawn. The saw is an "Azerrucho" for two hands above and below. The transom of unworked Timbers, in the form of a Grill, serves as the Horse(man). And it is under this that the men stand, to guide and assist the Sawyer, who manipulates the "Azerrucho" over the log Timbers.' Apart from the specific designation of the saw-yard as an 'English' one, the use of the word 'transom' shows that the installation was carried out by Englishmen. The word is not known in Spanish, while in addition to its shipbuilding connotations, the 'Shorter Oxford' gives: 'transom —a beam resting across a saw-pit to support the log. *dial.* 1885.' The word must have been used by the men who erected this yard in precisely that sense at least a century and a half earlier than the date given in the 'S.O.D.', and was picked up by the illustrator of the 'Diccionario'. It is significant that on another plate from the same work, showing the tools used by the shipwrights, joiners, and caulkers, a large trestle, described as a 'Banco para aserrar Maderos' (Horse for sawing Timbers) is given, together with a crude version of Moxon's and Diderot's large framed saw. This seems to indicate that in Spain at this period it was still normal to use the trestles and the framed saw, as in France, while this English-type saw-yard was a comparatively recent innovation, and consequently given a plate to itself. The saws shown in use in the pit were also probably English in origin, being the broad-bladed pattern with two large tiller handles. They were possibly obtained from the new water-driven rolling mills near Sheffield, which had then been in production for about a generation.

The only other known 18th-century picture of a saw-pit is illustrated in Fig. 375, p. 631 of the 'Oekonomisch Encyclopädie' of Johann Krünitz, Berlin, 1773–1858, and simply described as 'Holzsäger in der Schneidgrube'. The saw is a plain pit-saw with tiller and box.

A detailed account of pit-sawing in Belgium is given in Elisée Legros, 'Le scieur de long en Ardenne liègoise', Nos. 43–44 of 'Enquêtes du Musée de la Vie Wallonne', July–December, 1946. This describes the process of cutting a log into boards, undertaken for record purposes on behalf of the museum by two old sawyers, in the *hourd*, or covered saw-pit, at Bilotain, near Liège. This pit had been in use commercially up to 1935, when the owner installed machinery. The record was made in 1942. The saw used, a tapered pit-saw with a tiller handle, was known as the *fer aux planches*, while the box or *ménotte* differed from the standard English pattern in having a square middle section. There is no mention in this account of the antiquity or otherwise of the pit method in Belgium.

With regard to England, there is a picture in M. and C. H. B. Quennell's 'History of Everyday Things in England' of pit-sawyers at work at Rossway, Herts, in 1934, and another in H. L. Edlin's 'Woodland Crafts in Great Britain', London, 1949. The 'Woodworker' for June, 1957 also showed a photograph of two men sawing in a pit, in what looks like a boat-builder's yard, but the provenance of the picture is not known.* 'The Story of the Saw', by P. d'A. Jones and E. N. Simons, Spear and Jackson Limited, 1960, has an illustration of pit-sawing in Ghana recently, and the writer has photographs showing natives using a pit-saw to convert mahogany logs to sizes suitable for their power saws, at the Mt. Silendra Mission, Southern Rhodesia, in 1960, kindly communicated by Mr. S. J. Charles, of Umtali.

To sum up the evidence so far available, it seems that pit-sawing was common in England and Denmark, at least from the 18th century onwards, but although pits were used in other parts of Europe, for example in North-west Germany and Belgium, the normal practice everywhere else on the Continent, from Roman times to the advent of machinery, was to use one or two pairs of trestles.

To return to the saws themselves after this long digression, the pit-saw illustrated in

* There is a good picture of pit-sawyers in the new Folk Museum at High Wycombe.

Smith's 'Key' (Fig. 143) became the standard form in this country, whence it was exported all over the world. The blade, from 4 to 8 ft. long, tapers considerably from heel to toe; there is a slot at the wide (top) end to which the 'tiller' was bolted, the lower end being left plain and without teeth for some distance, to accommodate the 'box'. The typical English forms for these fittings are shown in Fig. 144, from the present-day catalogue of the Sheffield firm of Sanderson Brothers & Newbould. The tiller was a fixture, but after the first foot or so of the log had been sawn, the box was removed so that the blade could be taken out of the kerf. The support under the log was then moved along, the saw replaced and the box wedged into position again, for sawing to be continued.

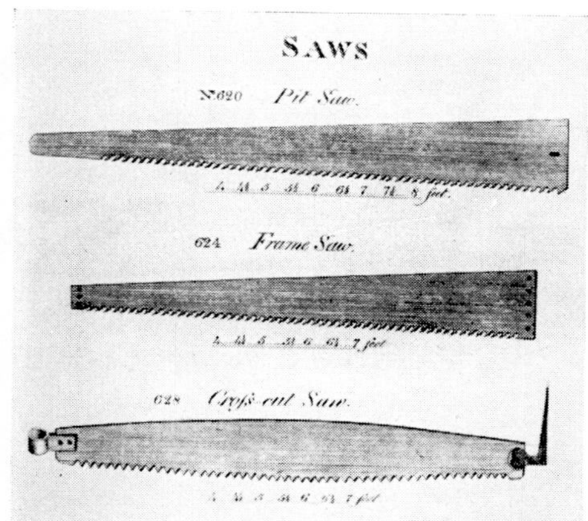

143. Pit, Frame, and Cross-cut Saws
Smith's 'Key', 1816

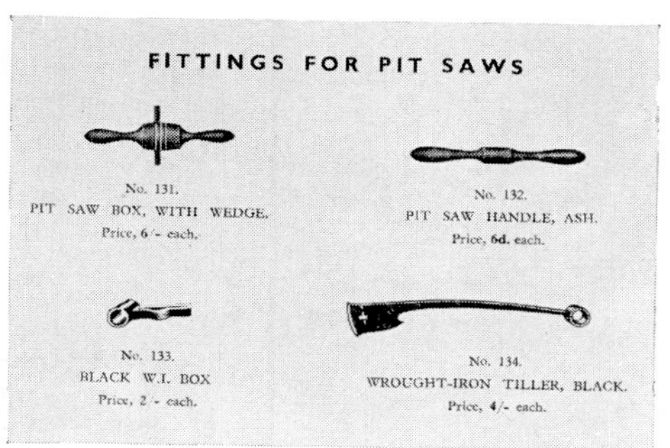

144. Fittings for Pit Saws
Sanderson Bros. & Newbould, Sheffield

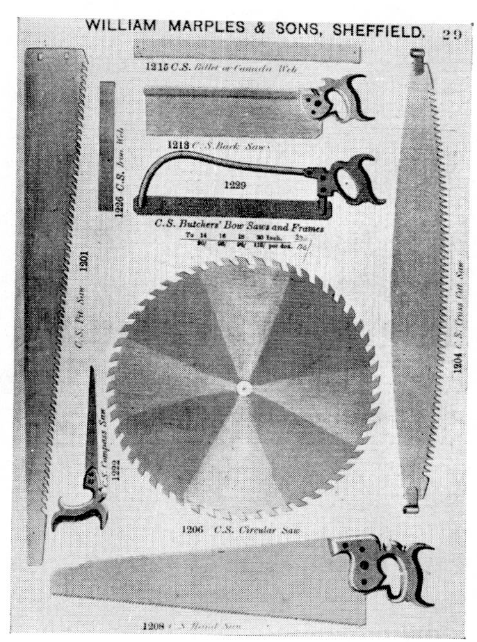

145. Saws in 1864 Catalogue
William Marples & Sons, Sheffield

It has been noted that the saws shown in the Spanish 'English' saw-yard in Fig. 142, roughly a century earlier in date than that in Smith's 'Key', are of uniform breadth throughout, and that there is a tiller handle at both ends. This was probably done to make it easier for the two men working in the pit. Dr. Gösta Berg, in the monograph on 'Sawing by Hand' already referred to, mentions that the earliest picture of a Swedish log or 'crane' saw, in a MS. history of military technology by J. Mollerheim, written in 1720–21, shows a saw of similar pattern, i.e., of uniform width throughout its length, but the type of handles used is not described. It may be assumed that in its earliest form the wider-bladed frameless pit-saw followed the shape of the narrow blades it replaced. It was then found that tapering the blade towards the toe not only economised in material, but resulted in a lighter and handier tool.

The pit-saw in the Marples catalogue of 1864 (Fig. 145) is practically identical with Smith's of 1816, except that there are two slots for alternative fixing of the tiller, while the blades shown in the present-day catalogue of Sanderson Brothers & Newbould have three, and the saws are made up to 10 ft. long. Mr. G. B. Callan, in a recent communication, states that these pit-saws are still made in considerable quantities for export to the following markets: India, Pakistan, Burma, Siam, South America, East and West Africa, and some to the West Indies.

The frame-saw in Fig. 143 was used for the same purpose as the pit-saw, but differs from it in having the teeth cut right down to the toe, and a row of circular holes at both ends for fitting in a large frame. There is a very fine example of this type of saw, complete with frame, in the Shelburne Museum of Woodworking Tools, Shelburne, Vermont, U.S.A. This is described in the catalogue as a pit-saw, but the text also states that 'trestles were used in the state of Vermont as early as 1800'. Judging from what we know now, it might have been better to say 'as late as 1800', but it is likely that a large numbers of sawyers in the United States in the early years of the 19th century were immigrants from various parts of Europe, and brought their tools and methods with them, some using pits and others trestles, according to the custom of their homeland. In the Goldenberg catalogue of 1901 these blades are described as 'Russian' frame-saws, and Mercer mentions that Disston was exporting similar blades to Russia in 1915.

In this connection it is a curious coincidence that the only illustration of a framed saw of this pattern in use known to the writer occurs in a picture by J. Maclise, R.A., of Peter the Great at Deptford Dockyard, painted about 1868, and shown in a recent Academy Winter Exhibition. All the tools shown are anachronistic, being the usual shipwright's tools of the mid-Victorian period, including this framed saw, but as has already been noted, sawyers are shown working on a scaffold, and not, as might have been expected, in a pit.

Marples also listed and illustrated these blades in 1864, but these were probably for export as well, as the English sawyers seem to have preferred the frameless type with the tiller. The frame-saws, in any case, seem to have disappeared from the present-day catalogues.

5: The Two-man Cross-cut Saw, Medieval to the 18th Century

The two-man cross-cut saw was apparently little used by the Romans, and only became common about the middle of the 15th century. At this period it is usually shown with a straight blade of the same width throughout, and two large handles let into sockets forged in the blade itself, and standing up at right angles on the side opposite the teeth. Traditionally St. Simon the Apostle, on a mission to the East, was martyred somewhere in Asia Minor by being sawn in half lengthways, and thanks to this we have many medieval representations of the saint with a book in one hand and a saw, as often as not a cross-cut, in the other. One of the earliest of these may be a statue in the north chapel of the cathedral of Notre-Dame, Strasbourg, and the saint is also shown on the shrine of St. Sebaldus in Nuremberg by Peter Vissler, dated between 1508 and 1519, a plaster copy of which is in the Victoria and Albert Museum.

The Wierix cross-cut saw of about 1600 (Fig. 68) differs from these in having a parallel-edged blade with a pronounced belly. Moxon's 'Whip-saw' however, has the back of the blade straight, with a convex cutting edge. The term 'whip' refers to the to-and-fro movement of the tool, from the German *Wippe*—seesaw, also used to designate the pole lathe. Moxon notes that this saw is used with the 'trussel' he illustrates on his Plate 5; nowadays this would be known as a sawing horse.

All these cross-cuts have had up to now ordinary or peg teeth, but as they were frequently used for cutting up green logs into billets, it was soon found advantageous to leave a blank between each pair of teeth, so that the wet sawdust could escape more easily. Feldhaus suggests in his book on the history of the saw that this type of tooth, known as M-tooth, was invented by Leonardo da Vinci, on the strength of a sketch in the notebooks, now in the Bibliothèque Nationale at Paris, dating from between 1488 and 1497. This is noted in the usual mirror script as a 'Double saw, which works by pushing and pulling'. Prior to this, the earliest example of this type of cross-cut saw known to the writer was the tool held by the St. Simon in Tilman Reimenschneider's carved altar-piece of the Twelve Apostles, now in the Kurpfälisches Museum at Heidelberg, dating to about 1509.

There is, however, a much earlier representation of the M-toothed cross-cut saw in the Unterlinden Museum at Colmar. This is also a figure of St. Simon the Apostle (Fig. 146), in black and gold, copied from an engraving by Martin Schongauer (*c.* 1450–1491), forming part of the decoration on the 'Chasse de St-Hippolyte', a small casket possibly used as a reliquary. In addition the casket bears the arms of Duke René II of Lorraine and his wife Philippine de Gueldres, and was probably presented to them on the occasion of their wedding, which took place in 1477. This gives a firm date for the painting, and shows that this type of saw was common in Alsace and South Germany some years before the mention in Leonardo de Vinci's notebooks. Incidentally, Schongauer's original engraving can be seen in the Musée de l'Œuvre Notre-Dame at Strasbourg.

This is important from the point of view of technological advance generally. It is

146. St. Simon the Apostle, 'Chasse de St. Hippolyte', 1477
Unterlinden Museum, Colmar

often assumed that since a new device or discovery is mentioned by a universal genius like da Vinci, he must have invented it himself. In this case, at any rate, it seems fairly certain that he merely noted an instrument he had seen his workmen using hundreds of times. The note and the sketch he made of it have been carefully preserved with the other records of his lively mind and observant eye, while the humble workman who perfected the idea in the first place, for no better reason, perhaps, than to lighten their work, lived their anonymous lives and died unhonoured and unsung.

Finally, a rather gruesome engraving by Lucas Cranach the Elder, dated to 1509, showing the actual martyrdom of St. Simon, is illustrated on p. 38 of Feldhaus' 'Die Sage'. The saint is portrayed trussed head downwards in a wooden frame, and the instrument in use is a large two-man cross-cut with M-teeth.

A curious variant of the cross-cut saw is the tool used in prisons in the 17th and 18th centuries for cutting up Brazil-wood, the sawdust of which was used by dyers to obtain a red dye. Two, and sometimes three cross-cut saw blades were fastened together and worked by a large tiller handle at each end. An engraving of a prison yard at Amsterdam, dated about 1612, showing convicts undergoing this form of hard labour, is reproduced on p. 288 of Jan and Annie Romein, 'De Lage Landen bij de Zee', W. de Haan N.V., Utrecht, 1949. Incidentally, the country, Brazil, was named after the wood, which originally came from the Far East, and not vice versa.

6: Dutch Hand-saws of the 17th and 18th Centuries

Reference has been made in an earlier chapter to the introduction about the middle of the 17th century of wider blades for hand-saws, the outcome of the newly discovered process of rolling steel strip in water-driven mills. It was suggested that these wide blades were probably the tools referred to by Joseph Moxon in 1683 when he advised his readers to purchase their steel saws from the ironmongers in Foster Lane. The new development, however, was confined to England and Holland, and in each country the typical pattern evolved along quite different lines, especially with regard to the shape of the handle and the method of fixing it.

Taking the Dutch saws first, the earliest example of the new type occurs on a token of the Carpenters' Guild of Flushing, dated 1627, and now in the collections of the Openluchtmuseum at Arnhem. It is illustrated in Jacob Dirk's 'De Noord-Nederlandsche gildepenningen . . .', Haarlem, 1878, Pl. 78, No. 20. The saw appears with other carpenter's tools, and is necessarily very tiny and the detail obscure, but the blade is comparatively wide for its length, while the handle has the characteristic pistol shape.

A much clearer example of the new pattern is shown in a carpenter's carved stone trade sign, dated 1643, from a house in the Botgensstraat 25, Dordrecht. Here the very wide blade, with the cutting edge slightly convex, the shaping at the toe, and the pistol-shaped handle, are entirely typical. The method of fixing the grip to the blade is not clear, owing to the weathering of the stone, but it was probably effected by means of the tang shown rather better in the later examples.

The further development of the type is shown by a very interesting saw (Fig. 147) from

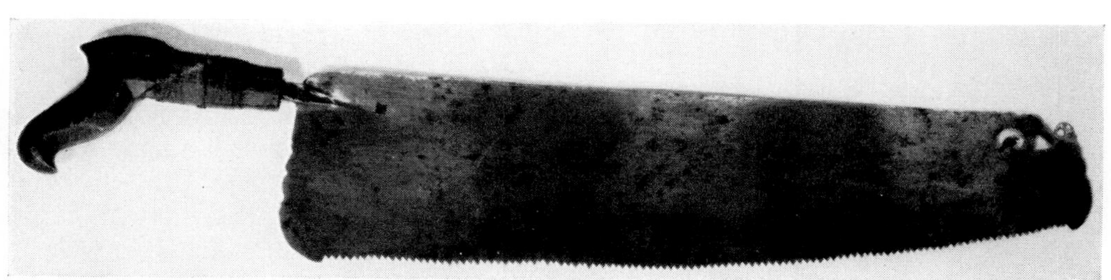

147. Late 17th-century Dutch Hand-saw, *c.* 1698 — *State Hermitage, Leningrad*

the Hermitage, Leningrad, one of a number of tools, including planes, a hack-saw, hatchet, and files, in the collections devoted to the relics of Peter the Great. It will be remembered that Peter visited Holland and later England in the last years of the 17th century to study Western methods of shipbuilding, spending some time at Zaandam and then at Deptford, returning in 1698 to quell a minor insurrection. This gives a fairly close date to this saw, which was probably taken to Russia by one of the Dutch craftsmen Peter induced to go back with him. It shows all the usual features: the wide blade, with the convex cutting edge, fixed to the handle with a tang forged on the upper edge, and the peculiar, and to modern eyes rather inadequate grip. The shaping at the toe is most elaborate, while the answering profile at the heel is a unique feature of the tool under consideration.

The final stage in the evolution of the 18th-century Dutch hand-saw is shown by the splendid example in Fig. 148, from Leeuwarden. Similar tools are illustrated in Mercer and in contemporary Dutch prints and drawings. The back of the blade is now perfectly straight, with the decoration at the toe reduced to a single curve. The toothed edge is straight for about half its length, but curves up considerably towards the toe.

148. 18th-century Dutch Hand-saw *Fries Museum, Leeuwarden*

149. 18th-century Swedish Hand-saw *Nordiska Museet, Stockholm*

The handle is fixed in the usual way to a tang on the upper edge of the blade, and is furnished with a wide brass ferrule and a single band of simple decoration. This type of saw appears to have died out towards the end of the 18th century, and the *handzagen* illustrated in the modern Dutch tool catalogues have the English-American type of blade and handle, whose development will be described in the next section.

These wide-bladed hand-saws were practically unknown outside this country and Holland, at any rate in the 18th century, although the idea was occasionally copied in Scandinavia and Germany, but the pattern never became really popular there. The saw in

Fig. 149, from Sweden, is a comparatively rare exception. It differs in important respects from the standard Dutch pattern; the toothed edge is perfectly straight, the blade tapers slightly from heel to toe, while the tang is part of the blade itself, let into a rather crude handle. This saw has been included here mainly because it shows the toe-end decoration in its most elaborate form. It may give an answer to that hardy annual in the school woodwork room: 'Please, sir, what is the little tooth at the top of the blade for?' It has no obvious purpose, and is most likely a vestige of the shaped toe of the first broad-bladed saws.

7: English Hand-saws of the 17th and 18th Centuries

The foregoing account of the evolution of Dutch hand-saws shows that the wood-workers of the Low Countries adapted the sword- or knife-like tool of the Middle Ages, with a tang to which the round handle was fixed, to the new wider steel blades, the only modification being the adoption of a pistol-shaped grip to get more pressure down to the cutting edge. The English saw-makers, however, made a complete break with this tradition; the handle being shaped from a flat blank as wide as the blade itself, which was slotted into it and fastened with rivets. This method seems to have been used from the beginning, and no transitional forms appear to have survived. It looks as if this is one of the rare cases in technological history of something entirely new, instead of the usual gradual modification of existing forms[1].

If only Joseph Moxon had read his proofs a little more carefully, he could have helped us considerably here. We have already noted the two tools which his engraver added to the Félibien plate, and that these are not referred to in his text. The omission of any reference to the saw is unfortunate, as it distinctly shows (Fig. 71) a wide blade with a straight cutting edge, let into the bulbous end of a flat, shaped handle, and fixed with two rivets. The handle itself is a remarkably early example of the so-called 'dolphin' handle, a modified pistol-shaped grip, which later became the characteristic 'open' handle of the English and American compass, dovetail, and small tenon-saws.

Since these wider steel blades were first made in and near Sheffield it is very appropriate that one of the earliest representations of the complete saw should come from Baslow in Derbyshire, where it was discovered by Mr. G. R. A. Wilson, of Spear and Jackson Ltd. It is illustrated on p. 32 of 'The Story of the Saw', the book issued to celebrate the second century of the firm. It takes the form of an iron inn sign, made by a local blacksmith for the 'Joiners' Arms', and carries the date 1696. The blade of the saw is slightly tapered, with large peg teeth, with the handle fixed to two small lugs by means of rivets. In its general appearance this saw is remarkably similar to the tool the drunken carpenter is trying to pawn in Hogarth's famous engraving 'Gin Lane' referred to by Mercer (p. 136), and dating to about 1741.

The saw in the middle foreground of a carved panel (Fig. 150) in the collection of Dr. J. F. Stent, of Shere, Surrey, shows all the main features of the new pattern. Here

[1] A saw of this type, with rivetted handle, described as an "English" handsaw is illustrated in Rålamb's 'Skeps Byggerij', Stockholm, 1691.

again the broad part of the handle is roughly the same width as the blade, which has a curved profile to the upper edge, the toothed edge being straight. No rivets can be seen, and the shape of the handle is plainer than Moxon's, with fewer curlicues. It has been suggested that from internal evidence this panel may be dated to the middle of the 17th century, with a Scandinavian or Dutch provenance, but if the saw is anything to go by, it may very well be English, and possibly a generation earlier than Moxon.

150. 17th-century Joiner's Shop *Coll. Dr. J. F. Stent, Shere, Surrey*

There is no doubt, however, that by the middle of the 18th century the new pattern of saw-blade and handle was well established in England, judging from the kit of tools carefully carved on the footstone to the grave of Mark Sharp, a local carpenter, in the churchyard of St. John-sub-Castro, Lewes, Sussex (Fig. 151). The hand-saw is possibly rather out of scale with some of the other tools, but the detail is beautifully clear, showing the 'closed' type of handle with two large rivets, fitted to a wide, slightly tapering blade with a straight cutting edge. This point is worth stressing, as it will be remembered that on all the contemporary Dutch saws this cutting edge is most distinctly curved. It is worthy of note that this carving also gives the first known example of the modern closed grip for large planes, set slightly off centre. This confirms the suggestion, made during the discussion of the Jennion trade card, that the new type of plane handle was developed at much the same time as that of the saw; it now seems likely that the saw handle came first, and that the plane handle was adapted from it.

Another trade card, that of Thomas Hattam, ironmonger, of the Cross Saws and Gridiron, 31 Barbican (Fig. 152), shows a pair of hand-saws almost identical with the Mark Sharp saw, except that the blade has more taper, with the toe rounded off instead of square. Although this card is dated to about 1780, it had probably been in use for some time without altering the block, for by this time the profile of these handles had been further developed to bring it nearer the modern shape.

This is exemplified by the tenon-saw formerly belonging to Samuel Crompton, the

151. Footstone to Grave of Mark Sharp *Lewes, Sussex*

inventor of the spinning mule, in the Science Museum, South Kensington. The solid part of the handle to which the blade is riveted is elliptical in shape, a reversion to the Moxon pattern, but the rest of the grip is definitely modern in profile, and there are now three rivets. This is the earliest known backed saw still in existence; it differs from modern tenon and other large backed saws only in having the blade slightly tapered towards the front, with the front edge at a slight angle. The blade itself is stamped 'HARRISON CAST STEEL'.

152. Trade Card of Thomas Hattam, *c.* 1780
'Signboards of Old London Shops', Sir Ambrose Heal, Batsford, London

8: Hand-saws, the 19th Century

The hand-saw in Peter Nicholson's 'Mechanical Exercises', 1812, is very simila to those in Fig. 152, while the larger backed saws, described as Sash, Tenon, and Carcas respectively, are very much like Samuel Crompton's. In addition he has a dovetail-sav with the open type of 'dolphin' handle, but none of his illustrations shows any screws o rivets. For this reason the pictures of saws of this period are taken from the roughl contemporary Smith's 'Key' (Fig. 153). The hand-saws, with three rivets or screws range from 22 in. to 30 in. in length, and there are two others, with only two screws the 'Gentleman's' (our modern 'panel'), from 10 in. to 20 in., and the 'Grafting', fron 10 in. to 14 in. long. Of backed saws, Smith has the dovetail, 8 in. to 10 in. long, an the 'Carcase', 12 in., both with an open handle and two screws, and the 'Sash', 14 in

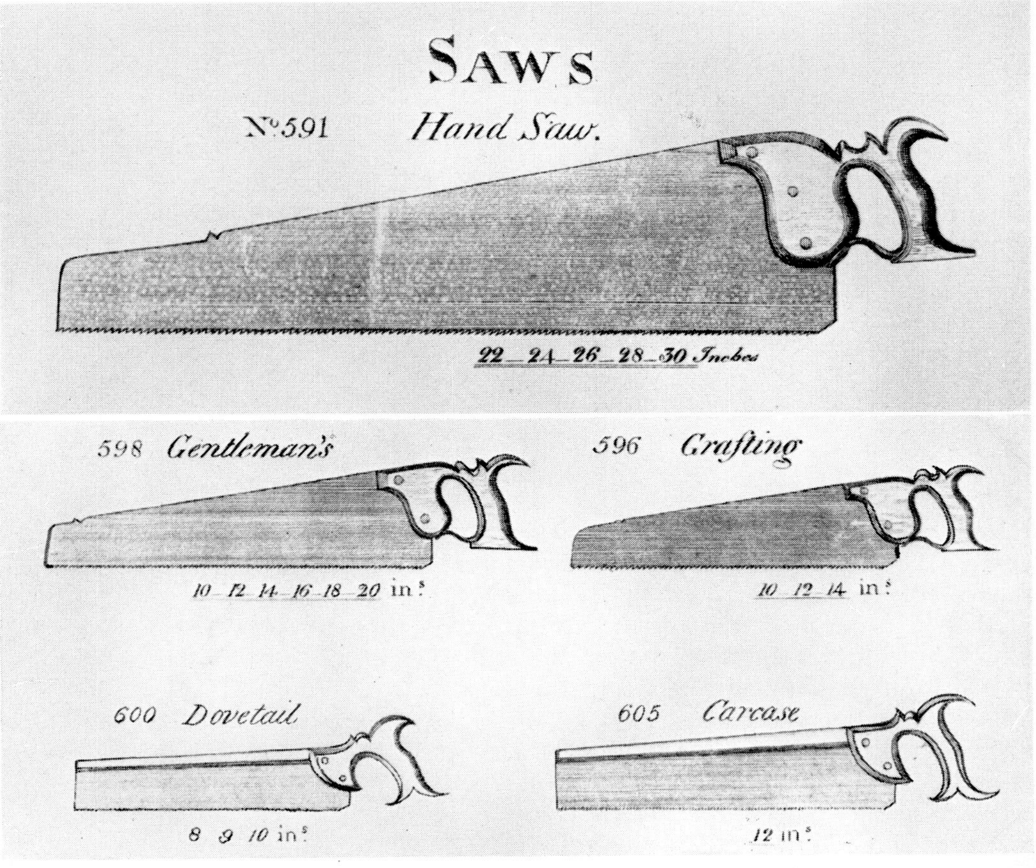

153. Hand and Backed Saws *Smith's 'Key', 1816*

and the 'Tenon', 16 in. to 19 in. long, with a closed handle and three screws. These saws differ but slightly from those in use today.

To complete the record, the saws in the 1864 Marples catalogue are shown in Fig. 145. The Hand, Panel, and Ripping Saws, ranging from 10 in. to 30 in. in the text, have wider blades with rather more taper, giving a better balance, while the larger sizes have the handle nearer the middle of the blade, and it can now accommodate four screws. The backed saws could be obtained from 10 in. to 24 in. long, and with brass backs instead of iron up to 18 in. The narrow 'Compass' saw, which also appeared in Nicholson and in Smith's 'Key', has been largely superseded by the modern pad- or keyhole-saw, but survives today in the sets of blades with a common handle, intended chiefly for the handyman. It is interesting to note that in the Goldenberg catalogue of 1901 these saws are called in the French translation 'Scies à guichet dites à voleurs (so-called burglars' key-hole saws).

Another interesting case of nomenclature is the small, fine-toothed backed saw with a straight, turned handle with ferrule, common in all the catalogues, and known as the 'Gents' saw. This term was rather puzzling at first, but may be explained as the survival of the description 'Gentleman's', noted above, frequently used in the 19th-century catalogues to designate smaller and lighter tools than those intended for craftsmen. This was of course before the days of 'Do-it-youself', but even then many gentlemen of leisure amused themselves with woodworking in various forms, and special tools were designed for them, but this saw, apparently, is the sole survivor.

The history of the saw in the 19th century would hardly be complete without mention of the name of Henry Disston. Learning his trade with Spear and Jackson's, of Sheffield, which was founded in 1760, he emigrated to the United States in the thirties of last century. In 1840 he began the manufacture of saws in Philadelphia. Up to this time most of the tools used in the States had to be imported, principally from England, but Disston soon captured the home market for saws, and it was not long before he was sending his products the reverse way across the Atlantic. Up to 1855 he had to rely on imported steel, but in that year he built his own furnace and cast the first crucible saw steel made in America. Ten years later he began the manufacture of files. The famous Disston 'skew-back' hand-saw was introduced in 1874. In its modern form it is shown in Fig. 154. It will be noted that the handle, as well as the blade, has been considerably simplified from the previous English shapes, and there are now five securing screws altogether. These saws range in size from 20 in. to 26 in. for cross-cutting,

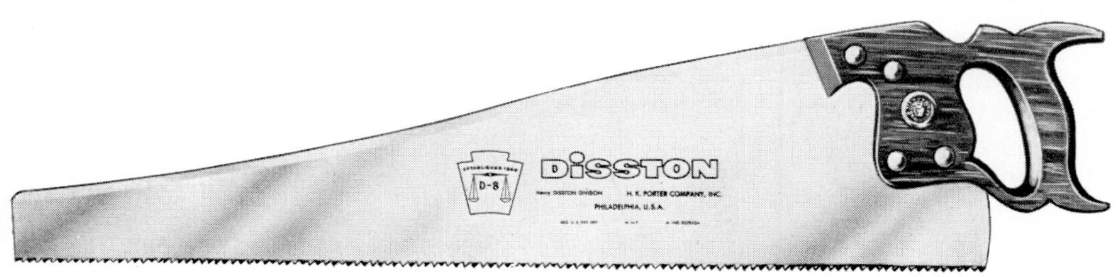

154. Disston D8 Hand-saw, 1959 *H. K. Porter Co. Disston Division, Philadelphia, U.S.A.*

and the rip-saws are 26 in. long with $5\frac{1}{2}$ points to the inch. Disston's also make straight-back hand-saws and the usual range of backed and dovetail-saws. The writer remembers using a Disston panel saw belonging to an old workmate some forty years ago, and remarking on the sweetness with which it did its work.

Disston's old firm of Spear and Jackson have returned the compliment by designing their 'Spearior' hand-saws on similar lines, including the skew-backed blade and the five securing screws. In the corresponding backed saws by the same firm the handles are again very much simpler in shape and more robust than the earlier forms. Although, as was mentioned before, these handsaws are not very popular on the continent of Europe, where most woodworkers still use various forms of framed saw, most of the foreign catalogues list them either as imports from America or this country or as direct imitations. The names they give them are of interest: in French *égoïne*; in German *Fuchsschwanz* (Fox's brush); in Russian *shirókaya nózhovka* (wide knife-saw); and in Italian *Sarraco* or 'English saw'. The Italians, by the way, call their framed saws *sega di San Giuseppe*, or 'St. Joseph's saw', probably because this kind of bow-saw, as we call it, is frequently depicted in the many pictures of the Holy Family in their churches, showing the husband of the Virgin with his tools.

This bow-saw, or turning saw, is the only representative of the framed saws with narrow blades which is in common use in this country today. The illustration of it in Smith's 'Key' (Fig. 155), apart from the rather fancy toggle-stick and the wider space

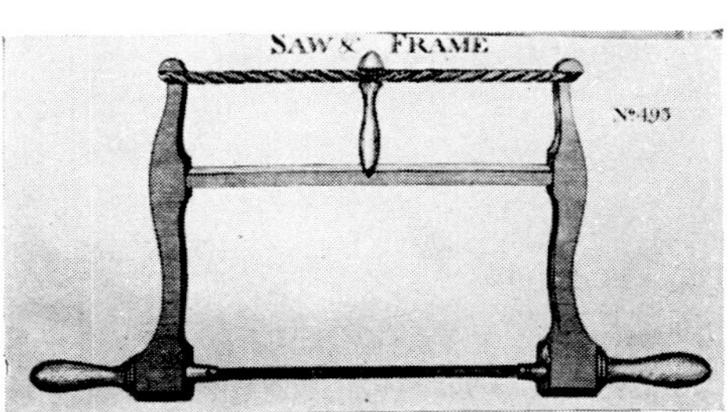

155. Bow Saw, 1816 *Smith's 'Key'*

between the cross-bar of the frame and the blade, is practically identical with those in use at the present time. There is one interesting constructional feature of these small framed saws. In the English pattern the stretcher across the middle is usually stub-tenoned into the side arms. Reference to Figs. 135 and 136 will show that in the continental pattern the stretcher is carried right across the side arms of the frame, usually with a bridle joint, in fact until the toggle-stick is tightened up it is free to move some distance either way. This is still the usual form of construction for these framed saws in Germany and Scandinavia at the present time, and is also shown in recent books on woodworking technology used in the Russian trade schools.

9: Special Saws, from the 16th to the 19th Century

Up to the end of the 15th century the decoration of woodwork, particularly furniture, had been confined almost exclusively to carving, but about this time the fashion set in for inlaying with patterns of various-coloured woods. At first these patterns were purely geometrical, and applied in the form of stringing or bands of chequer-work. The fashion originated in Northern Italy, and for this reason this particular form of inlay is known in some countries, e.g., Germany and Russia, as 'Certosian mosaic', from the Certosa di Pavia, the celebrated Carthusian monastery north of the ancient university city, and where a good deal of this work may still be seen. There are also some very fine examples of it in the Museo del Duomo at Orvieto, while the craftsmen of the Khan-al-Khalili bazaars in Cairo also produce a variety of this work to decorate their cigarette and trinket boxes. Since the early patterns were made up of squares and oblongs, the material was easily prepared with the ordinary plane and saw, but later the designs became more elaborate, taking the form of pictures or floral arabesques. These pictures were frequently architectural in character, and in some of the South German and Italian churches the decoration of the choir stalls and other woodwork takes the form of exercises in perspective. In England this fashion was used to decorate cabinets and boxes of various kinds, the subject being a stylised representation of the Palace of Nonesuch, built for Henry VIII at Cheam to the designs of the Italian Toto del Nunziata. For this reason these chests or cabinets are known as 'Nonesuch' chests. There is a particularly fine example of a writing-desk of this type in the Victoria and Albert Museum, illustrated in Ralph Fastnedge, 'English Furniture Styles', Penguin, 1955, Pl. 3. This work called for an especially fine saw for cutting out the curved shapes, and an entirely new pattern, with a U-shaped iron frame to give the thin blade sufficient tension, was invented for the purpose some time in the early 16th century.

The earliest known representation of a saw of this new type, known in Germany as the 'Laubsage' or 'leaf-saw', occurs on one of the inlaid panels of a wire-drawing and moulding machine made by Leonhard Danner, a Nuremberg joiner and engineer, in 1565 for the Elector Augustus of Saxony, and now in the Cluny Museum at Paris. Four saws of this pattern are mentioned in the inventory of the Elector's collection of tools, formerly at Dresden, and may be dated to the same period. One of them has an elaborately chased iron frame, and the handle is of turned ivory. The saw blade, 2–3 mm. wide, was made from a piece of clock spring, and the tension adjusted by means of a screw.

There are several of these saws on an inlaid panel of a cabinet made for Gustav Adolf of Sweden by the Augsburg cabinet-maker Baumgartner in 1632, now in the University Museum at Uppsala. One in particular is being used by one of the workmen, holding his work in a vertical, pedal-operated vice or 'horse'. Two others are shown hanging on the wall behind the bench. A very similar saw can be seen above the crossed guns among the tools engraved on the lid of the silver tankard of the Stockholm Joiners' Guild

(Fig. 156). A later but much clearer example occurs on an inlaid panel of the Copenhagen Guild chest of 1679 (Fig. 136). The steel parts of the tools in this panel are inlaid in metal. Unfortunately, the upper end of the iron frame has fallen out, but it seems likely that the tension of this saw was regulated by turning the handle.

Diderot, in the 'Encyclopédie' of 1765, illustrates two types of fret-saw; the one shown hanging on the wall on the left in the plate of the cabinet-maker's workshop (Fig. 157) has a tension screw at the upper end of the frame. This cheaper type is also figured on the plate of cabinet-maker's tools. The pedal-operated 'horse' for holding the layers of veneer while cutting out the marquetry designs is also shown in this plate, while the

156. Silver Tankard, dated 1671,
Joiners' Guild of Stockholm
Nordiska Museet, Stockholm

157. Cabinet-maker's Workshop, 18th Century *Diderot, 'Encyclopédie'*

two workmen in the foreground are sawing out the veneer with a special framed saw. In the section of the 'Encyclopédie' devoted to the craft of the *Boisselier* (bushel-maker), however, the *scie à decouper*, almost identical with the fret-saw on the Copenhagen Guild chest, is shown with the mechanism of the handle separated, and the text has the note: 'C'est en tournant la manche dans la virole que l'on tend ou détend la lame' (by turning the handle in the ferrule the blade is tightened or slackened).

In this connection it is possible that our coping-saw, a comparatively modern fret-saw where the blade may be swivelled to any position required, owes its peculiar name to this *scie à decouper*, a term which is now obsolete in France itself. It is interesting to note, however, that the 1957 catalogue of the Amsterdam firm of tool dealers, C. G. Sieben & Co., mentions *decoupeerzaagjes* (little fret-saw blades), although the saw itself is known in Dutch as the *figuurzaagbeugel* (fret-saw bow).

Generally speaking these fret-saws have changed very little since the 18th century, except in improving the actual material or accuracy of cutting the fine teeth of the blade. Towards the end of the 18th century, after the introduction of the treadle lathe, the new mechanism was adapted to work a vertical jig-saw, the blade of which was tensioned either by a bow or a spiral spring. There is a very fine example of a jig-saw of this latter type, used for making the famous 'Tunbridge ware', a form of Certosian mosaic very popular in Early Victorian England, in the Pinto Collection of Wooden Bygones at Northwood, Middlesex. Nowadays a good deal of this work is done with power-operated jig-saws, which are rather outside the scope of this study.

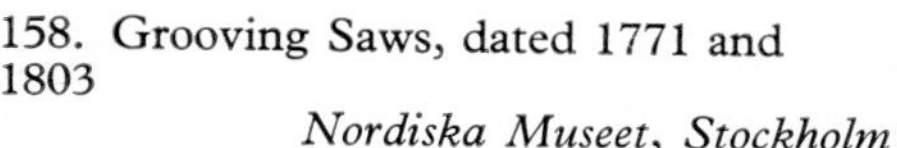

158. Grooving Saws, dated 1771 and 1803

Nordiska Museet, Stockholm

Another special saw is quite common on the Continent but so completely unknown here that it is difficult to find a name for it.* Some 18th-century examples are shown in Fig. 158 from Scandinavia, but almost identical tools appear in the present-day German,

* In the United States they are known as staircase-saws.

French, and Swiss tool catalogues. In German they are known as *Gratsagen*, or 'edge' saws; in French *scies à queue*, or 'tail' saws. They are used for cutting the sides of a groove across the grain. In the modern German handbooks on woodwork technology they are described as being pull saws, but the upper tool is clearly a push saw, while the middle one may be used either way. The saw at the bottom is a veneer saw for cutting thick veneers against a fence or guide.

Saws of this type appear to be unknown in this country, but the writer has found that a similar arrangement with a fixed fence is a very useful tool in the school workshop. It can be used for cutting the shoulders of lapped housing joints for the corners of boxes or small cabinets, especially by boys who cannot manage a dovetailed joint. Three sizes, $\frac{3}{8}$ in., $\frac{1}{2}$ in., and $\frac{5}{8}$ in., to cover the standard board thicknesses, with the blade, about 6–8 in. long, cutting to half these thicknesses respectively, have been made from old tenon-saw blades, and they are in constant use. It might seem a little strange to go back to the 18th century for tools to use in a modern workshop, but after all the methods adopted in school handicraft are, or should be, based on those of the Golden Age of hand craftsmanship.

Another special saw which is not often seen in this country is the 'dowel'-saw, for cutting pins flush with the frame before cleaning up, a thing which is sometimes difficult to do with an ordinary backed saw. In the 18th century these dowel- or pin-saws sometimes took the form of a mason's trowel, with both edges serrated, and one of these is shown in Félibien's 'Principes' of 1676. The modern pattern has the two edges parallel, with the handle bent away from the plane of the blade.

10: Cross-cut Saws, the 19th Century

Cross-cut saws have changed very little in essentials since the 17th century, but there have been a number of minor improvements, particularly in the shape of the teeth. The large cross-cut saw in Smith's 'Key' (Fig. 143) is a typical example of the English pattern, with both the back edge and the tooth line bellied. The socket for a handle at the left-hand end, bolted to the blade, is more usual in English saws; the alternative tang was probably fitted to saws for export to particular foreign countries, as will be seen later. The equivalent saw in the Marples 1864 catalogue (Fig. 145) shows the socketed lug at both ends, but is otherwise identical with Smith's.

Through the courtesy of Mr. R. A. Salaman the writer has been able to consult the 1901 catalogue of the Alsatian firm of Goldenberg et Cie, of Saverne, near Strasbourg. This listed, about sixty years ago, the remarkable number of no less than sixteen basic types of cross-cut, besides several sub-types. The list includes Swedish, Russian, Bohemian, Hungarian, Tyrolean, Croat, Swiss, Harz, Breslau, Swabian, Hanoverian, Bavarian, Saxon, English, American, and French. Of these only the English and the Swedish have both the back edge and the tooth line bellied; the Saxon, Tyrolean, Croat, and Swiss have the tooth line bellied and the back edge concave. All the others have the back straight and the tooth line bellied, except one sub-type of the Breslau saw, and a variant of the French, the only two of the sixteen in which both back and toothed edges are straight and parallel.

Most of these saws have ordinary peg teeth, sometimes with a flat gullet, but the Hungarian, Breslau, and Bavarian have M-teeth, while one variant of the Tyrolean half-moon saws has the teeth raked towards the handle on each half of the blade.

The Russian, Tyrolean, Croat, Swiss, Swabian, and Hanoverian types are shown with tangs, of which the Croat tangs are welded to the blade; all the others have socketed lugs for turned handles, with slight variations in detail and two, three, or four rivets or fixing screws. The American saws have a reversible handle fixed with a winged nut.

It is difficult to understand why there should have been so many different types: one for almost every province of Germany, besides the 'national' types such as English, Russian, French, American, and so on. Perhaps the only explanation is the innate conservatism of the craftsman, but it made the task of an international firm like Goldenberg's very much more difficult in having to cater for so many varying tastes. But 1901, the date of this catalogue, must have been very near the end of the period when manufacturers had to carry stocks of tools of the local traditional patterns. Since then the emphasis has been the other way; with the improvement of communications and the decline of regional traditions, the larger firms, with their international prestige and higher standards, have been able to impose their own designs to a large extent. Consequently the modern lists show a reduced number of variants, although the national characteristics still reveal themselves; e.g., Disston's 'Champion' No. 152 has the straight back with the bellied tooth edge of the Goldenberg 'American' type, but they also list several types of hollow-back saws. The Sandvik 221 has the same straight back, but slightly hollow backs are also popular with them. The majority of the cross-cut saws in the Sanderson Brothers & Newbould list are of the 'English' pattern, with round back and bellied toothed edge, but there are one or two with straight or hollow backs. All these saws have the socketed lugs, but it is probable that tanged lugs are still used in Germany and Eastern Europe, as they were sixty years ago.

The main differences nowadays are in the shape of the teeth, and a good deal of ingenuity has been displayed in devising a tooth shape which will cut green wood sweetly and efficiently. The main variations are shown in Fig. 159, arranged according to complexity and date of introduction.

The first group consists of variants of the ordinary Peg tooth, known on the Continent as the Wolf's tooth. This is sometimes cut with a flat space between the teeth, and sometimes, to make for quicker and vibrationless cutting, the flat gullets vary in size in groups of three or four.

The second group is based on the M-tooth, which we have shown to have originated towards the end of the 15th century. A hand-saw with this type of tooth is sometimes known in this country as a 'log' saw. The sides of each pair of teeth are vertical, with a deep, rounded gullet between them, the other two bevels are equal and opposite. The Sanderson Brothers & Newbould catalogue has a variation of this called the 'Tasmanian' tooth, with a small perforation in the gullet of the paired teeth.

The 'Great American Tooth' is a further elaboration of the M-tooth, with three points instead of two in each group, and has been widely adopted for general-purpose saws.

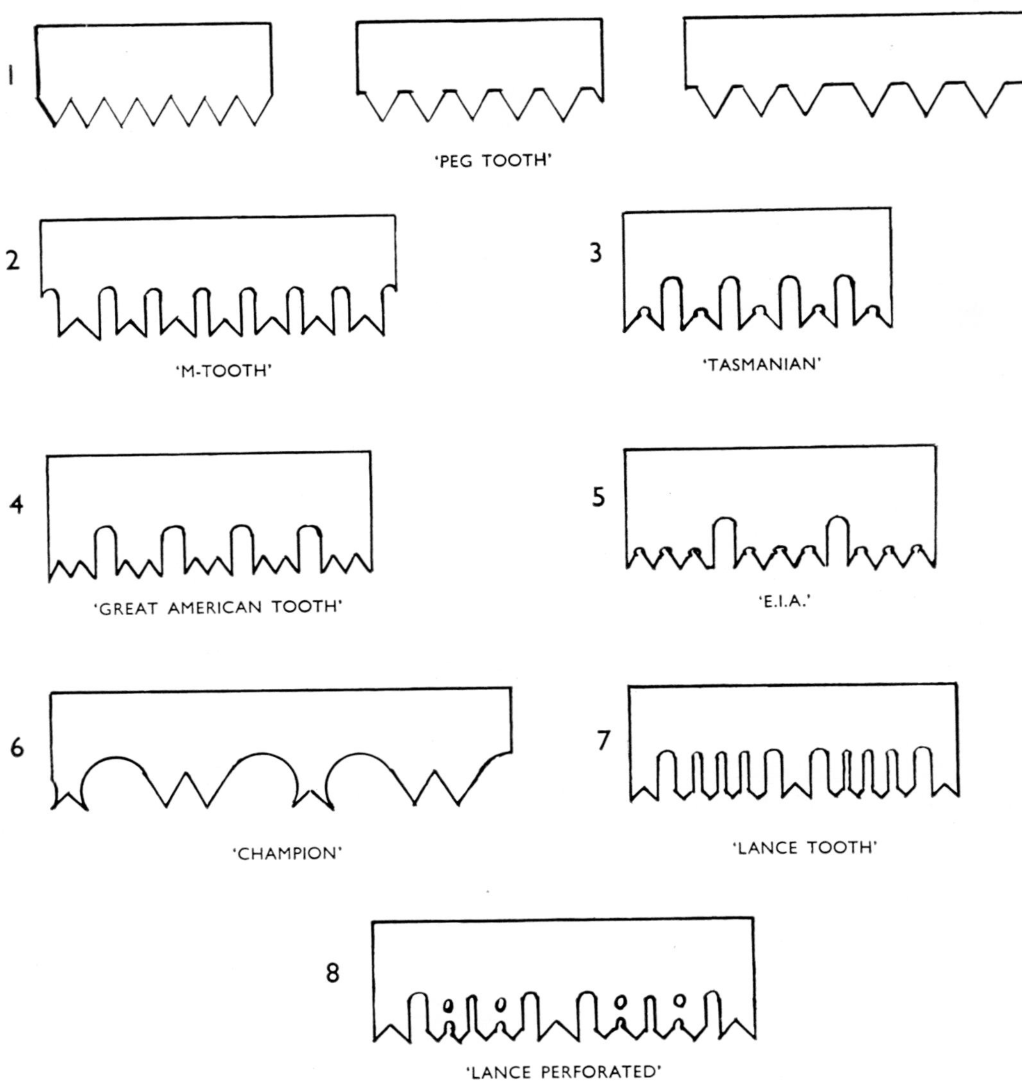

159. Saw Teeth Profiles

The process of elaboration has been carried still further in the Swedish 'E.I.A.' tooth, used a good deal on the Continent for tubular bow-saws. Here the teeth are in groups of four, sometimes with the 'Tasmanian' perforation in the gullet of the smaller teeth.

In the M-tooth and its later derivatives the groups of smaller teeth do the actual cutting, while the vertical edges with the deeper gullet help to clear the sawdust from the kerf. These two functions are separated completely in the 'Champion' tooth, which is composed of pairs of long peg teeth separated by a small M-tooth which acts as raker. Saws with teeth of this type are listed by Disston, Sanderson Brothers & Newbould, and Sandvik's.

The 'Lance' tooth carries this idea a stage further by providing a group of four cutting teeth to each pair of clearing teeth. In its earlier form the four cutting teeth were of the ordinary peg shape, but in later models a thin gullet was cut between each one to the same depth as that of the rakers. In the latest form of Lance tooth only the central gullet is so treated, the other two are cut about half-way, with a perforation as shown in the figure. Disston's call this a 'Lance perforated tooth', while Sandvik's describe it as the 'Raked' tooth.

Other variations of these tooth shapes are possible, but those described above have become the most usual types for varying conditions of work.

Supplementing the traditional two-man cross-cut, the present-day manufacturers list a one-man saw like a very large hand-saw. They are made from 2 ft. 6 in. to 5 ft. 0 in. long, and the additional handle on the back edge can be adjusted to any position. The most usual form of teeth for this saw is the Great American, with a short length of peg teeth near the toe, but Disston's also list one with Champion teeth, while Sandvik's also have a plain peg-toothed version with the teeth hooked towards the toe for quicker cutting, and another with their Raked (Lance perforated) tooth.

Finally the tubular frame-saw, sometimes called erroneously the 'bow'-saw, has become very popular for rough carpentry and similar work in recent years. The most usual form of tooth is the 'E.I.A.', which has retained its popularity since it was first introduced on this type of saw, but Sandvik's list a blade with a form of 'Champion' tooth, and another pattern with grouped peg teeth in their hard-pointed range. It is not without interest from a historical point of view that this most modern saw of all as regards date is, apart from its size and the material used for the frame, essentially the same as the tool from the Roman period of Egypt (Fig. 125) and the medieval bow-saws from Russia. A similar point could be made about the modern American wedge axe, whose streamlined shape recalls that of the early flat-butted polished flint axe of the Neolithic period. Like languages, some tools have a tendency to get simpler as they develop.

SECTION IV

BORING TOOLS

1: The Bow Drill

ONE OF the mysteries of Ancient Egypt from the point of view of the history of technology is that although simple copper awls were used by both carpenters and leather workers in the Archaic Period (about 3000 B.C., W. B. Emery, 'Archaic Egypt', Pelican, A 462, 1961, p. 221), the only tool shown in use on mastaba reliefs, tomb frescoes, and coffin texts from Early Dynastic times onwards (from 2700 B.C.) for boring is the comparatively complicated instrument the bow drill. In other words the Egyptian craftsmen seem to have missed out altogether the two-handed auger, which to us seems the logical successor of the piercer or awl. Yet judging from the surviving woodwork, whatever form of drill they used must have been one of the most important tools in their kit, for since they had neither nails nor screws, almost everything was fitted together with wooden pins or dowels, or sometimes lashed together with leather thongs or rope, and the drilling of an accurate hole for this was essential. The idea of lashing woodwork joints together may seem rather strange to modern craftsmen other than boat-builders, but the method had a long history in Egypt. Some of the earliest woodwork known to us, in the form of planks with sets of holes bored just inside the edge to enable them to be overlapped vertically and lashed together, was used to make the walls of the temporary cabins, which the Egyptians of the earliest times, well before 3000 B.C., built for their work in the fields near the Nile. A good many of these, found by Sir Flinders Petrie at Tarkhan, have only survived because they were used some centuries later to form the sides and bottoms of crude coffins. This method of constructing the cabin or house with overlapping vertical boards may explain why the walls of the early mastaba tombs, although built of brick, show the deep vertical recesses mentioned by I. E. S. Edwards in the Penguin, 'Pyramids of Egypt', although he makes no attempt to account for this feature.

Later the corners of coffins and other box-like constructions were jointed in a very efficient manner. Each corner was accurately mitred, with a single dovetail near the top, and a slight shoulder on the ends, and pinned together with half-inch wooden pins arranged roughly in pairs. There are a large number of outer and inner coffins and wooden boxes for Canopic jars in the British Museum, the Louvre, and the Egyptian Museum at Cairo fitted together in this way. It was the standard method of jointing corners in

Egypt from about 2500 B.C., and like many things in that mysterious country, was kept unchanged for many hundreds of years. In the case of the coffins, it is likely that this method made it easy for the sides and ends to be fastened temporarily, and then dismantled for the painters to cover the inside surfaces with the traditional inscriptions and ritual spells before the coffins were finally assembled. In some of the coffins in the British Museum there are grooves connecting the pairs of dowel holes, to allow the joint to be lashed together.

But as was mentioned above, no Egyptian augers are known, and all the representations of carpenters drilling holes show them using the bow drill. A reconstruction of one of these tools is displayed in the Science Museum, with a copy of a tomb fresco, dating to about 1400 B.C., showing a workman boring a hole in a chair frame, presumably to take the plaited cane of the seat. He is holding the nave of the drill stock, possibly a piece of soft stone, in his left hand, and using the 'bow' with his right. The reconstruction of the drill below it has a hardwood stock, with vertical fluting on the part which takes the thong of the 'bow'. The latter is, however, a perfectly straight piece of round wood, and it would require considerable skill to hold it away from the stock without tilting the bit.

A much earlier picture than this of the bow drill occurs in a sculptured relief on the walls of the mastaba of Tiye, at Saqqara, of the Vth Dynasty, dating to about 2540 B.C. (Fig. 35). The drill stock and nave also figure in the hieroglyphic inscription above the workman's head. There are also two coffin friezes depicting carpenter's tools which include the drill stock and bow, complete with cord: one on the inner coffin of Sen, a physician of the Middle Kingdom, No. 30842 in the British Museum; and another on the outer coffin of Hereschefhotp I, of about the same date, in the Museum of the Egyptian Institute of Leipzig University (Greber, 'Geschichte des Hobels', Abb. 24).

It is also very surprising that the only boring tools shown in use from Greek and Roman sources are also bow drills. The Greek example occurs on a red-figured *hydria* by the Gallatin painter in the Museum of Fine Arts, Boston, Mass., where the 'bow' is also a straight piece of wood like those shown in the Egyptian drawings.

The Romans appear to have been the first to use a curved stick for the bow, as shown by the shipbuilder in the Catacombs gold-glass vessel (Fig. 160), but here the artist has

160. Roman Workman using Bow Drill, Catacombs Gold-glass Vessel

Vatican Museum, Rome

made a mistake, as the workman is holding the middle of the drill stock instead of the nave at the top. A similar Roman bow and drill stock, complete with shell bit, appears on the right-hand side of the relief of the two Greek freedmen in the British Museum (Fig. 161). These tools are said to be sculptors', but although the bow drill was and still

161. Roman Sculptor's and Die-casting Tools *Trustees of the British Museum*

is used extensively by sculptors, owing to the ease with which the depth of the hole may be controlled, the remaining tools on the panel, consisting of a knife, a very typical Roman adze-hammer, and what looks like the blade of a paring chisel, are all woodworker's tools. Those on the pediment, however, are implements used in coining (Publicus Licinius, the patron for whom the relief was made, was a Roman magistrate who struck coins, *c.* 12 B.C.). Other Roman examples are: a relief from the side of the gravestone of Eutyches which shows a plane; a similar gravestone at one time in Rome, from an engraving made in 1603 (Greber, *op. cit.* Abb. 41); and a fresco in the House of the Vettii, Pompeii, showing Daedalus making the wooden cow for Pasiphae (Fig. 189).

After the Roman period the bow drill was little used by woodworkers, who preferred the more powerful tools like the breast auger and later the brace, but in addition to the sculptors, it was taken over by workers in the more fragile materials. B. A. Kolchin, in the Novgorod reports, describes two iron bits for bow drills from the 12th and 13th centuries, but suggests that they were used for working bone. The iron part of the drill is shown in Fig. 162, and consists of a square middle section, with a long tapered pin at the upper end to take the nave, and a spoon bit about 3 mm. ($\frac{1}{8}$ in.) in diameter at the lower end. A wooden or bone bobbin was fitted to the square shank to take the bow cord. Kolchin states that a similar tool was found in 1902 in an 11th-century burial mound in the Smolensk district.

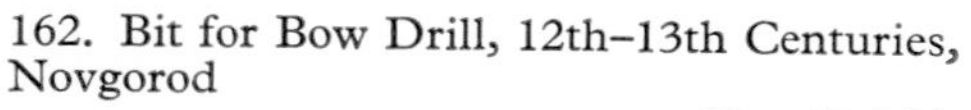

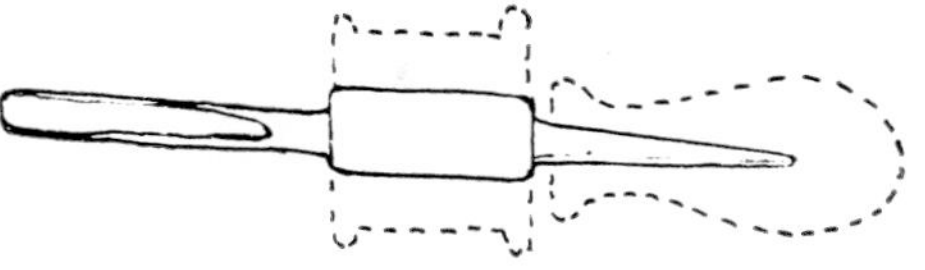

162. Bit for Bow Drill, 12th–13th Centuries, Novgorod
After Kolchin

163. The Rosary Makers, J. Luyken, *c.* 1720
Author's Collection

A further adaptation of this drill is shown in J. Luyken's engraving of the rosary-makers, published about 1720 (Fig. 163). Here the drill stock is held horizontally in a wooden fitting attached to the bench, while the workman applies the workpiece to the drill with the left hand. Some pieces with the holes drilled in them may be seen on the bench. Later they were cut up and fashioned into beads.

A *taladro de arco* is illustrated among the Spanish coppersmith's tools in the 'Diccionario de Construccion Naval' of the early 18th century, but the details are vague. Diderot shows bow drills in use by sculptors, but the only evidence that they were also used by woodworkers about this time comes from Bergeron's 'Manuel du Tourneur' of 1816. A full range of bow and fiddle drills (a later refinement) is given on Plate XI (Fig. 164). On the extreme right is a flexible steel bow, the tension of the cord being adjusted by a pawl and ratchet device; a hand-drill stock on the left with the wide, turned nave, and other types of drill stock with tapered pins, which were supported by the breast-plate (Fig. 4 on Bergeron's plate). This is described in the text as the 'conscience, qui s'applique contre l'estomac'. This is a striking anticipation of James Laver's remarks in the second chapter of 'Nymph Errant' on where a Frenchman keeps his conscience. Various fiddle-drill accessories are also shown, including a device which could be attached to the bench like that in the picture of the rosary-makers.

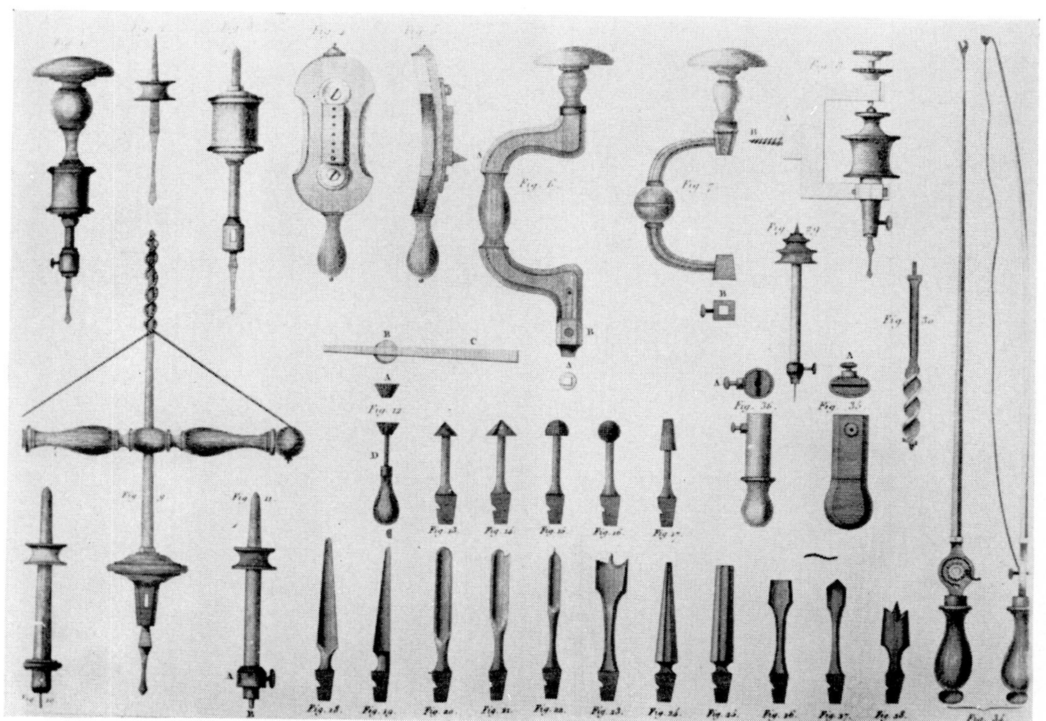

164. Bow, Fiddle, and Pump Drills *Bergeron, 'Manuel du Tourneur', 1816*

A fiddle-drill stock almost identical with Bergeron's Fig. 3 is illustrated in the Marples 1864 catalogue, but these tools are now mainly used by jewellers. The bow drill, however, is still used extensively by woodworkers in the Middle East and down as far as Kenya in Africa, while the writer has seen and photographed the bead-makers in the Khan-el-Khalili bazaar in Cairo using a small bow-driven lathe. It is interesting to note that the handle of the 'bow', as used by both the Arab bead-makers of Cairo and by an Arab carpenter on a photograph taken at Terschicha in North Israel in 1959 by Dr. S. Avitsur, of the Tel-Aviv Museum, in the author's collection, is the same straight piece of wood as used by the Ancient Egyptians and the Greeks.

2: The Auger

Although the only boring tool shown in use by Roman woodworkers is the bow drill, a fair number of iron spoon bits have come down to us which were probably used with a handle as augers. None of these handles have survived, but Pliny states that auger handles were often made of olive, box, holm-oak, elm, and ash, while there is a small gimlet at Shrewsbury fitted with a handle of bone. One of these larger bits, 8 in. long overall and $\frac{1}{2}$ in. in diameter, was found at the corner of Poultry and Princes Street in the City, and is illustrated in 'London in Roman Times', Pl. XXXII, No. 7. Very similar bits, differing only in size, have been found at Newstead, and there are other examples at Leeuwarden and Saint-Germain. The two show-cases of Roman tools, showing how they were probably used, recently installed in the Landesmuseum at Zürich, display a number of augers, with conjectural, but highly probable plain handles of wood.

The auger is a very common tool in the medieval illuminated MSS., but very few actual tools have been preserved. A complete set of five shell or spoon augers are included in the kit of shipbuilder's tools of the Late Viking Period (Fig. 128), with flattened tangs to take the handles, and a similar bit, 13 in. long with the cutter 1 in. in diameter, is included in the hoard of Saxon tools from Hurbuck, Co. Durham (Wilson, 'The Anglo-Saxons', Fig. 11). The auger from Ragnildsholmen (Fig. 165) is a smaller version of the same type, with a very characteristic handle, improvised from a suitable piece of crutched wood. That this was common practice is shown by the almost identical

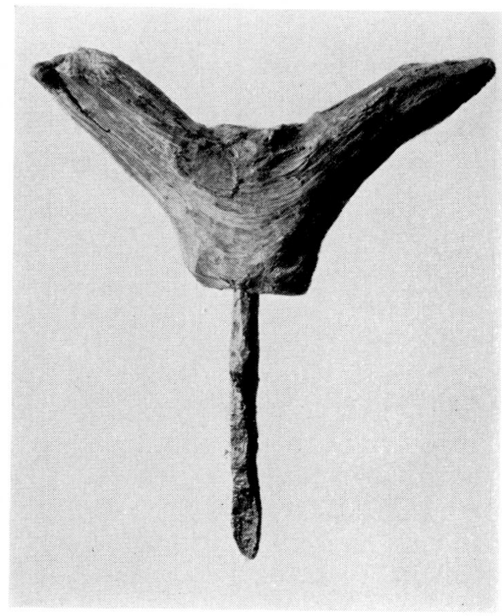

165. Handled Auger, *c.* 1320. Ragnildsholmen
Antikvitetsakademien, Stockholm

tool in the Bedford Book of Hours Noah's Ark; another hanging in the tool rack in the 13th-century joiner's shop stained-glass window in Chartres Cathedral, and many others too numerous to mention.

Kolchin (*op. cit.*) gives several examples of spoon augers in his description of the 10th–13th-century carpenters' tools from Northern Russia, where they are known as *perovidnie* (pen- or plume-shaped). Three of these are shown on the right in the diagram from his book (Fig. 166). Their diameter ranges from 14 to 26 mm. (½ in. to 1 in.), and the length

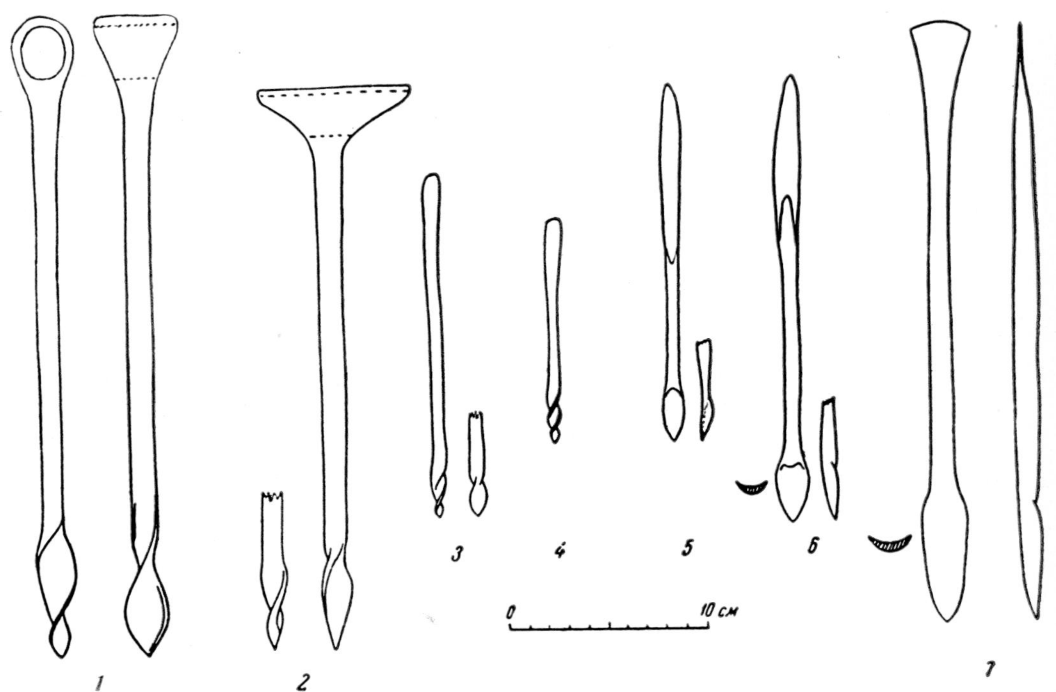

Рис. 87. Сверла по дереву
1 — 4 — спиральные, 5 — 7 — перовидные

166. 10th–13th-century Russian Augers *B. A. Kolchin*

accordingly from 7 in. to 13 in. He also describes some twist augers (*spiralnie*), and remarks that as a rule they were used for the smaller-sized holes, from ¼ in. to ¾ in. in diameter, with lengths similar to the 'pen' bits. He further states that 'all the spiral bits of the period known to him, amounting to over thirty examples, have the cutting edge on the right-hand side of the spiral, i.e., the workman turned the auger clockwise (as at the present time)'. It is also notable that two of his larger spiral augers have the shank provided with an eye to take the handle.

In the same writer's description of the medieval tools found during the 1951–56 Novgorod excavations at the Nerevski End ('Trudi Novgorodskoi Arkheologicheskoi

Ekspeditsii', Vol. II, M.I.I.A., Moscow, 1959, pp. 38 and 39) he lists twelve spoon bits with diameters ranging from $\frac{1}{4}$ in. to $\frac{11}{16}$ in., and three twist bits all about $\frac{1}{4}$ in. in diameter. Some wood details, however, preserved almost intact in the damp subsoil, particularly parts of looms and the ribs and decking of boats, had clean round holes, obviously bored with an auger, up to $1\frac{1}{8}$ in. in diameter. Metallurgical analysis of the bits showed that a strip of steel had been welded to the iron for the entire length of the spoon or spiral section, and the steel showed evidence of hardening and tempering. Several wooden handles similar in shape to that of Fig. 165 were also found, but these are being described in detail in a later volume of the reports which Kolchin has in preparation.

Although the shipwrights had already evolved their specialised breast augers by the 11th century, and later the cabinet-makers and joiners used the brace, for general building work and wheelmaking the two-handed auger continued in use right up to modern times. The Jost Ammann woodcut of 16th-century carpenters at work (Fig. 23) shows a workman drilling a deal with one in preparation for mortising, and a similar eyed shell auger leans against the sawing-horse in the foreground. The companion picture of the wheelwright shows a conical spoon auger in use for reamering out the hub of a wheel. A similar picture by the Dutch artist Jan Luyken, dated to about 1718, gives a clearer view of the process (Fig. 167). In both pictures the tool appears to be held still and the wheel pushed round by the workman's foot.

167. The Wheelwright, Jan Luyken, 1718
Author's Collection

Among the ship's carpenter's tools abandoned by the Novaya Zemlya Expedition (Eig. 168) there is a long, eyed auger and a rather shorter shell auger with the tanged shank. Moxon illustrates an 'Augre' at K in the plate of joiner's tools (Fig. 71) and

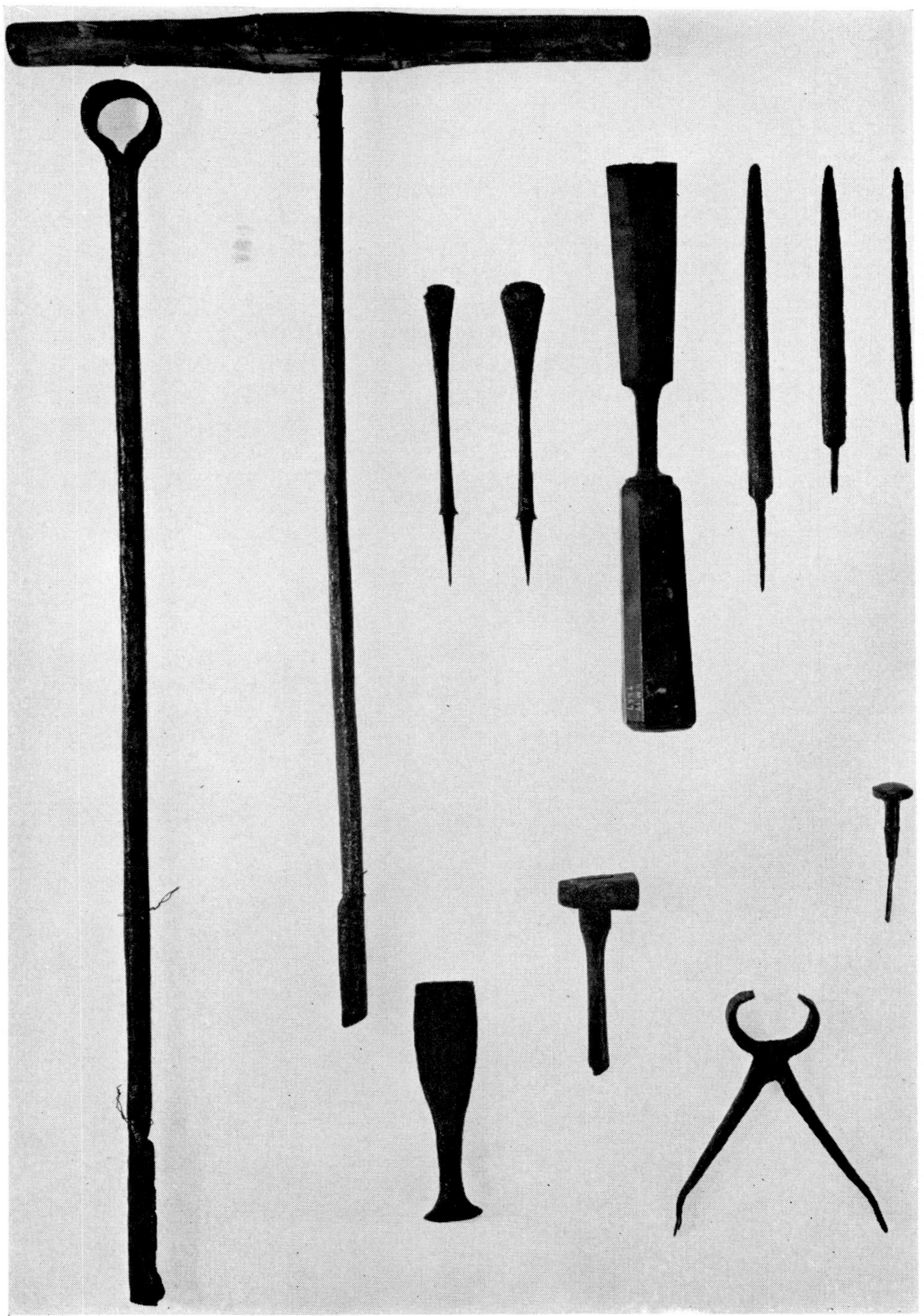

168. Ship's Carpenter's Tools, Novaya Zemlya Expedition *Rijksmuseum, Amsterdam*

remarks that it is used for boring 'Great Round Holes . . . usually with the Stuff laid low under you'.

The auger, dated 1785, from Finland (Fig. 169), has a tanged shell bit with the characteristic crooked handle which survived in the Baltic countries long after the Middle Ages. This particular example is said to have been used for boring shingles.

169. Handled Auger, dated 1785
Suomen Kansallismuseo, Helsinki

The plate of augers in Smith's 'Key' (Fig. 170) gives a wide selection of cooper's, shipwright's, and carpenter's tools, all with tangs. The screw auger No. 208 is the earliest representation known to the writer of the modern twist bit, and this particular type, with the square scribing cutters, was later known as the 'Scotch' screw auger. Mercer, in this connection, quotes on p. 200 Knight's 'American Mechanical Dictionary', which states that the spiral auger was invented by Lilley, of Connecticut, and afterwards (?) by Gurley, of Mansfield, Conn. about 1800. But the earliest U.S. patents are for Hoxie (1804), Hale (1807), and L'Hommedieu (1809). Since these augers were already being made in Sheffield in 1812, and were later known in this country as 'Scotch' augers, it seems likely that they were in use here at least as early as in the States. Ch. Holtzapfel (*op. cit.*) mentions that a Mr. Phineas Cooke was rewarded by the Society of Arts in 1771 for inventing a screw auger, but owing to manufacturing difficulties it did not become common until much later.

The 'Scotch' auger is named as such, and illustrated, at the top of the selection of augers in the Marples 1864 catalogue (Fig. 171). The other type of screw auger shown, described as 'Gedge's Pattern', has curved instead of square scribing cutters. These are more difficult to keep sharp, but less liable to break and are rather quicker in action. A brace bit of the same type is shown lower down, side by side with a 'Jennings' Pattern',

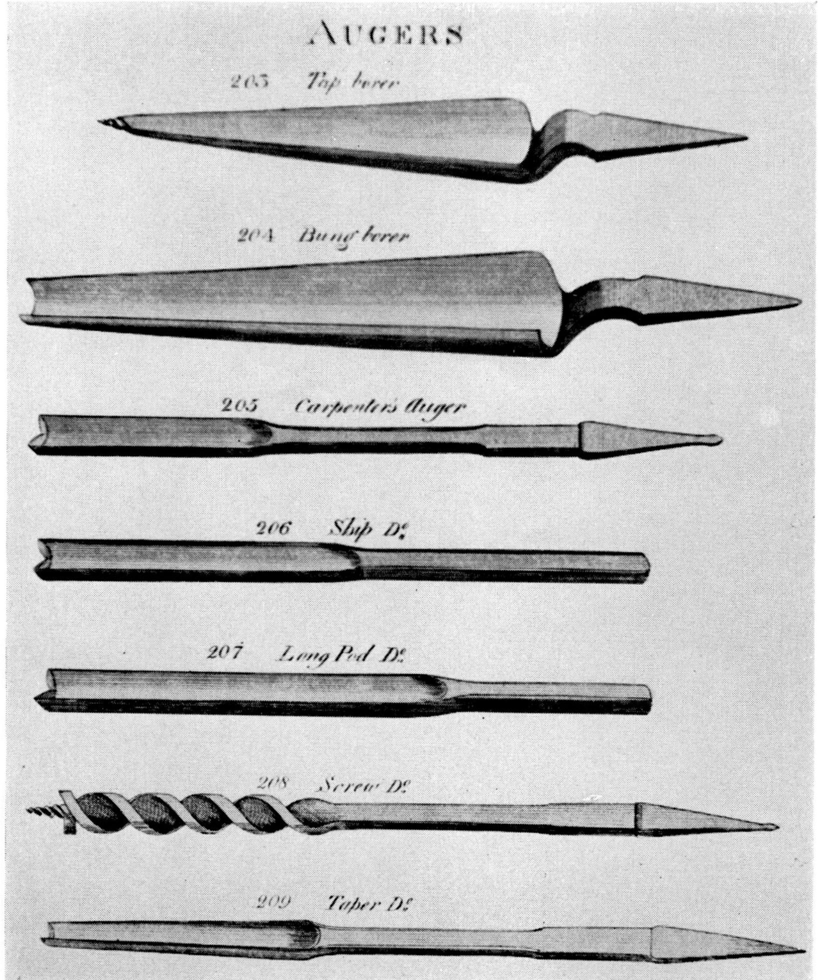

170. Augers, 1816 *Smith's 'Key'*

which is a combination of the square scribers of the 'Scotch' and the thinner spiral of 'Gedge's'. The Marples augers could be obtained either eyed or tanged, according to taste, the eyed variety being, as a rule, 25% to 50% dearer. The sizes ran in eighths from $\frac{3}{8}$ in. to 2 in., but the bright Scotch-screw eyed augers ran up to 3 in. in diameter. The lengths are not specified, except in the case of the carpenter's eyed shell augers, with a 12-in. shank. Among the other types listed occur: Dod's Pattern ship augers, ship augers, long shell, black and bright screw augers, and Gedge's Pattern bright screw augers. It will be seen that the tangs vary in shape; those for the black screw auger and the carpenter's shell auger having a shield-like extension which was bent round over the handles. Ash auger handles of various sizes are listed later in the catalogue.

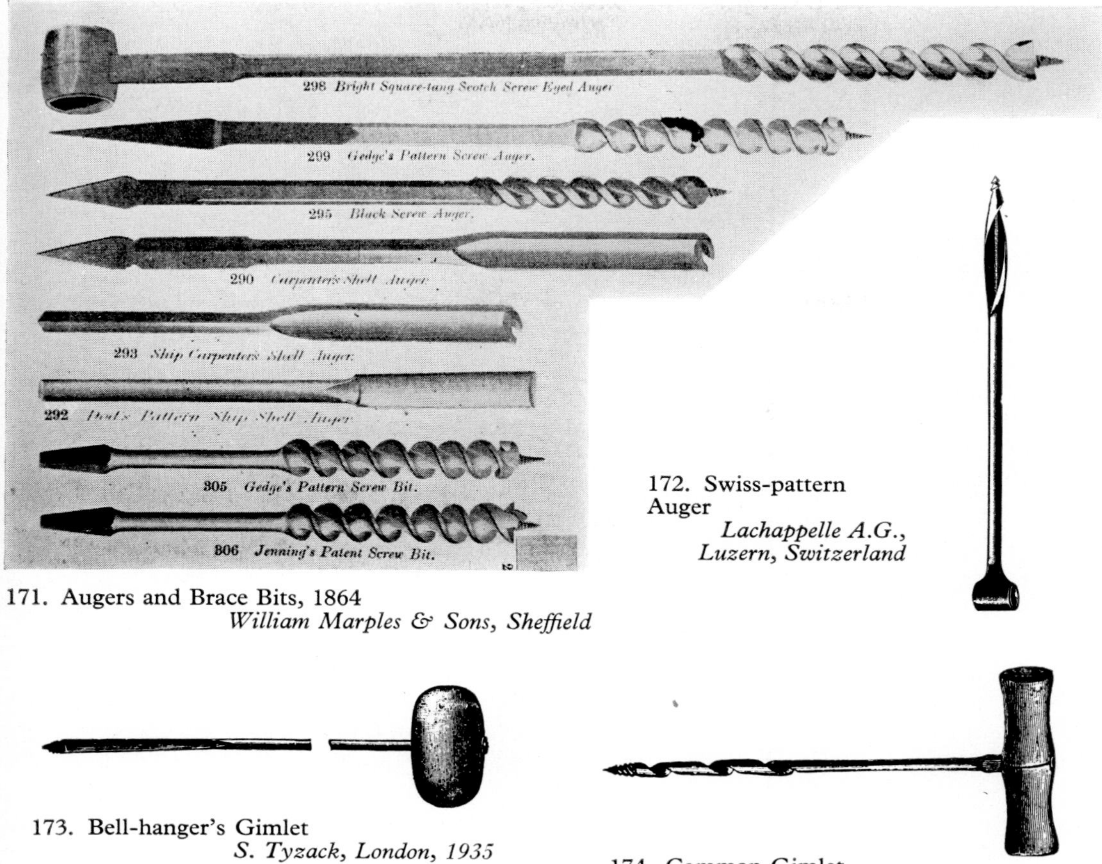

171. Augers and Brace Bits, 1864
William Marples & Sons, Sheffield

172. Swiss-pattern Auger
Lachappelle A.G., Luzern, Switzerland

173. Bell-hanger's Gimlet
S. Tyzack, London, 1935

174. Common Gimlet
S. Tyzack, London, 1935

Modern examples of augers are usually eyed, as in the tools in the 1935 Tyzack list, and similar tools are shown in Buck and Hickman (1953), while the Lachappelle catalogue (1952) shows an identical tool with a Swiss-pattern bit (Fig. 172). The modern English augers are all about 2 ft. long overall, one half of which is twist, with diameters from $\frac{3}{8}$ in. to 2 in. The Swiss tools are about the same length, but thinner, from 10 to 38 mm. ($\frac{3}{8}$ in. to $1\frac{1}{2}$ in.).

The last survivor of the auger family in common use at the present time is the gimlet. This is illustrated in Moxon with an egg-shaped handle, which has become standard in the bell-hanger's gimlet (Fig. 173). Tyzack listed these up to 30 in. long, but the Marples 1864 catalogue shows them up to 42 in., any size from $\frac{3}{16}$ in. to $\frac{3}{8}$ in., with box-wood handles. The cutter in both cases is of the shell-spike pattern, which gives a quick entry and a clean hole. The common gimlet is usually of the twist-spike type, as in Fig. 174. Heurtematte shows a similar tool, with the metal shank bent round to form the handle, something like a sardine-tin opener, under the caption *vrille*, while the

Swiss catalogues call them *perçoirs à main* or *Nagelbohrer*, with, of course, a Swiss-type bit.

3: The Breast Auger

As has already been pointed out, by the end of the 10th and the beginning of the 11th century the shipwrights had evolved a more efficient form of auger, where the power used for turning the bit was separated from the direct pressure on the tool, in this case applied to a loose nave, which was held against the chest, hence the name 'breast auger'. This not only gave the extra force needed to bore the large holes required in shipbuilding work, but made the tool handier in the somewhat cramped positions often encountered when building boats. Three of the known medieval illustrations showing this tool in use are in a shipbuilding context, and there is also the negative evidence offered by Salzman, on p. 345 of 'Building in England': '. . . although I have found the "breast-auger" in shipbuilding accounts, it does not seem to figure in ordinary building.'

The tool may first be noted (as mentioned by Mercer) in that section of the Bayeux Tapestry (*c.* 1085) showing the Duke William supervising the building of the ships for his invasion of England, but the actual details of the tool being used by the workman in the middle of the upper boat (King Penguin, No. 10, Fig. 38) are not particularly clear.

A very much finer illustration of the breast auger in use occurs in the 13th-century MS. Psalter from St. John's College, Cambridge (Fig. 175). The college librarian, Mr. F. P. White, M.A., has been good enough to supply the information that this picture is one of forty-six full-page illustrations to a psalter given to the library in 1672 by one Charles Baker. Nothing is known of its earlier history, but part of it seems to have been written between 1397 and 1400 for a member of the Holland family, probably Sir Thomas Holland, 3rd Earl of Kent. The pictures, however, are of the 13th century, and are said to be by unknown English artists.

The third example occurs in the 13th-century French 'Bible Moralisé' (MS. Bodleian 270b, fol. 9v.) showing a group building the Ark; Noah himself with a very large axe, another workman in the boat using a breast auger with a large nave, turned stock, and short handles, and a third caulking the seams with a spoon.

Another 13th-century illustration of the breast auger in use is found in 'Illustrations to the Life of St. Alban', M. R. James, Clarendon Press, Pl. 48, also reproduced on Plate 4 of Salzman's book referred to above, and attributed to Matthew Paris. It is curious that Salzman, usually such a careful writer, should have missed this, as it is contrary to his remark quoted earlier, but there is no doubt that the workman on the ladder in the top right-hand corner is boring a hole in a scaffold pole (a very naughty thing to do, by the way) with a breast auger with a conspicuously large nave and short handles.

The remaining examples of this tool known to the writer come from Scandinavia and the Baltic countries, but it is not unlikely that it was also used, at any rate by shipbuilders, in this country. The earliest of these, dated to 1662, has a slightly twisted, flat-ended bit let into a hexagonal stock which has lost its ferrule. The plain cross arm is pinned to the stock, which is provided with a roughly carved loose nave at the upper end. Other breast augers in the Nordiska Museet collections at Stockholm from the 18th century have turned stocks and nave, while one example has a shaped wooden breast-plate instead of the nave. A similar tool, but lacking the nave, dated 1716, and now in the Science Museum, was found recently in Sweden by a friend of Mr. J. F. Chalkley, who described the tool in the 'Hardware Trade Journal' of 30th November, 1951. There are other smaller breast augers in the Finnish National Museum at Helsinki, one dated 1802 (Fig. 176).

It is, however, surprising to find that the breast auger is still in use to this day in some backward districts near the Baltic Sea. In his book, previously cited, on Esthonian rural crafts, A. Viires gives several examples of this tool, and a photograph, taken by himself in 1957, of a workman using one. They are all clearly home-made tools, and obviously preferred to the plain auger for some jobs, and often handier than the equally crude wooden braces they sometimes use.

175. Noah Building the Ark, 13th–14th Century

By permission of the Master and Fellows of St. John's College, Cambridge

176. Breast Auger, dated 1802

Suomen Kansallismuseo, Helsinki

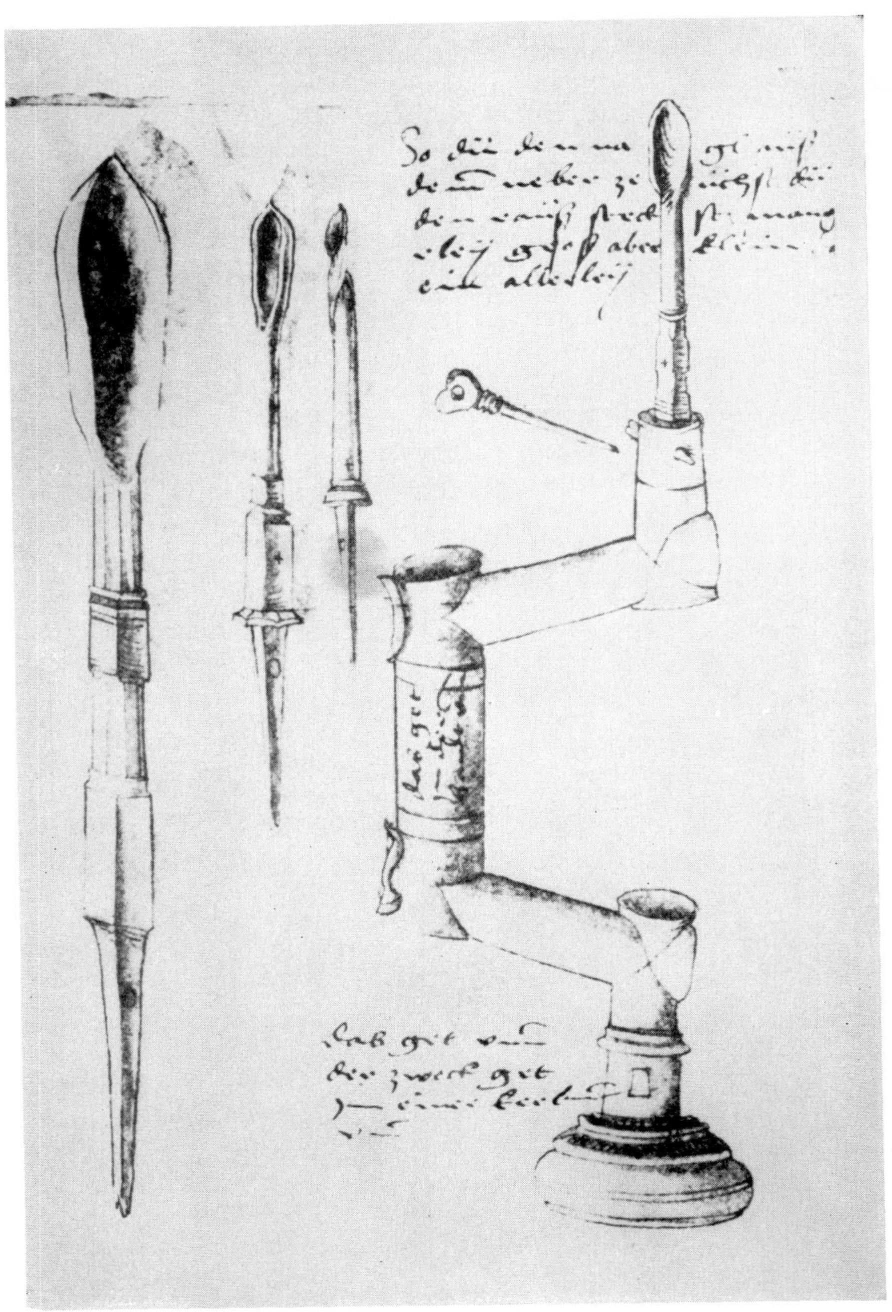

177. Brace and Bits, *c.* 1505 *Nürnberger Buchmalerei. Courtesy J. M. Greber*

4: The Brace

In spite of the modern fashion of assuming that one thing invariably develops from another, there seems to be no connection between the brace and any other form of boring tool which preceded it. It first appears in Northern Europe as a more or less fully developed tool early in the 15th century, and it has been suggested, by R. F. Chalkley and others, that it may have been brought here from the Near East by the returning Crusaders. So far, however, no evidence has been found to substantiate this theory.

The main advantage of the brace is that the turning movement imparted to the bit is continuous and positive, and not intermittent, as with the augers, or with an idle return stroke as in the various bow, pump, or strap drills. Its earliest use was as an auxiliary tool for boring a pilot hole, which was then enlarged by the more powerful auger, for dowels or trenails in building work.

The first representation so far known is the well-known panel showing St. Joseph in the Maître de Flémalle's 'Annonciation' triptych, dated 1438. The brace also appears in the early 15th-century Bedford Book of Hours Noah's Ark picture, and in the 'Livre de Rustican', a French MS. of the same period.

The metal brace shown in Fig. 177, reproduced by the courtesy of J. M. Greber, shows how far the tool had been developed by South German craftsmen by the beginning of the 16th century. The drawing also shows large and small spoon bits and a primitive twist bit, held in position by the long metal pin.

The earliest actually surviving brace is one of the relics of the ill-fated Novaya Zemlya Expedition of 1596 (Fig. 178). The stock is of wood, with a turned nave, and

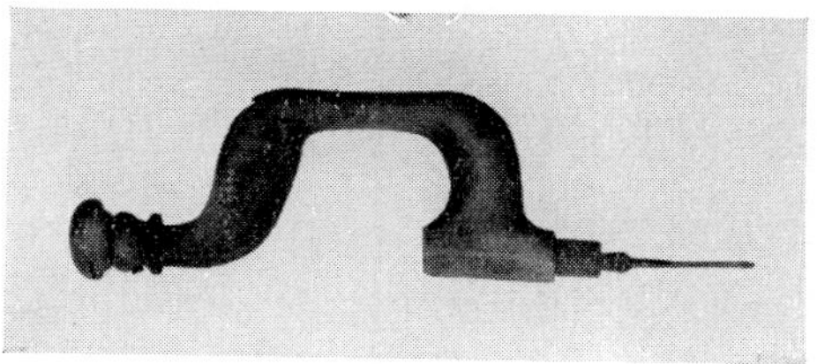

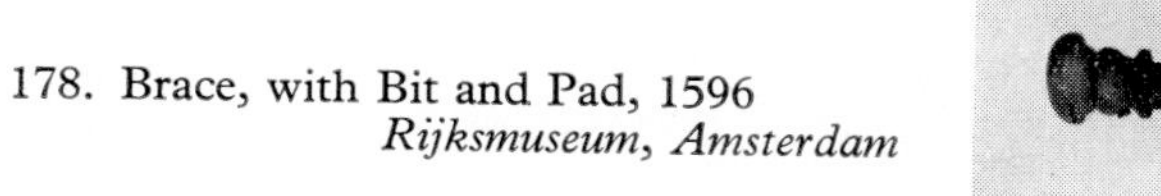

178. Brace, with Bit and Pad, 1596
Rijksmuseum, Amsterdam

the bit is held in a manner common right up to the end of the 18th century. Nearly a hundred years after the Dutch tool Moxon, describing the brace, shows a similar method. 'In the figure:* . . . a is the Head; b, the Pad; c the Stock; and d, the Bitt.' He remarks further that there are: 'Bitts of several sizes, fitted into so many Padds'. He calls the tool the 'Piercer', which is confirmation of its earlier use for drilling pilot holes. A still more advanced method of fitting the pad (with its bit) into the stock is shown in the carved wooden brace (dated 1764) from Stockholm (Fig. 179). The springed bifurcated pad held itself firmly in the square hole in the stock, and could easily be removed by pressing the two halves together with the fingers. A similar

* H, Fig. 71, p. 69.

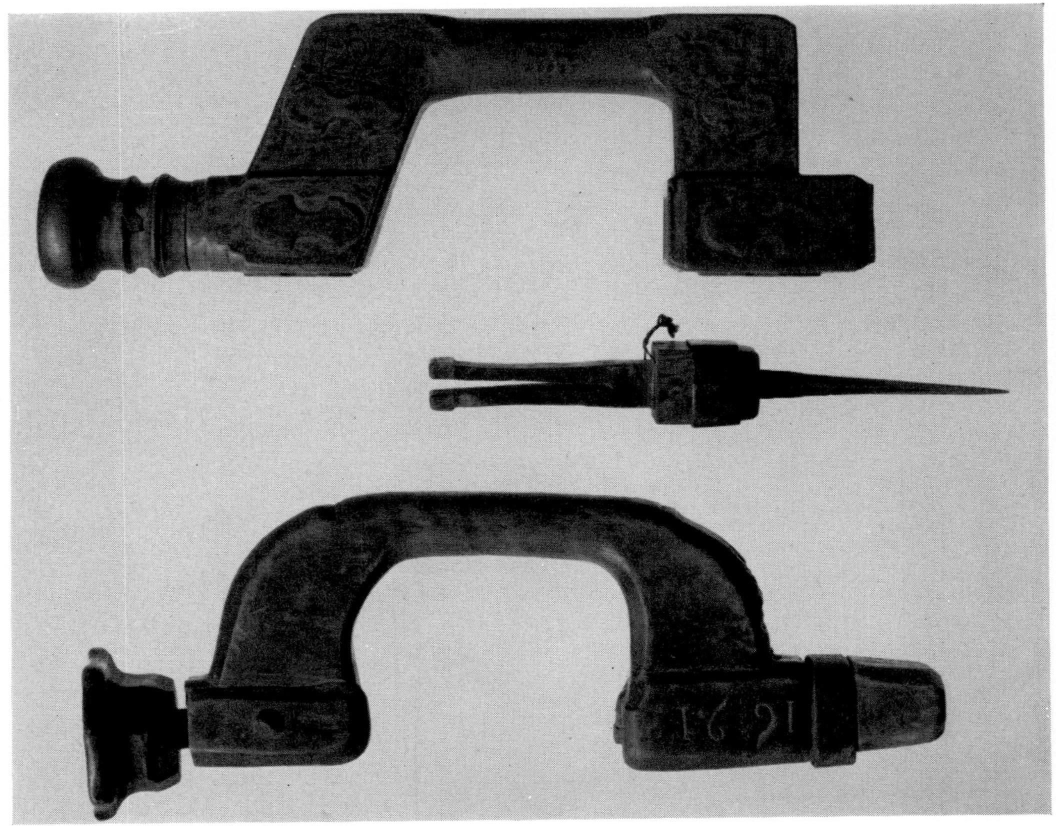

179. Braces, dated 1691 and 1764 *Nordiska Museet, Stockholm*

arrangement is shown as late as 1812 in Pl. IX of Bergeron's 'Manuel du Tourneur', but during the 18th century most of the commoner tools had square pads simply held by pressure in the square hole.

A more positive way of holding the pad with a thumbscrew is used in the wooden brace, dated to about 1800, in the Science Museum (Fig. 180). This picture also shows an early form of centre bit. Bergeron shows a similar tool on his Plate XVI, but here the pad is let into the stock directly, while the bit is held in the split section of the pad with the thumbscrew.

The braces in the middle of Plate XI by the same writer (Fig. 164) are practically identical with those in Smith's 'Key to the Manufactories of Sheffield', and that is where they probably came from originally. Fig. 6 is described in the text as: 'Vilebrequin en bois, tête en cuivre, ressort interior pour retenir et fixer les mèches par bouton B' (Wimblekin of wood, with brass head and interior spring to hold and fix the bits by button B). It will be noted that the bits shown in this picture all have a notch cut in the square, tapered shank. This was clipped into the stock, and released by pressing button B. The other iron brace (Fig. 7) has a tiny screw to hold the bit, but the corresponding figure in Smith's

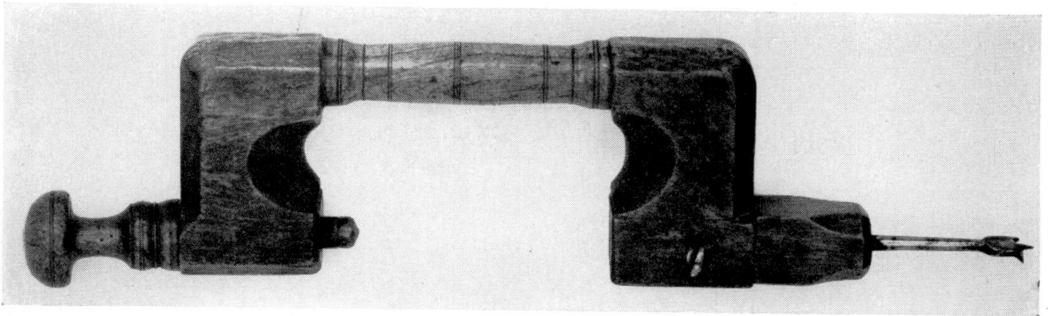

180. Brace, *c.* 1800 *Crown Copyright, Science Museum, South Kensington*

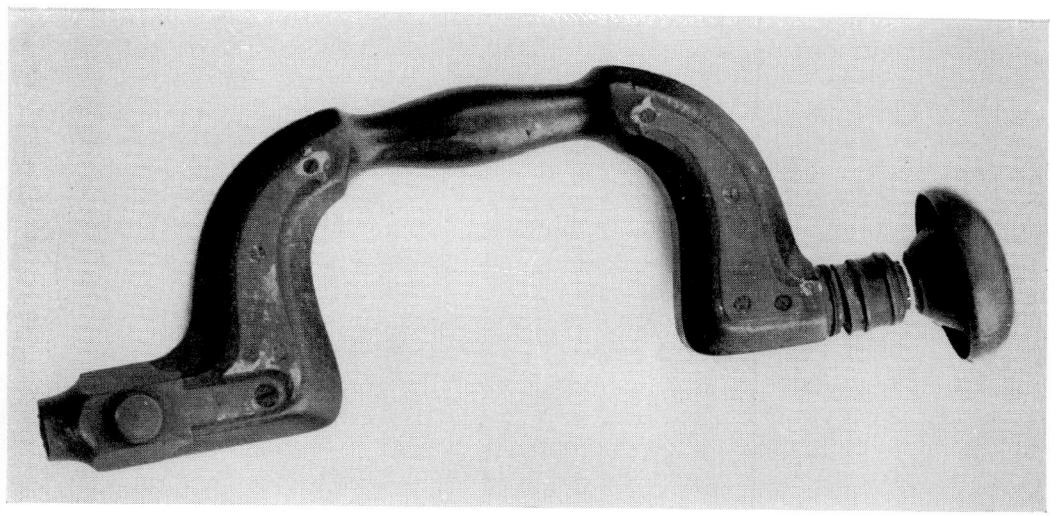

181. Beech Plated Brace *Author's Collection*

'Key' shows a proper thumbscrew, making the tool practically identical with the modern 'linesman's' brace. Referring back to the Bergeron plate, it is interesting to note that the bit shown in the middle at Fig. 23 is described as: 'Mèche à trois pointes, dites à l'anglaise' (Three-pointed, so-called 'English' bit). This shows that the bits were also imported from Sheffield, or at any rate the prototypes, as Bergeron remarked that those he shows were 'made under our own eyes'. The similar stouter and shorter bit at the far end on the right (Fig. 28) is described as a cooper's bit.

According to Mr. A. O'Connor Fenton, of William Marples & Sons, Ltd., the original patentee of the springed button chuck brace as illustrated by Bergeron was the founder of the firm, the first William Marples, but they have no information about the date of the patent. In any case, these braces were still being made without any change of shape or construction right up to the end of the 19th century; indeed, a friend of the writer in the hardware trade remembers that they were still kept in stock for the more conservative craftsmen when he started business in about 1910.

One example, in fairly good condition, is in the writer's collection (Fig. 181). It is made of beech, with brass plates to brace the stock (possibly the origin of the term 'brace'), and a head of lignum vitae. This particular tool is of interest as having been made by Robert Marples, who broke away from the family business in the sixties or seventies and set up on his own at the Hermitage Works. The head carries a brass insert with the maker's name and address surrounding the arms of the Cutler's Company of Hallamshire, with a device of four crossed arrows.

The *ne plus ultra* of the wooden brace was undoubtedly the Marples Patent Brass Framed Brace, an example of which was purchased by the writer some years ago in an antique furniture shop. It was not part of the ordinary stock in trade, but had at one time belonged to one of the workmen connected with the business. The sweep is made of two pieces of ebony, reinforced by brass plates $\frac{1}{8}$ in. thick, cast solid with the bearings for the rotating handle and the head. The rotating handle was one of the major improvements of this brace; previously they had always been made solid. The plates are stamped with nearly as many inscriptions as an iron golf club: 'Hibernia', with Marples shamrock device; 'By Her Majesty's Royal Letters Patent' in black letter; 'William Marples Sole Manufacturer of the Ultimatum Framed Brace Sheffield'; and the Royal Arms. The head carries a brass plate with the device of a harp, surrounded by the inscription: 'William Marples & Sons, Hibernia Works, Sheffield', and is further embellished by an inlaid ring of ivory. There are in addition four name stamps of the former owner, 'J. Bale'. I have never got round to putting my own name stamp on it yet; if ever I did, it would be difficult to find any room.

The method of holding the bit, which was the actual object of the patent, is very ingenious, and for a long time defeated all attempts to find out how it was done. Showing the tool to an engineer friend one day, he was at once attracted by the eccentrically placed hole in the ferrule (which I had been vainly trying to twist), which he found could be pushed across in the direction of the long axis. This ferrule is attached to a strong spring, riveted at the other end to the brass casting of the pad, and carries a pawl which engages in a triangular notch in the shank of the bit. For some time no notched bit could be found to fit, but a visit to Club Row in the East End one Sunday morning on the advice of Mr. Stevens, of the Geffrye Museum, resulted in the acquisition of two nose bits, one of which, as chance would have it, fitted the ebony brace, and the other the Robert Marples beech brace.

In the Marples tool catalogue of 1864 this ebony brace, as the masterpiece of its inventor, is given a page to itself, with a display of the complete set of bits to go with it. There seems to have been some doubt as to what to call it, as it is referred to in various places in the catalogue as the 'Patent Metallic-Framed Ebony Brace', the 'Patent Brass-Framed Brace', and the 'Ultimatum Framed Brace'. It was certainly the ultimate, in every sense, and in ebony, boxwood, or rosewood it was listed at 23s., while an identical model in beechwood was 20s. This was a very expensive tool compared to the plain wooden one at 9s., or the simple iron brace at about 1s. retail, especially when we remember that the wages of the average carpenter of the period were 37s. 8d. for a 56½-hour week (R. W. Postgate, 'The Builders' History', App. 1). Both tools could be bought complete with sets of bits, from twelve to sixty, in groups of six; the complete set with the brace costing 54s., making the bits just over 6d. each. Straw-coloured bits were dearer at about 7½d. each. Messrs. Marples state that these braces were in regular demand until the introduction of the American-type joiners' braces towards the end of the 19th century, and they discontinued listing them about 1900. The ebony-framed brace must have been used exclusively by first-class joiners and cabinet-makers in the shop, as its enormous weight, 2¾ lbs., would have made it far too heavy for a carpenter to carry about in his bag.

The final stages in the development of the brace took place across the Atlantic. According to information supplied by Mr. Fred J. Gross, Manager of the Educational Department of Stanley Tools in New Britain, Conn., kindly passed on to the writer by Harry R. Jeffrey, of Wilbraham, Mass.: 'In 1859 the Spofford split socket chuck with thumbscrew was developed and patented, but it was only popularised by the J. S. Fray Co. of Bridgeport, Conn., who purchased the patent in 1866, and produced the braces.' One of these Spofford braces (Fig. 182) was brought in to me some years ago by two

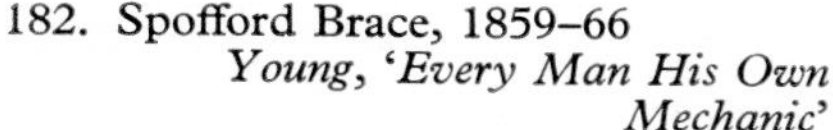

182. Spofford Brace, 1859–66
Young, 'Every Man His Own Mechanic'

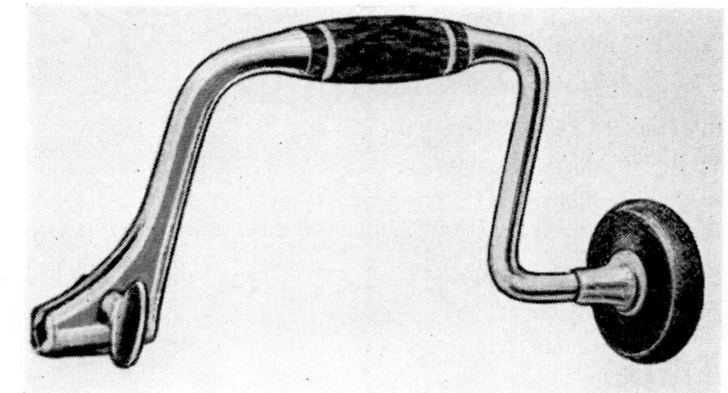

pupils who had been interested by my talks to the class about old tools. They had picked it up at a jumble sale for a few pence. It was heavily corroded, and the rosewood head had one half missing, but otherwise the tool is still quite serviceable. The chief advantage of the Spofford brace over the springed button type was that it could take any square-shanked bit, with or without a notch. The size and position of the notches on the bits varied according to different manufacturers, and were consequently not interchangeable.

To quote Mr. Gross further: 'In 1864 the first shell-type chuck with adjustable jaws was patented by Barber. Again the J. S. Fray Co. offered it shortly afterwards with interlocking jaws. We (Stanley Tools) purchased the J. S. Fray Company around 1919. The development of the ratchet-type followed right on the heels of the shell-type chuck, so it must have been soon after 1864.' The Barber braces soon ousted both the Spofford and the European wooden braces, and since the end of the 19th century have monopolised the market all over the world.

5: Miscellaneous Drills

In addition to those already mentioned, various other methods of applying the rotating motion to the bit have been in use from time immemorial. One of these is referred to in the 'Odyssey', Bk. IX, in the description of the putting out of the Cyclops' eye: 'Like a man boring a ship's timber with a drill which his mates below him twirl with a strap they hold at either end, so that it spins continuously'. This account comes down to us from the Late Bronze Age, and the episode is depicted rather crudely on a Proto-Attic amphora of the 7th century B.C. in the museum at Eleusis. A better representation of the method occurs on the tombstone of an Early Christian sculptor of sarcophagi, one Eutropus, from the cemetery of Sant' Elena, near Rome, now in the Archiepiscopal Museum at Urbino. A workman is shown guiding a drill driven by a strap worked by an assistant. Similar strap drills have been in use until quite recently in China by boat-builders and other woodworkers.

Another primitive method still in use by retarded Stone Age peoples like the Eskimos, Laplanders, and natives of New Guinea is the pump drill, of which a Scandinavian example is shown in Fig. 183, with a flywheel made of stone. A similar tool is illustrated on a plate of sculptor's tools in Diderot (1779), while an almost identical 'Drille' is shown on Bergeron's Plate IX, No. 9 (Fig. 164). This is described as being used by goldsmiths and jewellers. The flywheel here is of metal, probably brass. The 'Ironmonger' of

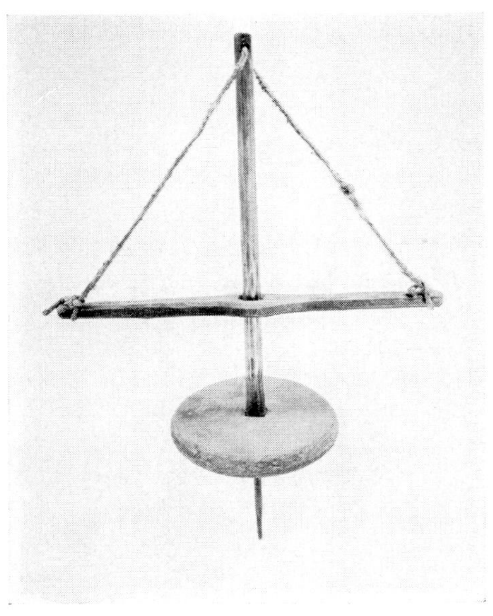

183. Pump Drill
Nordiska Museet, Stockholm

184. Archimedian Drill
S. Tyzack, London

185. 'Yankee' Reciprocating Drill
S. Tyzack, London

3rd March, 1956 gives an example from New Guinea with a wooden flywheel. Both the pump and strap drills, in common with the bow drill, had a reciprocating action, and are normally used with bits that cut either way, or more or less burn their way through.

Although its Greek name might suggest an Early Classical origin, the Archimedian drill appears to be a comparatively modern tool. It does not figure in Diderot or Bergeron, and the earliest illustration of it occurs in the Marples 1864 catalogue. It also figures in most modern catalogues (Fig. 184), the bits, up to about $\frac{1}{8}$ in. in diameter, having a cylindrical shank, held in a two-jaw collet chuck by means of a winged or knurled nut. The tool shown in Buck and Hickman 1953 is very similar, with a plastic handle and head.

Working on much the same principle, the 'Yankee' reciprocating drill (Fig. 185) is of a more robust construction, and is provided with a shell chuck. It was first introduced as a rapid-action ratchet screwdriver, but it can also be used for boring holes. It will take drills up to $\frac{3}{16}$ in. and twist bits up to $\frac{3}{8}$ in. The final stage of this method of turning the bit by means of a reciprocating action is shown in the push brace, where the spiral is enclosed and the head is pulled out and pushed back. All these drills have an idle return stroke, which gives them their inherent ratchet action, but is a disadvantage when boring holes.

The earliest illustration of the breast drill known to the writer occurs in Bergeron, *op. cit.*, Vol. II, Pl. IX, Fig. 16 (Fig. 186). Both the handle and the gears (with a ratio of 1:1)

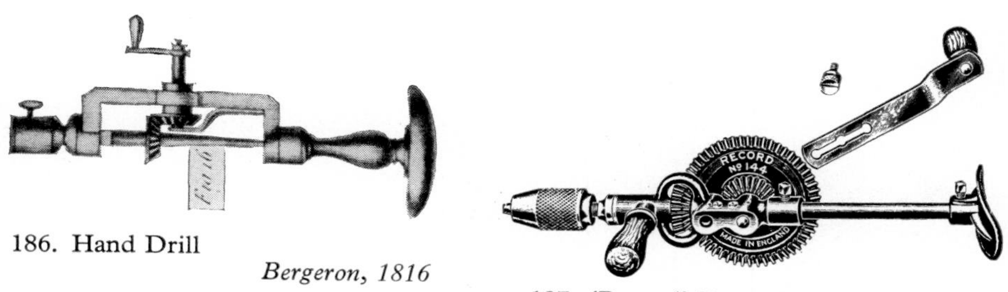

186. Hand Drill
Bergeron, 1816

187. 'Record' Breast Drill
S. Tyzack, London

are extremely small in proportion to the nave and the chuck, which is simply a hollow collar with a thumbscrew. It should be noted that there is no handle at the side for holding the tool to the work, which increases the probability that this is one of the very earliest forms of this instrument. In Holtzapfel (1846) it is called a 'French brace' so it is also likely that Bergeron's tool was actually invented by one of his compatriots possibly towards the end of the 18th century. The illustration from the 'History of the Portable Drill' in the 'Ironmonger' referred to above, shows an 'English bench gear-driven Brace (mid-19th century)', which is almost identical with Bergeron's except that the driving gear bevel is much larger, giving a ratio of about 4:1. This example also has no side handle, so it may be earlier than the date given above. The 'Improved Brace Drill' in the Marples 1864 catalogue has a much larger gear ratio and a longer handle, with a side handle in addition. The method of holding the bit in the chuck is not shown, but the thumbscrew was probably on the far side when the artist drew the picture.

The breast drill (Fig. 187) shows one pattern of the final stage of this tool's development, and will take drills up to $\frac{1}{2}$ in. in diameter. The crank handle may be extended to give extra power, and there are two gear positions for fast or slow speeds. The head has a shaped breast-plate so that the weight of the body may be applied to the tool. The chuck is of the modern, three-jaw shell type. These tools have now been almost completely superseded by portable electric drills.

Finally, if only for sentimental reasons, mention must be made of the 'Improved Boring Machine' (Fig. 188). The writer used one of these about forty years ago for boring holes for mortices for tusk-tenon joints in trimmer joists. One sat astride the platform, and the right-hand gear drove the auger bit, while the left-hand pinion engaged in the rack and provided a rather savage feed. It was a crude but very effective instrument, and one wonders how many are still in use today.

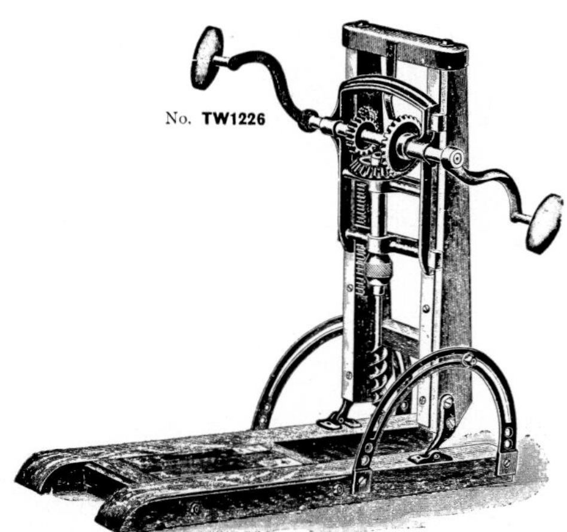

188. Boring Machine (U.S.A.)
S. Tyzack, London

SECTION V

THE CARPENTER'S BENCH

THE INTRODUCTION of the carpenter's bench may be connected with the invention of the plane in Roman times. Previously the work was done on a small horse or trestle, or on a plain block or stump. But as soon as it became necessary to lay the wood flat for truing the surface with a plane, some form of table was found essential, with some provision for fixing the workpiece. Indeed the German word for bench, *Hobelbank* (plane-bench), has preserved the usage to this day. The earliest and most primitive bench was a length of stout flat or half-round wood with two pairs of splayed legs, often left in the round, at each end. The workpiece was held by pegs driven into

189. Roman Joiner at the Bench.
House of the Vettii, Pompeii
Author's Photograph

holes in the bench-top itself, as in Fig. 189, which shows Daedalus making the wooden cow for Pasiphae, or sometimes a hold-fast or dogs were used (Fig. 54). Mr. J. Wymer has made a small bench of this type for his delightful model of a Roman carpenter's shop based on finds at Silchester and elsewhere, which forms an interesting feature of the re-arranged exhibition of Roman material at Reading Museum. According to A. Viires (*op. cit.*) the low benches used by workmen in the rural districts of Esthonia to this day are almost identical with this Roman pattern.

That the Romans sometimes had more elaborate benches than this is suggested by the discovery at Saalburg in Germany of three planks with mortices for legs and bench stops, and provision for what may have been some kind of vice. Two of the pieces are shown in Fig. 190, with a suggested reconstruction of a bench, using the third. None of

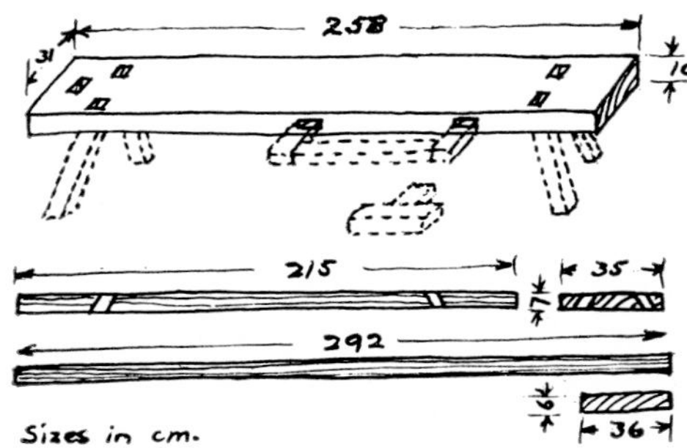

190. Reconstruction of Roman Bench
Courtesy J. M. Greber

191. Roman Last-maker working on 'Horse'
Museo di Civilta Romana, E.U.R., Rome. Author's photograph

the boards has holes for holdfasts, but the front edge of the stoutest board has two mortices which may have taken a T- or U-shaped piece, to hold the wood against the side of the bench. All this is highly conjectural, and up to the present there are no known representations of Roman benches showing this feature, but it is difficult to see why the workmen should have gone to so much trouble to cut these mortices unless it were for some such purpose as this.

The Romans also used a form of 'horse' for holding small workpieces during processing. In the Archaeological Museum at Rheims there is a relief showing a cobbler making a wooden last (Fig. 191). He is sitting astride a small bench, and the workpiece is held firmly on a sort of anvil by means of a strap passing down through the bench top, and held taut with his left foot.

Throughout the Middle Ages the more primitive type of Roman bench described above was retained with very little variation, and there are a number of drawings, MS. illuminations, and paintings showing this construction, one of the earliest being a picture in the 'Mendel'schen Stiftsbuch' (cartulary) of about 1400 at Nuremberg. The top of the bench is a simple plank, with two pairs of round, splayed legs, while the workpiece is held by pegs at one end and along one side, almost exactly as in the Pompeii fresco over 1,000 years earlier. A rather more elaborate example, with stout square legs, still with a considerable splay, is shown in a misericord of about 1495 in the Cluny Museum, Paris. The details of the underframing are not clear, but each front leg had a vertical row of holes, presumably to take a board on edge when truing to width, but there is no sign of a vice. In fact none of the joiners' benches known to the writer up to the second half of the 17th century shows any vice at all.

According to J. M. Greber, in his history of the bench ('Fachblatt für Holzarbeiten', Berlin, 1937), there is a complete project for both side and end screw vices in a book in the Nuremberg Municipal Library, designed by the engineer Löffelholz of that town in 1505. The side vice is in the usual position at the left-hand end, and was tightened up by two nuts, the screws being fixed into the side of the bench-top. The end vice has a long wooden screw, fitted with a cranked and forked bench-stop, with the wood held firmly between this and another stop let into one of a series of holes in the bench. This is a very remarkable anticipation of the modern vice, but it was not generally adopted for something like two hundred years.

Judging from the available material, the development of the ordinary bench-vice was in fact very gradual and slow. The Wierix bench of about 1600 (Fig. 68) does not show one, but there is a small toothed bench-stop at one end. The same applies to the bench in Félibien's book of 1676 (Fig. 192), which has a similar bench-stop and a row

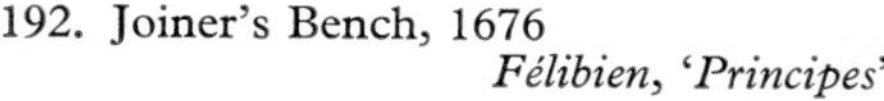

192. Joiner's Bench, 1676
Félibien, 'Principes'

of holes for the hold-fast shown, to hold the wood, while the vertical legs are here provided with holes, as in the Cluny misericord. The bench in the Stent panel (Fig. 150) is similar in construction, except for the absence of rails between the legs, and the addition of a notched piece of wood nailed to the front left-hand end of the bench-top. This was evidently intended to take the end of a board laid on its edge and supported by pegs driven into the holes in the legs. Oddly enough, a similar arrangement is shown for a temporary bench in the Russian textbook for joiners' apprentices: 'Stolyarnoe Delo', Moscow, 1958, and according to Mr. Chr. Waagepetersen, of Kalundborg Museum, the Danish carpenters often use the same device when working outside the shop.

The bench shown by Moxon (Fig. 71) is identical in construction with Félibien's, except for the addition of a double-screw vice at the right-hand end of the bench-top, and at the left-hand end a notched piece like that in the Stent panel, with what looks like the handle of a screw. The whole thing is completely out of perspective, and seems to have been fudged in after the original engraving had been cut. In the text Moxon is not much clearer than in his illustration:

> 'A. A Work-bench. b. the Hook in it, to lay Boards or other Stuff flat against, whiles they are Trying or Plaining. c. the Bench Screw (on its hither side) to Screw Boards in while the edges of them are Plaining or Shooting; and then the other edge of the Board is set upon a Pin or Pins (if the Board be so long as to reach to the other Leg) put into the holes marked a a a a a down the legs of the Bench: which Pin or Pins may be moved into higher or lower Holes, as the Breadth of the Board shall require . . .
>
> 'd. The Hold-fast, let pretty loose into round holes marked b b b b b in the Bench. Its Office is to keep the work fast upon the bench while you either saw, tennant, Mortess or sometimes Plain upon it, &c. . . .
>
> 'Sometimes a double Screw is fixed to the side of the Bench as at g: or sometimes its farther cheek is laid on Edge upon the flat of the Bench, and fastened with a Hold-fast or sometimes two on the Bench.'

It is clear that if the right-hand vice is fixed as shown, the board could not have been supported on the pins in the other leg, as it would have been in the way. Probably the second alternative Moxon mentions, using a hand-screw fixed to the top of the bench in any suitable place with hold-fasts, was the more usual arrangement.

This difficulty was eventually got over by moving the vice round the corner, leaving the front of the bench-top clear, and by providing square holes for additional bench-stops, to make a true back vice, as shown in the Arts Décoratifs carved panel (Fig. 135). In this illustration the left-hand screw vice is shown rather more clearly than in Moxon's, but the perspective is still at fault, possibly due to the fact that the panel is carved in such low relief; the screw is shown pointing upwards. Apart from this, the arrangement is very similar to that shown on two German benches, of 1764 and 1770, in Greber's articles previously referred to.

The next step in the development of the vice was to make the cheek itself movable, using either two screws, or one screw with a guide or runner at the other end, to keep the cheek parallel. The latter method is clearly shown on the bench in Peter Nicholson's 'Elements' of 1812 (Fig. 193). No back vice is fitted, and the only improvement since, as far as English benches are concerned, has been confined to turning the vice cheek from the horizontal to the vertical, with the runner or spacer working in a box along the cross-rail under the bench.

At about the same time as Nicholson, Bergeron in Paris used an elaborate form of bench with a vertical vice cheek and back vice (Fig. 194). He describes this in the text as an 'étable de menuisier à l'allemande' (German joiner's bench). An almost identical bench without the back vice is given by Greber as dating from 1877, but he calls it a 'French' bench. In the modern catalogue of Féron et Cie, Paris, the Bergeron bench is still known substantially as it was a hundred and fifty years ago. Here the back vice is called a *presse parisienne*. It is curious that the French writer calls it a 'German' bench, while the German says it is French. Greber confuses the issue a little by giving the bench from Holtzapfel's book of 1846, with the back vice, and calling it English. It is certain, however, that benches with an end vice are very rare in English workshops, and in our catalogues they are usually, and correctly, called 'continental' benches.

Fig. 195 is taken from the 1952 catalogue of the Lucerne firm of Lachapelle A.G. The left-hand front vice still survives with the horizontal cheek, and the Swiss call this a *presse française*, while the end vice is known simply as a *presse de derrière*. One may wonder why the tremendous convenience of this device for fixing the workpiece for planing or other processing never seems to have been fully accepted in this country.

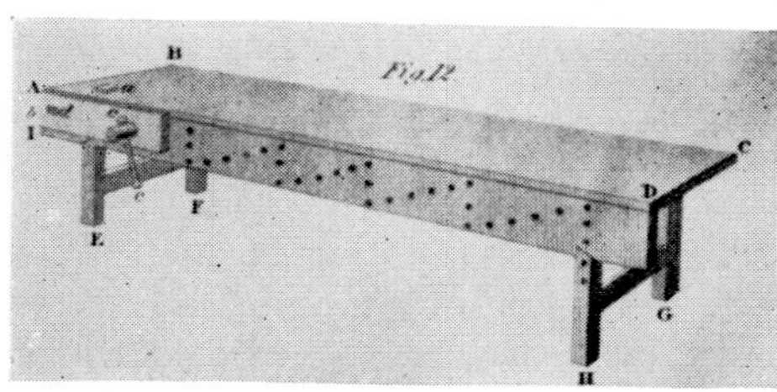

193. English Bench, 1812
Peter Nicholson, 'Elements'

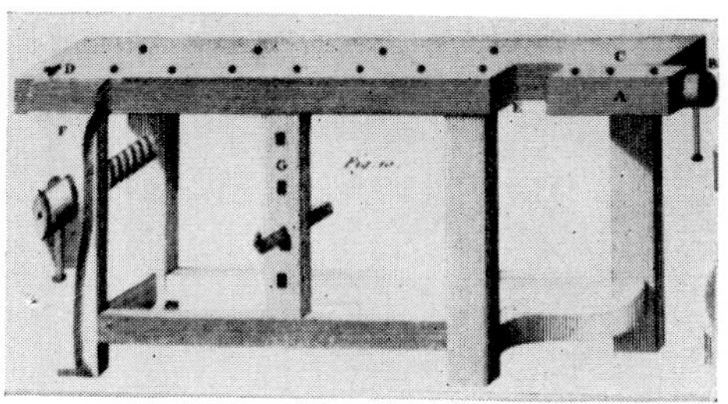

194. German Bench, 1816
Bergeron, 'Manuel du Tourneur'

195. 'Record' Joiner's Bench, 1952
Lachappelle A.G., Luzern

SECTION VI

THE RULE

1: Egyptian and Roman

THE STANDARD Egyptian measurement of length was the 'Royal' or 'Memphis' cubit, about 20·7 in. or 52·8 cm. long. This was divided into two halves, and also into seven palms, 2·95 in. long, some or all of the palms being further divided into four digits. The commonest type of Egyptian rule, used by masons, carpenters, and other craftsmen, was one cubit long, divided as described, with the two left-hand palms subdivided into digits, but a few two-cubit rules have also survived. It usually consisted of a strip of wood, about 2 in. by 1 in. in section, with one edge bevelled at about 45 degrees to about half the thickness, the graduations being scribed across the face and bevel, and down the front edge. A curious feature of some Egyptian rules is the way smaller units were obtained. Instead of repeated subdivisions, into halves, quarters, and so on, the digits were divided separately into smaller and smaller units; for example, one wooden cubit rule in the British Museum from Abydos, dated to about 1250 B.C., has one palm divided into four digits, each digit in turn subdivided into 2, 3, 4, and 5 parts. On a similar rule of 2600 B.C. in the Science Museum the digits are subdivided in this manner from the right-hand end into 2, 3, 4, and so on parts, up to 10. Normally there are no figures or other markings, but a fragment of a slate rule from Abydos in the British Museum, also dated to 1250 B.C., has the last three digits subdivided into 12, 13, and 14 parts, with the number of parts indicated by numerals.

The Roman rule (*regula*) was also a plain strip of wood (our printers' 'reglet' is a modern use of the same word). The practical Roman foot, or *pes monetalis*, was about 29·5 cm. or 11·61 in. long, and usually divided into four 'palmi', 2·94 in. long, or slightly smaller than the Egyptian palm. The palma was further subdivided into either three unciae, or twelfths, the origin of our word 'inch', or four digiti, or finger widths. Apparently the Romans guessed anything smaller than the digita. In Cyrenaica, Germany, and Gaul a longer foot, measuring respectively 30·8, 33·2, and 32·4 cm. was also used.

The funerary reliefs of Roman woodworking craftsmen give great prominence to measuring tools such as rules, squares, levels, dividers, and so on, an indication of the Roman flair for the essential. The difficulty with the rules shown in these sculptures, however, is that where the markings are still visible, the methods of graduation vary. The commonest appears to be the simplest: the foot is divided into four palmi, one or more of which being subdivided into four digiti, the palmi being sometimes indicated by a cross or circle over the mark (like the Egyptian rules, there are no numbers at all).

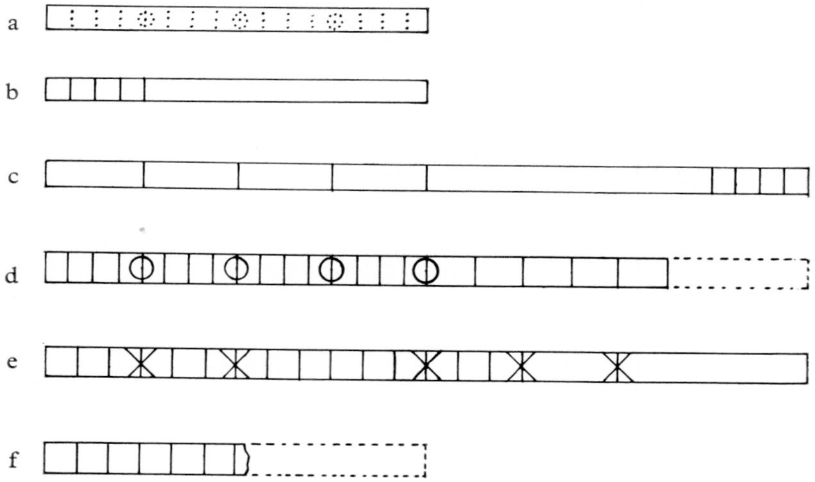

196. Roman Rules on Funerary Reliefs: (*a*) Museo Capitolini, Rome; (*b*) Uffizi, Florence; (*c*) Capitolini, Rome; (*d*) Ostia Antica; (*e*) Aquileia; (*f*) Bordeaux

Fig. 196 shows a selection of rules on funerary reliefs, all except (*d*) from casts in the Museum of Roman Civilisation at the Universal Exposition just outside Rome; (*d*) was measured on the site at Ostia Antica. The first example is a foot rule divided into palmi and digiti, the graduations being indicated by a row of three dots, with the palmi picked out by a circle of dots round the line. The monument is to one T. Statilio Apro, a *mensor aedificorum* or builder, and also shows other instruments of his profession: a cane, a measuring rod, and a writing tablet. The second is that of a woodworker P. Ferrarius Hermes, and shows a foot rule with only one palma indicated, subdivided into digiti. Other tools on this relief include an axe-adze, a square, a plumb-bob, and a chalk-line on a winder. The third is not so easy to decipher, as some of the graduations are rather vague, but the scheme seems to represent a 2-ft. rule, with 1 ft. divided into four palmi and the other having only one palma at one end divided into digiti, as in the previous example. This relief also shows a level, plumb-bob, dividers, and a square. The rule shown at (*d*) from Ostia is also not easy to interpret. It appears to be a 2-ft. rule, with 1 ft. divided into four palmi and sixteen digiti, the palmi being marked by scribed circles over the line. To the right of this there are five divisions, each exactly two digiti long. It may be that the complete rule had eight of these divisions, but one end was cut off to accommodate the handle of an axe-adze which forms the central feature of the relief. Other objects shown include a pair of dividers and two oars or sweeps for a boat. The relief was a memorial to a young man who died at the age of eighteen years eleven months, and the lettering is of the second century A.D., but there is nothing on the inscription to indicate his trade. As Ostia was at this time the port of Rome, he may have been a boat-builder or repairer. The two remaining examples use the uncia, or twelfth. The rule shown at (*e*) is 2 ft. long, with the left-hand end divided into unciae, but only two of the palma divisions are marked with a cross. The other half also has the same palma divisions, but only the first one is subdivided into unciae. The memorial was to a *faber carpentarius*, or coachbuilder, and the relief also shows an eight-spoked wheel and a pair of dividers. The last example is from the well-known relief of the bearded carpenter of Bordeaux, illustrated in Olwen Brogan's 'Roman Gaul'. He holds an adze in one hand and a rule in the other, just over half of which is visible; it shows six divisions, evidently unciae. There are several other reliefs showing these plain strip rules, but the graduations have been worn away by time and exposure, and consequently the method of marking cannot be deciphered.

Besides this graduated straight-edge type of rule, the Romans also used folding rules of bronze, made in two parts, hinged in the middle, and provided with a clip which locks on two studs when the rule is extended. They are usually 1 ft. long overall, and divided into sixteen digiti on the wide outside face, the inside wide face into four palmi, and one edge into twelve unciae, thus making the best of both worlds. There is a particularly fine example in the London Museum at Kensington Palace, and others at the National Museum of Wales, at Cardiff (Fig. 197), Lyons, Zürich, and at Naples. In this last museum, and

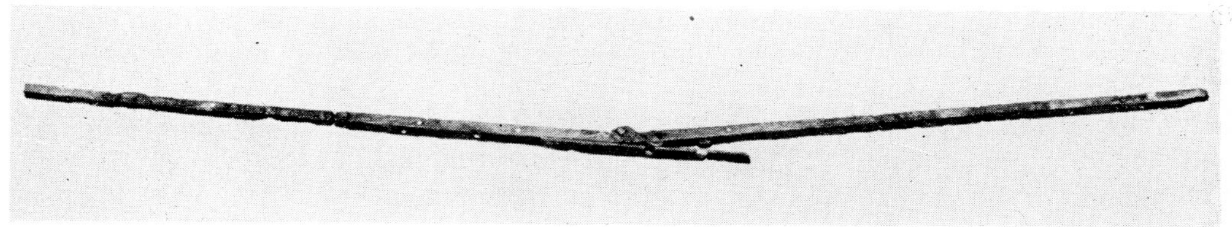

197. Bronze Folding Rule from Caerleon *By permission of the National Museum of Wales, Cardiff*

also in the Antiquarium at Pompeii, there are two folding rules of the same general form, but only 6 in. long when extended. It is curious that although these folding rules appear to have been in fairly common use all over the Empire, and are all practically identical, they have never been found on the funerary reliefs, as far as is known. It is also curious that, as remarked above, they normally show both the uncia and the digita method of subdivision, whereas the plain strip rules always stick to one or the other. This may indicate that they were pocket instruments used by officials of some kind, and not the ordinary rules used by the woodworkers in the workshop. Another point is that they would be rather expensive, and beyond the pockets of the ordinary craftsman.

2: Medieval to Modern Times

There is remarkably little evidence of the rules used for measuring purposes in the Middle Ages and during the Renaissance. Most of the references to 'rewles' for masons and other workmen in Salzman (*op. cit.*, p. 339) are to tools we would now call straight-edges. They were usually made from well-seasoned oak from casks or barrels bought for the purpose. The straight-edge shown in the foreground of Dürer's 'Melancholia' engraving is a tool of this type. A graduated strip very similar to the Roman rules described previously is shown hanging up in the background of the portrait of an architect by Tom Ring the Elder in the Kaiser Freidrich Museum in Berlin. It consists of a plain piece of wood with a hole at one end for hanging up, divided rather curiously into thirty-five parts by lines drawn across the width. There are seven groups of five spaces each, every fifth mark having a circle inscribed over it, with a matching semi-circle at each end. The artist was born in Münster in 1496, and died about 1547, so this rule could be dated about 1525. Another graduated stick reminiscent of the Roman rule shown at (*e*) in Fig. 197 is shown on a picture of the Madonna with Jesus and Saints, by Andrea Mainardi (1550–1613) in the Museo Civile, Cremona. Just over half of the complete rule is visible, showing thirteen divisions, the sixth and twelfth from the right marked by crossed lines. This was evidently a 2-ft. rule graduated in inches.

The 'Childhood of Jesus' engravings by Hieronymus Wierix (*c.* 1600) show two rules, that on the frontispiece (Fig. 68) being a straight stick about 3 ft. long divided into eight parts. A similar rule is shown in the picture entitled 'Les tronçons', showing St. Joseph and the Holy Child cross-cutting a log. One of the assistant angels is holding a rule with seven large graduations visible, that at the end, partly concealed by her hand, is further subdivided into eight or ten parts. A rule similar to this, consisting of a plain stick graduated into eight parts, occurs among the wooden models of tools used during the initiation of new members to the journeyman joiners' guild of Enköping, in Sweden, now in the Nordiska Museet, Stockholm, Judging from the appearance of the remaining tools, which include try- and smooth-planes, squares, chisel, and hatchet, they date from the middle of the 18th century. Another similar example is shown on the carved wooden 'Du Buf' cartouche in the Pinto Collection of Wooden Bygones at Northwood, Middlesex. The remaining tools appear to be coopers', and this enigmatic object may also have been connected with a guild.

Although the inventory of Thomas ffowler (see p. 128) in the Guildhall Records Office lists both 'rules' and 'joynt rules', there is no mention of folding rules in Moxon (1683). He illustrates a plain foot rule in the plate showing carpenters' tools, graduated into inches and quarters, the inches being numbered up to twelve. This is the earliest known instance of numbers applied to the divisions of a rule. Discussing this Plate 5, Moxon remarks: 'The use of the Rule is to measure Feet, Inches, and parts of Inches, which for that purpose are marked upon the flat and smooth sides. Numbered with Inches, and every Inch divided into two halfs and every half into two quarters, and every quarter into two half quarters, so that every Inch is divided into eight equal parts . . .

Commonly in all 24 inches; which is a Two-Foot rule.' This seems to indicate that, as shown on his plate, the ordinary rules were graduated into quarters, but about this time they were beginning to mark eighths as well. This explains his curious manner of describing fractions as parts of quarters; the rules were so divided, and anything less had to be estimated. For instance, in describing the width of the iron for a grooving plane he states that they range from 'a half-quarter of an Inch to an Inch and a half'. Again: the 'Tennant Saw Kerf is seldom above half a half-quarter of an Inch wide', a very roundabout way of saying a sixteenth.

An early representation of a graduated folding rule occurs in a group of joiners' tools on one of the Workum painted guild biers, now in the Openluchtmuseum at Arnhem, figured on p. 105 of Sacheverell Sitwell's 'The Netherlands'. The drawing is very rough, but the tool looks like a 2-ft. folding rule, with the knuckle hinge at the left-hand end. There are twelve divisions right across both faces, but only one edge is sub-divided into quarters. These painted biers, used at the funerals of members of the guild, date from about 1740.

The trade card of John Brailsford, Cutler, in the Broad part of St. Martin's Court, Leicester Fields, illustrated in Sir Ambrose Heal's 'London Tradesmen's Cards of the XVIIIth Century' (Batsford), shows a folding rule of a very modern type. The joint is shown very clearly, but the graduations are naturally very sketchy on a drawing as small as this; all one can be sure of is that there are twelve divisions, apparently sub-divided into halves. This tradesman is listed in the companion book 'Signboards of Old London Shops' under the heading 'Fishing Tackle Makers', at the sign of the 'FISH AND CASE OF KNIVES' at the same address, the date being given as 1769.

A group of folding rules in ivory and brass in the Musée des Arts Décoratifs in the Louvre, Paris (Fig. 198) offers many points of interest. The four-fold rule on the right,

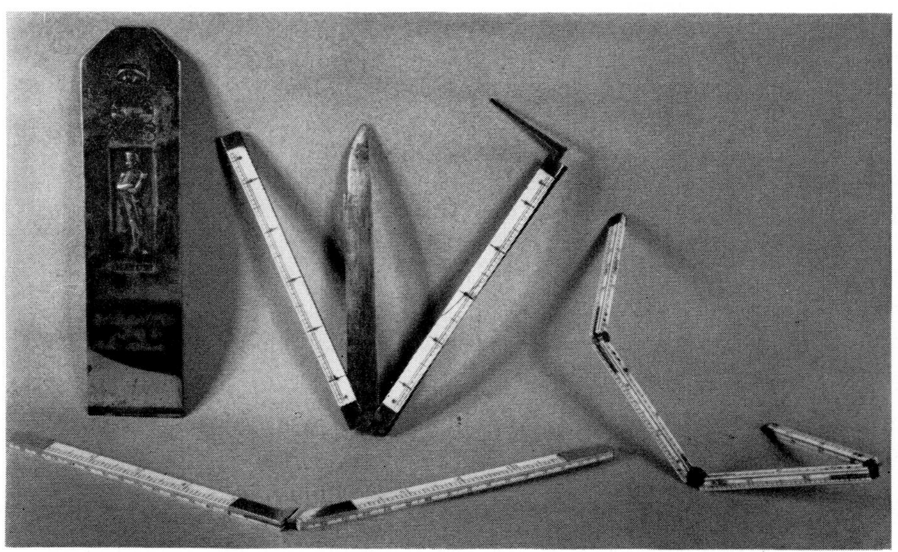

198. Folding Rules in Ivory *Musée des Arts Decoratifs, Paris*

one *pied* (or French foot) long, 12·789 in., is graduated in four different ways. The four faces are inscribed: PARIS–HAMBURG–BURGOS–LONDON; this suggests that the rule was English, a French maker would have used the spellings 'Londres–Hambourg'. Two of these names of cities are visible on the photograph: the PARIS face, on the outside, is divided into 12 *pouces*, each of 12 *lignes*. The inside edge, marked LONDON, is graduated up to 12 in., subdivided into eighths. The markings on the inside face stop at 12, approximately coinciding with the English 11 in. Each of these divisions are divided into twelve parts. This must be the Spanish 'pie', equivalent to 0·9146 ft. or 10·96 in., the subdivisions being *pulgadas* and *líneas*. The German measurements are not visible. This rule was given to the museum by M. le Comte de Montesquiou-Fezensac, who is described in Larousse as '(l'abbé François de —), homme politique français, né à Marsan (Gers) (1756–1832).

The reason why the names of cities are given on this rule, and not those of the respective countries: France, Germany, Spain, and England, may seem obscure to us in these days of standardisation, but the fact was that up to the end of the 18th century every large town in Europe had a different standard foot. In the 'Lexicon Technicum' of John Harris, London, 1714, a list is given of foreign measures, with the equivalents in English feet. The list includes five cities in the Netherlands, three in France, two in Belgium, four in Germany, six in Italy, and others in the Baltic States and Scandinavia. Neither Hamburg nor Burgos are cited in this list, the nearest being Bremen, 0·946 ft., or Dantzick, 0·944 ft., and Toledo, 0·899 ft. The adoption of the metric system on the Continent in the 19th century put an end to this confusion, which must have been a great nuisance to merchants and traders.

Returning to Fig. 198, the folding knife-case rule in the centre, which when extended gives a *pied du Roi* graduated in 12 *pouces* and 12 *lignes*, and is without numbers, is very similar to the *pied pour Bourrelier* (harness-maker) of Diderot. According to the museum authorities, it dates from before 1812.

The rule at bottom left of the photograph is of similar date. It is a two-fold foot rule in ivory and copper gilt, divided into 12 *pouces* and 12 *lignes*, numbered on the principal face, with centimetres and millimetres on the edge (1 *pied* is equal to 0·325 m.). According to Larousse, the metric system became legal in France by the decree of 2nd November, 1801, and finally obligatory after 1st January, 1840. M. Bale, of the Musée des Arts Décoratifs, has kindly offered the information that in 1812, in order to make the two systems (the old *pied* and the new *metre*) easier to adopt, the length of the foot was altered to make it exactly equal to one quarter of a metre, instead of the former 0·325 m. This 'metric foot' survived until 1837. For this reason the two previous rules can be ascribed to before 1812, and the one with the metric graduations to between 1801 and 1812.

It is curious, however, that a little book picked up on one of the second-hand bookstalls along the Seine near Notre Dame some years ago, entitled 'Nouveau Petit Manuel des Poids et Mesures', by M. Tarbe, dated 1840, makes no mention of this 'metric foot'. It describes the advantages of the new system, and gives conversion tables for each unit. It is clear that the adoption of the new system was by no means universal even at that date.

It is even more curious that the inserted price list of tools, dated 1st July, 1873, in a copy of William Marples & Sons 1864 catalogue, gives a conversion table from French to English measurements of length, from *lignes* to inches! This means that thirty-odd years after the official adoption of the metric system in France it was still necessary to use the old units. There is, in fact, no mention of the metric system at all.

Mercer suggests that the mass production of the modern boxwood brass-plated rules dates from about 1840, and his estimate is probably as good as anybody's. In any case, the rules shown in the Marples catalogue referred to above, in colours with the brass parts shown in gold, are to all intents and purposes identical with those obtainable in the toolshops today. These are all graduated in sixteenths, so that this innovation may have come about at this time.

SECTION VII

CHISELS AND GOUGES

THE CHISEL as a specialised woodworking tool goes right back to the Stone Age, and many examples of comparatively long, narrow pieces of flint or hard stone with one end carefully ground to a sharp edge have been found in Neolithic settlements. The earliest metal tools of copper and bronze had a similar general form, and were used without handles, but later, when the technique of casting socketed weapons and tools had been mastered, these methods were applied to chisels and gouges.

Among the hoards of Bronze Age tools and weapons found in various parts of South Wales many examples of both tanged and socketed chisels occur. In the same group as the bronze saw from Monkton (Fig. 116) there was a plain chisel, about 4 in. long, with a pointed tang without stop and an expanded edge $\frac{5}{8}$ in. wide. Another group of bronze socketed chisels were found near Cardiff about 3 ft. below the level of the turf (Fig. 199). The widest (not shown in the figure) has had the socket damaged, but the others show a small collar between the socket and the blade and two rivet holes near the top. No. 3 has a plain socket, but Nos. 1 and 2 have another narrow collar round the rim. The length of these tools overall is about 60 mm. and the width of the blade varies from 69 mm. to 37 mm. The small collar at the base of the socket in these chisels is unusual, and most chisels and gouges of this type, whether found in Siberia or in South Wales, have plain tapered sockets with the rounded collar on the rim.

The Egyptians used both solid and handled tanged chisels of copper and bronze,

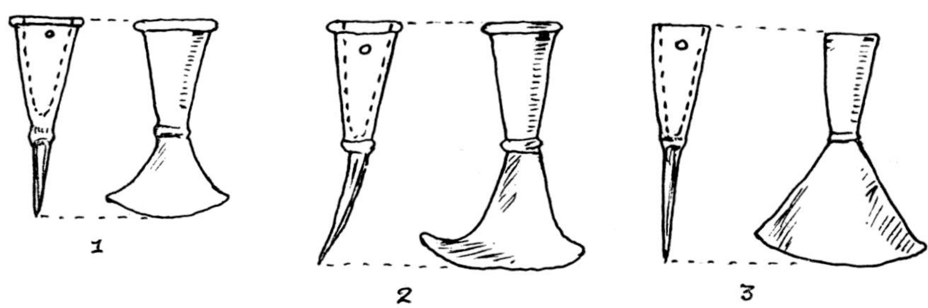

199. Socketed Bronze Chisels, Cardiff *National Museum of Wales*

and carpenters using these tools to cut mortices, with a round wooden mallet to drive the chisel, are shown on the Saqqara reliefs of 2540 B.C. and in the well-known model of the workshop of the XIIth Dynasty, about 2000 B.C.

The Early Iron Age gouges and chisels, being forged instead of cast, were usually rather cruder than their bronze predecessors, and in most cases have not survived so well. An iron gouge, however, with a socket formed by bending over two flanges, as in the Early Iron Age axes and adzes, complete with a turned oak handle, was found in the Glastonbury Lake Village. This dates to about 200 B.C., and the handle is 27·3 cm. long, with maximum diameter 3·5 cm., while the gouge itself is 11·1 cm. long, with a cutting edge 4 cm. wide, curved to a segment of a circle 5⅛ in. in diameter.

The Romans used both tanged and socketed chisels and gouges, and there are dozens of examples of both types in the collections at Shrewsbury, Reading, London, Saint-Germain, and in Italy, many of them badly rusted and battered, but in most respects almost identical with those in use today. The Silchester Collection at Reading includes a series of socketed mortice chisels ranging in width from ¼ in. to ¾ in., a solid chisel something like a modern plugging chisel, and socketed gouges of various shapes and sizes. Some of these are shown in Fig. 200. The carpenter in the Pompeii fresco (Fig. 189) is using a tanged mortice chisel with a long wooden handle. The blade of the chisel appears to be slightly curved, but this was probably not intentional, while the curiously small, diabolo-shaped mallet seems rather light for the job. There is a similar workman on the Vatican gold-glass vessel of the shipwrights at work, but here the chisel is more like a modern firmer, with a short blade and long stem. On the funerary relief of the Roman coiners in the British Museum (Fig. 161), at the bottom of the right-hand pilaster below the adze-hammer, there is a wide tanged blade very similar in shape to a socketed iron chisel from the Poultry in the London Museum, illustrated at Fig. 18 in 'London in

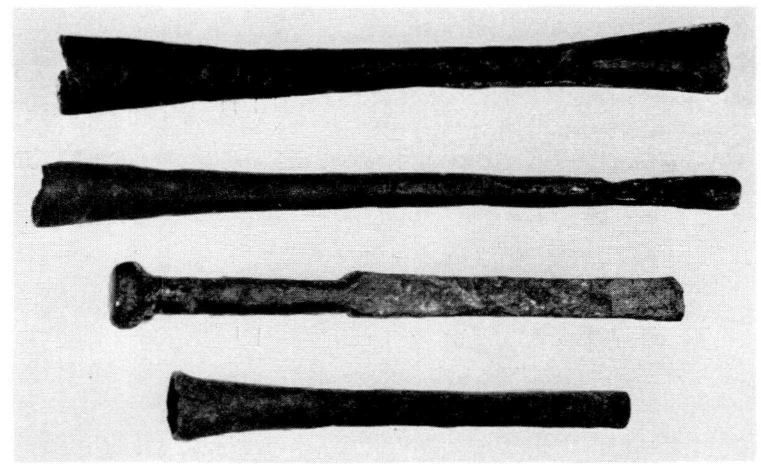

200. Roman Iron Chisels and Gouges *Photo. Reading Museum From H.G. the Duke of Wellington's Collection*

Roman Times', and to others found at Newstead in Scotland. It has the same hollow-sided blade, but if it is intended to represent a chisel, it is difficult to understand why it is shown without a handle, although at the same time the adze above it has only a very short shaft.

B. A. Kolchin's discussion of the chisels of the 10th–13th century in 'Blacksmith's Work in Pre-Mongol Russia' is confined to solid and socketed mortice chisels, known as *doloti*, very similar to the Roman tools described above. He mentions the wider *stameska*, or paring chisel, but does not illustrate any. The solid chisels were forged from a rectangular iron bar, with a strip of steel welded to the end of the blade to form the cutting edge. These were the most common type found; the blades were usually narrow, from 9 to 16 mm. wide, and ground to a bevel of about 25 degrees. The socketed chisels, which were somewhat rarer, had either a round socket welded to the steel blade or a square one forged directly from the shank of the tool, which was of iron with a steel strip at the cutting edge. These were presumably fitted with stout wooden handles, but none of these have survived.

Coming to the tools used by the medieval craftsmen in the West, most of the illustrations of the period show chisels with short turned handles and the cutting edge expanded to about twice the width of the stem, a shouldered tang, and no ferrule, similar to the two small chisels in Fig. 168. On the other hand, the Bedford Book of Hours Noah's Ark scene (15th century), and the Bourdichon Holy Family group (1510) have splayed chisels with distinct ferrules, while the latter picture also shows two wide paring chisels with parallel, shouldered blades. But in spite of this, ferrules on the handles appear to be uncommon, and the majority of the tools, whether parallel or splayed, have plain square or octagonal handles, as in the Wierix title-page (Fig. 68) and the large bevelled-edge chisel in the Novaya Zemlya group (Fig. 168).

Both straight and splayed types are illustrated in Félibien, the parallel-bladed tool being known as the *ciseau* and the splayed blade as the *fermoir*. Moxon copies the latter under the name of 'Formers', and states they are used with the mallet. The *ciseau de lumière* he calls the 'Paring Chissell', which 'has a very fine edge, and is used without a mallet, the blade being held with the fingers and pressing the shoulder against the handle'. In accounting for the term 'Former' Moxon introduces a typical piece of folk-etymology. He says: 'they are so called because they are used before Paring Chissells, as in the Fore-plaine'. It may be, however, that the original French word *fermoir* has something to do with the *ferme* or roof-truss. The modern term 'firmer chisel' tends to cloud the issue still further. Moxon calls Félibien's *fermoir à nez rond* (fourth from the left) the 'Skew-former', '. . . a tool not much used by Joyners', for cleaning out acute angles, while the *bec d'âne* (ass's snout) is called the 'Mortiss Chisell'. It is 'ground to a Broad Basil and is made in several breadths according to the size of the Mortisses'. A feature of all Félibien's chisels is the relative shortness of the handles and their simple octagonal shape, which Moxon copies faithfully. But on the plate of carpenter's tools in the 'Doctrine of Handyworks' (Pl. 8) he also gives a large socketed chisel with a short, stout wooden handle, and a 'Ripping Chisell', similar in shape with a longer handle. He notes, however, that most carpenters use an old chisel for this purpose.

Two firmer gouges in the Peter I Collection at the State Hermitage, Leningrad, are of interest here. They date from the end of the 17th century, and were probably taken to Russia by Dutch shipwrights. The larger of the two is about 2 in. wide, with a long socket and a turned handle, the blade being stamped 'RICHARD NOCK'. The smaller gouge, about $1\frac{1}{4}$ in. wide, has a roughly rounded handle with a ferrule, and is stamped with a device rather like a Madonna and Child. This shows that both socketed and ferruled types were in use at this time.

Diderot (1759) gives a similar group of chisels and gouges as Félibien, but his joiners' tools have round, turned handles, with a rolled shoulder on the face of the stem, while the plain octagonal-handled chisels are confined to carpenters. He also clears up one or two doubtful points of nomenclature. The *ciseau* proper has a parallel-sided, shouldered blade with a distinct sharpening bevel on the upper face. The *fermoir* has no apparent bevel, but a splayed blade thinning gradually to a cutting edge, which in the *fermoir en nez rond* is slightly skewed. The *ciseau de lumière* has the shouldered parallel-sided blade of the *ciseau*, with the gradually tapered point of the fermoirs. The mortice chisel of *bec d'âne*, now shortened to *bedane*, carries the rolled shoulder all round the stem. Diderot, in the section 'Charpente', gives in addition a range of solid steel *ébauchoirs*, similar to the Russian *doloti* previously described. The stem of the tool was forged from an octagonal bar, the cutting edge being formed to three different shapes: the *ébauchoir plat*, with a flat blade and square cutting edge; the *ébauchoir en grain d'orge*, with a V-shaped blade like a wheelwright's bruzzer; and the *ébauchoir à gouge*, with a very solid, spoon-shaped blade. Diderot, like Félibien and Moxon, does not show socketed mortice chisels, but they must have still been used, as they have survived to this day.

As late as 1812 Peter Nicholson, in 'Mechanical Exercises', shows both firmer and mortice chisels without ferrules, the latter with the characteristic stout oval handles. In the early sixties, however, the Marples catalogue, although still listing tapered octagonal handles exactly like those of Félibien, shows the full range of present-day beech and boxwood handles with a brass hoop or ferrule. The ordinary carpenter's chisel handles had a turned body with a neck, and were usually in beech, but the joiner's tools frequently used boxwood, with either a plain turned body, or with the grip having an octagonal section. These distinctions are maintained to the present time.

SECTION VIII

MISCELLANEOUS WOODWORKING TOOLS

THE EARLIER chapters of this book have dealt more or less systematically with the main tools for chopping, sawing, planing, and boring timber, but there are in addition a number of others in the carpenter's bag which cannot be classified very easily under any of these headings, all of which have had their history. Take the bag itself, for example. We have no evidence on how the Roman carpenters carried their tools, but one of the finds at Saalburg was a large bucket, the wooden part of which had rotted away, containing a varied collection of axes, chisels, and other iron hardware. In the Middle Ages the usual receptacle was a basket of some kind; there is a particularly good example in the foreground of Breughel's 'Adoration of the Kings' in the National Gallery in London, and another on the fresco of Noah building the Ark in the Campo Santo at Pisa. The numerous Dutch pictures of the Flight to Egypt almost invariably show St. Joseph carrying his tools in a basket slung over his shoulder, with his long-handled saw thrust through the handles. The more sedentary joiners and cabinet-makers kept their precious tools in large chests, on which they lavished their utmost skill and ingenuity. There is a very good example in the Pinto Collection of Wooden Bygones, and another in the Scarborough Museum.

One family of tools which are of great practical importance are those concerned with testing the work for accuracy and with setting out. As has already been remarked, the Romans showed their appreciation of this by showing tools of this kind very frequently on their funerary reliefs. Fig. 161 is an exception to this, but most of the others show, in addition to the rules discussed above, instruments such as the square, level, or compass. A particularly clear example of the Roman level is shown in Fig. 42. The Romans inherited this pattern from the Egyptians, who were using levels of exactly the same form many hundreds of years before. It consisted of three strips of wood jointed together like a letter A, with a plumb-bob and line suspended from the top corner. One of the earliest of these levels in the Egyptian Museum at Cairo came from the tomb of one Senutem at Deir el-Madina, and dates from the 14th century B.C. This type of level was in constant use throughout the Middle Ages—there is a terra-cotta of the Madonna and Child by Andrea della Robbia in the Bargello at Florence, dated 1475, showing one—and the same tool is illustrated in Diderot's 'Charpente' of 1769. A rather more elaborate pattern is sometimes shown in the medieval pictures, consisting of a long straight-edge forming the base, with a short upright plumb-rule in the centre, like an inverted letter T, with or without side struts (Fig. 60). The master carpenter in the illustration to the 'Livre de Rustican' is carrying one, and a similar tool is shown on the Mark Sharp gravestone at Lewes. This type of level, in fact, survived up to the middle of the 19th century, and is illustrated by Moxon (1683), Nicholson (1812), and Young in 'Every Man His Own Mechanic' (1882). The earliest known reference to a 'Spirit Levil' [*sic*] is in Smith's 'Key to the Manufactories of Sheffield' (1816). Spirit levels were used by surveyors and the like in the 18th century, but were only available to carpenters much later.

Among the other tools from the tomb of Senutem mentioned above there is an ingenious form of plumb-rule, consisting of an upright about 2 ft. long and 3 in. by $1\frac{1}{2}$ in. in section, with two pieces about 6 in. long mortised and tenoned into it at right angles, dividing the length into three equal parts. The bob is suspended on a line attached to the top of the upright and passing over the ends of the two short horizontal members. Obviously if these two pieces are exactly the same length, when the plumb-line just touches the lower piece the long upright must be perpendicular. But although the plumb-bob is shown quite frequently in Roman reliefs, and beautifully turned examples in bronze have been found at Pompeii and other places, there is no evidence to show whether they were used with a rule or not. No plumb-rules are known from medieval sources either, and even Moxon in 1683 shows a plumb-line being used without one, the line itself being sighted to give the perpendicular.

The Senutem tools also include a wooden square, formed by two strips about 12 in. long jointed at right angles, and carved with a hieroglyphic inscription. The Romans had several patterns of square, or *norma*, one similar to the Egyptian example, sometimes with a narrow strip along the shorter edge to act as a fence when setting out, and others made of flat pieces of board with a stop along one edge, some with a right angle cut out of the middle to mark out a mitre. In the Landesmuseum at Zürich there is an iron square from Neftenbach, consisting of three strips roughly 6 in., 8 in., and 10 in. long, welded together to form a right-angled triangle, with another strip at one corner making an angle of 45 degrees with the side carrying the stop. This must have been a very handy tool for setting out large timber-work or masonry.

Squares of both Roman types were used throughout the Middle Ages, but as they were all made by the craftsmen themselves from suitable well-seasoned hardwood, usually old oak barrel staves, they vary somewhat in detail. The wide square for setting out is clearly shown in the right-hand foreground of the Wierix title-page (Fig. 68), and also on Fig. 136. On the French carved shop sign (Fig. 135) one edge of the tool is square and the other at 45 degrees, while on the tankard lid of Fig. 156 the mitre square is a separate tool. All these illustrations also give the L-shaped pattern for testing purposes. Félibien shows the *équaire* or plain square; the *fausse équaire* or bevel; the *triangle quarré*, a wide square for setting out; and the *triangle anglé*, a mitre square similar to that on Fig. 156. Moxon remarks of both plain and mitre square that the handles are 1 in. thick and the blades $\frac{1}{4}$ in., 'glewed and pinned' together.

A prominent tool on the Roman reliefs is the compass, or more correctly, a pair of dividers. These usually have straight, pointed legs; the pair of calipers on the wall in Fig. 127 is unusual, although a similar instrument to this was found at Pompeii. The straight-legged compass was used not only for scribing circles, but also for transferring measurements from the rule to the work, and as the Romans apparently knew nothing of the marking gauge, they may also have been used for scribing a line parallel to the face side or edge. These tools have remained virtually unchanged until modern times.

The method of marking timber by stretching a cord primed with colouring matter and releasing it sharply to leave a straight line on the surface was known to the Egyptians, and a list of carpenter's tools in the Greek Anthology ('Anthologia Palatina', VI, 205) includes 'the line and ochre box'. The method is illustrated in the Campo Santo fresco at Pisa, and a 'Holy Family' by Annibale Carracci of about 1600 shows St. Joseph and the Holy Child marking a plank on the bench in this manner. A chalk-line and box are shown in the foreground of Fig. 23, while the carpenters in the Rodler woodcut illustrated on p. 196 of Salzman's 'Building in England' are marking a balk with a line issuing from a small box with an upright handle.

As remarked above, the Romans do not appear to have used the marking gauge, in fact the earliest known representation of this tool is that shown on the bench in the Wierix title-page. The 15th-century poem 'The Debate of the Carpenter's Tools' (Hazlitt, 'Early Popular Poetry', Vol. 1, pp. 79–90) mentions a 'skantyllyon', which may have been some kind of gauge, but no examples of the tool occur in the medieval pictures. Félibien has two gauges, the ordinary marking gauge and one with an extra long point, probably a cutting gauge. Neither of these tools show any fixing for the fence, and Moxon merely remarks that the Oval, as he calls the block, is 'fitted stiff upon the staff'. Peter Nicholson, in 1812, shows a perfectly plain gauge similar to this, with no provision for securing the block, but Diderot's *trusquin* of 1759 has a thin, narrow wedge, while Bergeron's of 1816 has a small screw. Nicholson in his text mentions that separate gauges must be set when marking mortice and tenon joints, but on the Continent over a hundred years earlier a double gauge was in common use. Examples can be seen on Figs. 135, 136, and 156, each with a wide fence carrying two separate stems, both secured by the same wedge driven between them. The tool on Fig. 156 clearly shows the two spurs at different distances from the face of the block. This type of mortice gauge was apparently never very popular in this country, but by the time of the Marples catalogue of 1864 the modern patterns, with both spurs on a single stem, fixed either by means of a wedge or a screw, had come on to the market, and were identical with those in use today. In the present-day Dutch and Swedish catalogues, however, the gauge with two separate stems, in metal, is still listed.

Of the auxiliary tools for striking, the mallet has a comparatively simple history. The Egyptians often used a short billet of round, hard wood, with one end reduced in thickness to form the handle, but it was soon discovered—'soon' on the Egyptian time-scale means about 1,000 years—that this type had a comparatively short working life, so the head was perforated and fitted to a handle, using the end grain for the striking face. The Romans preferred this round-headed mallet, frequently waisted, as on the Pompeian fresco (Fig. 189). In the Middle Ages similar mallets were used for striking chisels and other tools, and for driving in wooden pins and trenails. The square-headed carpenter's mallet as used today is illustrated as early as Félibien (Fig. 192), and little variation is possible with such a simple tool.

The story of the hammer is rather more complicated. In general it followed the same line of development as the axe and the adze, in fact these have often been designed as dual-purpose tools, as on Figs. 14*b* and 34. The perforated stone 'axe-hammer' of

Fig. 3 could hardly be described as a woodworking tool, but the smiths of the Bronze Age made and probably used themselves small socketed hammers, which were lashed to knee-shaped wooden handles in the same manner as their axes. They were sometimes also fitted with loops, while in the Ashmolean Museum at Oxford there is a small square-headed, socketed bronze hammer head from Versecz, Hungary, with two loops, like the Spanish and Siberian socketed axes, a technological curiosity, both in its design and provenance. As with the axes, the perforated head was introduced in the Early Iron Age, and by Roman times it had assumed its familiar appearance, even to the extent of being sometimes provided with a claw for withdrawing bent nails. The usual hammer of the medieval joiners had a head of square section, with a plain tup or striking face and a wedge-shaped pene, similar to that shown on Fig. 150. This type is still widely used on the Continent, and in the English catalogues it is described as the French pattern. The English equivalent, now somewhat rare, has a similar shape except for a round tup with a neck, and is known as the Exeter or London hammer. The modern joiner's hammer, with a circular eye, round tup, necked on both sides of the eye, and symmetrical pene, was introduced some time in the early 19th century, and for some reason is known as the Warrington hammer. It is interesting to note that although most types of axe are given county names, Kent, Suffolk, Yorkshire, and so on, the names of hammers go by towns. The exception to this is the 'Kent', a stout claw hammer with a square tup and two straps or languets forged solid with the head, and giving an additional fixing for the shaft. A variety of this with a circular tup instead of square, reverts to the usual custom and is called the 'Canterbury' hammer. This type with the straps must have had a long history, as a claw hammer with a square head and similar straps is shown in Dürer's 'Melancholia' engraving of 1514, while Moxon shows a very badly drawn example in his plate of carpenter's tools. The modern American, or adze-eye claw hammer dispenses with the straps, and relies on a deep socket, like that of an adze, as its name implies.

Of cutting tools not previously dealt with, perhaps the most important are the drawknife and the spokeshave. An early form of drawknife, with the tangs for the handles bent up at right angles to the plane of the blade, is shown in the group of Viking shipwright's tools in Fig. 128, one with a straight cutting edge and the other slightly curved. Tools of this type, known as the *skobel*, were widely used in medieval Russia for smoothing the surface of the timber after using the axe or adze, but no examples have been noted on medieval illustrations in the West. The modern form of carpenter's drawknife, with a straight cutting edge and the tangs bent round in the same plane, fitted with short, turned handles, is shown among Moxon's carpenter's tools. He explains that it is used 'for the legs of Crickets, Rounds of Ladders, and rails to lay Cheefe or Bacon on'. This sounds more like the work of a spokeshave, but his illustration is clear enough. The drawknife turns up again in Smith's 'Key' of 1816 under the heading 'Drawing Knifes' [*sic*], and the full range is given of carpenter's , wheeler's, and cooper's, the latter group including heading and hollowing knives; the jigger, with one half of the blade straight and the other half curved; and various circular and round shaves. These coopers' tools had evidently undergone considerable specialisation during the 18th century, so that early in the 19th they had assumed their modern form.

The spokeshave is rather more of a problem. Although the word is recorded from as early as 1510, Félibien, Moxon, and Diderot do not refer to it, and the earliest known illustration occurs in the invaluable Smith's 'Key', curiously enough, on the page of coopers' tools. This is a rather crude-looking instrument, but it is in essentials identical with the present-day wooden spokeshave, the stock having rounded handles at each end, and the straight, wedge-shaped iron with two short tangs turned up at right angles is driven into corresponding square tapered holes in the stock. This seems to indicate that the tool must have had a long development behind it, but the French *bastringue* or *wastringue* and the German *Speichenhobel* are not known before the early 19th century. The earliest actual tool at all resembling a spokeshave known to the writer is in the Hall i' th' Woods Museum near Bolton in Lancashire, formerly the home of Samuel Crompton, the inventor of the spinning mule. It occurs in conjunction with a standard Dutch *blokschaaf* dated 1766, and may itself have come from Holland. The stock of the tool is carved in the shape of a fish, the tail end forming the handle, and near the fish's head a narrow cutter is screwed to the face, opposite a slot cut through the head. Greber, in his History of the Plane, illustrates similar tools from Germany, the Tyrol, and Switzerland, known as *Bandhobeln*, as used by coopers to split willow twigs for binding wooden kegs or tubs. The addition of a second grip on the other side of the cutter would give a passable version of the spokeshave, but whether the tool was evolved in this way, or the *Bandhobel* followed a different line of development altogether, it is not at present possible to say. What is worth noting is that the spokeshave itself, originally, as its English name implies, a specialised tool of the wheelwright, is now used for various purposes by craftsmen of many other trades, a case of a tool having been generalised rather than specialised. The modern metal spokeshaves, like the corresponding metal planes, were popularised by the Americans in the middle of the 19th century, but there were none listed in the 1864 Marples catalogue.

Another cutting tool which does not appear to have been used in this country at all, but which was very popular with cabinet-makers on the Continent from the 16th century to the late 18th, is the shoulder knife. It was used exclusively for cutting out veneers for inlays and marquetry work, and was essentially a narrow, pointed knife set in a long, curved, and often elaborately carved handle, the end of which was held under the armpit to give extra pressure when cutting several thicknesses of veneer. A typical example can be seen on Fig. 156, lying across the hammer. It was eventually superseded by the fret- and buhl-saws and the jig-saw machine.

A most essential accessory for the joiner and cabinet-maker was the glue-pot, but this was usually overlooked by the medieval illustrators, and we have no idea what it may have looked like during this period. Moxon illustrates a crude octagonal 'Glew-pot', and says it is commonly made of good thick lead, so that the glue will not chill. In the 17th and 18th centuries the Continental cabinet-makers used a three-legged kettle, sometimes with a handle. There is a good one shown on Fig. 156, just below the turning saw, and another under the bench in Fig. 135. They were probably heated by charcoal braziers set under them; the modern double glue-pot was probably evolved after the introduction of gas for heating.

BIBLIOGRAPHY

BERG, DR. GÖSTA: *Sawing by Hand of Boards and Planks.* Folk-Liv, Stockholm, 1957–58

BERGERON, H.: *L'Art du Tourneur.* Paris, 1816.

BIELER, K.: *An der Hobelbank.* Braunschweig, 1951.

CHILDE, G.: *Dawn of European Civilisation.* London, 1947.

CLARK, J. D. H.: *Prehistoric Europe.* London, 1952.

DAREMBERG ET SAGLIO: *Dictionnaire des Antiquités Grecques et Romaines.* Paris, 1877.

DIDEROT: *Encyclopédie.* Paris, 1765.

FELDHAUS, F. M.: *Die Säge.* Berlin, 1921.

FÉLIBIEN, A.: *Principes de l'Architecture, etc.* Paris, 1676.

GOODMAN, W. L.: *Woodwork.* Oxford, 1962.

GREBER, J. M.: *Geschichte des Hobels.* Zürich, 1956.

——: *Alte deutsche holzbearbeitungswerkzeuge.* Deutsche Volkskunde, Berlin, 1940, No. 4.

——: *Die Alten Zunftladen.* Zürich, 1952.

——: *David Roentgen.* Neuwied, 1948.

——: *Der Werdegang unserer Holzsägen*: Fachblatt für Holzarbeiten, Berlin, 1937.

HARRIS, J.: *Lexicon Technicum.* London, 1714.

HAWKES, C. F. C.: *Prehistoric Foundations of Europe.* London, 1940.

HEURTEMATTE, J.: *Cours de Technologie du Bois.* Paris, 1948.

HIBBEN, T.: *The Carpenter's Tool Chest.* London, 1933.

HOLTZAPFEL, CH.: *Turning and Mechanical Manipulations.* London, 1846.

HOOPER, J.: *Handcraft in Wood.* London, 1952.

JACOBI, DR. L.: *Das Romerskastell Saalburg.* Homburg, 1897.

JONES, P. D'A. and SIMONS, E. N.: *The Story of the Saw.* Sheffield, 1960.

KOLCHIN, B. A.: *Chernoe Metallurgie v Drevnoi Rusi.* Moscow, 1953.

KUKSOV, V. A.: *Stolyarnoe Delo.* Moscow, 1958.

LEGROS, E.: *Le Scieur de long en Ardennes liègeoise.* Enquêtes du Musée de la Vie Wallonne. Liège, 1946.

LEROI-GOURHAN, A.: *L'Homme et la Matière.* Paris, 1951.

——: *Milieu et Techniques.* Paris, 1945.

MERCER, H. C.: *Ancient Carpenters' Tools.* Doylestown, Penn., 1929.

MOXON, J.: *Mechanick Exercises.* London, 1683.

NICHOLSON, P.: *Mechanical Exercises.* London, 1812.

NORMAN, G. A.: *Hovelens Historie.* Lillehammer, 1954.

PETRIE, SIR F.: *Tools and Weapons.* London, 1917.

PINTO, E. H.: *Treen.* London, 1949.

RICH, A.: *Dictionary of Roman and Greek Antiquities.* London, 1884.

ROUBO, A.: *L'Art du Menuisier.* Paris, 1769.

SALZMAN, L. F.: *Building in England.* Oxford, 1952.

SLOANE, ERIC: *A Museum of Early American Tools.* New York 1964.

SMITH, R.: *Key to the Manufactories of Sheffield.* Sheffield, 1816.

VIIRES, A.: *Eesti rahvaparane puutoondus.* Tallinn, 1960.

WAAGEPETERSEN, CHR.: Forsvunde Tømreøkser. Kalundborg. 1965.

WILDUNG, F.: *Woodworking Tools at the Shelburne Museum.* Vermont, 1957.

WILSON, D. M.: *The Anglo-Saxons.* London, 1960.

YOUNG, F.: *Every Man His Own Mechanic.* London, 1882.

WYATT, E. M.: *Common Woodworking Tools: Their History.* Milwaukee, 1936.

SOME BRITISH MUSEUMS WITH DISPLAYS OF WOODWORKING TOOLS

Alton (Hants), Curtis Museum.
Ayr, Carnegie Library and Museum.
Bolton (Lancs), Hall i' th' Woods.
Bristol, Blaise Castle Folk Museum.
Bury St. Edmunds, Moyse's Hall Museum.
Cambridge, University Archaeological Museum.
Cardiff, National Museum of Wales.
Edinburgh, National Museum of the Antiquities of Scotland.
Farnham, Pitt-Rivers Museum.
Glastonbury, Lake Village Museum.
Halifax, Folk Museum.
Haslemere, Educational Museum.
High Wycombe, Folk Museum.
Kingussie, Folk Museum.
London, Science Museum.
London, Victoria and Albert Museum.
London, British Museum.
London, Geffrye Museum.
London, London Museum, Kensington Palace.
London, Guildhall Museum.
London, Horniman Museum.
Luton, Bagshawe Collection.
Maidstone, Museum and Art Gallery.
Manchester, University College Museum.
Northwood (Middx), Pinto Collection of Wooden Bygones.
Oxford, Ashmolean Museum.
Reading, Silchester Collection.
Salisbury (Wilts), Museum.
Scarborough, Museum.
St. Albans, City Museum.
St. Fagans, Welsh Folk Musuem.
Verulamium Museum.
York, Castle Museum.

N.B. This list is by no means complete.

Index